Glencoe Science Earth Science

Leveled Resources

for Above-Level, On-Level, and Below-Level Learners

with Leveled Labs

and Leveled Assessment

New York, New York Columbus, Ohio Chicago, Illinois Woodland Hills, California

Glencoe Science

Photo Credits
Cover: (t) Corbis
(b) DAL

The McGraw·Hill Companies

Send all inquiries to:
Glencoe/McGraw-Hill
8787 Orion Place
Columbus, OH 43240-4027

ISBN: 978-0-07-879312-7
MHID: 0-07-879312-2

Printed in the United States of America.

1 2 3 4 5 6 7 8 9 10 047 11 10 09 08 07

Table of Contents

BL Below-Level Learners OL On-Level Learners AL Above-Level Learners

BL Below-Level Learners OL On-Level Learners AL Above-Level Learners

To the Teacher

In the science classroom, there are two key challenges to teaching a diverse group of students. The first is labs. How can you challenge your advanced learners yet give the struggling learners the support they need? The second is assessment. Accurately assessing understanding means that assessments must be tailored to various student abilities. This resource contains materials to help you meet these challenges. Within you will find reproducible pages for:

- hands-on activities
- meeting individual needs (below, on, advanced)
- student assessment
- answers for the worksheets

Meeting Individual Needs (Below, On, Advanced)

Lab Versions A (Below-Level) and B (On-Level and Above-Level) Worksheets: These worksheets are an expanded version of the end-of-chapter lab found in the student textbook. The materials lists, procedures, and questions are repeated so that students do not need their textbooks open during the laboratory activity. Write-on lines are included for most questions. Tables, charts, and graphs are included for students to record their observations.

The labs are further expanded to be accessible for all students. Lab Version A, for below-level learners, includes slightly modified and expanded steps, as well as check boxes next to the key steps so students are better guided and can track their progress. Lab Version B, for on-level and above-level learners, is the same student edition lab with the addition of a *Challenge* section. *Challenge* includes several questions that will engage your advanced learners and ask them to extend what they did in the activity.

ASSESSMENT ADVANTAGE

Assessment

Chapter Tests A, B, and C (Below, On, Advanced): The chapters tests are written to accommodate all students. Test A, for below-level learners, provides students with guided questions, such as multiple choice, matching, and fill-in-the-blank with word banks. Test B, for on-level learners, tests average students with short-answer and completion questions. Test C challenges advanced learners with more difficult and open-ended questions.

All chapter tests require students to use process skills and understand content. Although all questions involve memory to some degree, you will find that your students will need to discover relationships among facts and concepts in some questions and will need to use higher levels of critical thinking to apply concepts in other questions. Answers are provided in the *Teacher Guide and Answers* section.

____
Teacher Approval Initials
____
Date of Approval

Student Lab/Activity Safety Form

Student Name: ____________________

Date: ____________________

Lab/Activity Title: ____________________

In order to show your teacher that you understand the safety concerns of this lab/activity, the following questions must be answered after the teacher explains the information to you. You must have your teacher initial this form before you can proceed with the activity/lab.

1. How would you describe what you will be doing during this lab/activity?

2. What are the safety concerns associated with this lab/activity (as explained by your teacher)?
   - ______________________________
   - ______________________________
   - ______________________________
   - ______________________________
   - ______________________________

3. What additional safety concerns or questions do you have?

Adapted from Gerlovich, et al. (2004). The Total Science Safety System CD, JaKel, Inc. Used with Permission.

Name Date Class

LAB Testing Variables of a Pendulum

LAB A

Lab Preview

Directions: *Answer these questions before you begin the Lab.*

1. What will you use to make a pendulum in this lab?

____

2. What will you use to determine the angle of release? ______________________

A pendulum is an old, but accurate, timekeeping device. It works because of two natural phenomena—gravity and inertia—that are important in the study of Earth science. Gravity makes all objects fall toward Earth's surface. Inertia makes matter remain at rest or in motion unless acted upon by an external force. In the following lab, you will test some variables that might affect the swing of a pendulum.

Real-World Question

How do the length of a pendulum, the attached mass, and the angle of the release of the mass affect the swing of a pendulum?

Materials

string (60 cm)
metal washers (5)
watch with a second hand
metric ruler
paper clip
protractor

Goals

- **Manipulate** variables of a pendulum.
- **Draw** conclusions from experimentation with pendulums.

Table 1

The Length of the Pendulum			
Length of String (cm)	Swings Per Minute		
	Trial 1	Trial 2	Average
10			
20			
30			
40			
50			

Safety Precautions

Procedure

- ❑ 1. **Study** the three data tables.
- ❑ 2. Bend the paperclip into an S shape and tie it to one end of the string.
- ❑ 3. Hang one washer from the paper clip.
- ❑ 4. **Measure** 10 cm of string from the washer and hold the string at that distance with one hand.

Table 2

Amount of Mass on the Pendulum			
Units of Mass	Swings Per Minute		
	Trial 1	Trial 2	Average
1			
2			
3			
4			
5			

(continued)

LAB A

Table 3

Angle of the Release of the Mass			
Angle of Release	Swings Per Minute		
	Trial 1	Trial 2	Average
90°			
80°			
70°			
60°			
50°			

5. **Use** your other hand to pull back the end of the pendulum with the washer so it is parallel with the ground. Let go of the washer.

❑ 6. **Count** the number of complete swings the pendulum makes in 1 min. Record this number in **Table 1**.

❑ 7. **Repeat** steps 5 and 6, and record the number of swings in **Table 1** under "Trial 2."

❑ 8. **Average** the results of steps 6 and 7 and record the average swings per minute in **Table 1**. To average, add both trials together and divide by 2.

❑ 9. **Repeat** steps 4 through 8, using string lengths of 20 cm, 30 cm, 40 cm, and 50 cm. Record your data in **Table 1**.

❑10. **Copy** the data with the string length of 50 cm in **Table 2**.

❑11. **Repeat** steps 5 through 8 using two, three, four, and five washers. Record these data in **Table 2**.

❑12. **Use** 50 cm of string and one washer for the third set of tests.

❑13. **Use** the protractor to measure a 90° drop of the mass. **Hint:** *Hold the protractor so the straight edge is vertical. Move the string to the 90° mark on the protractor, so it's parallel to the ground.*

❑ **Repeat** this procedure, calculate the average, and record the data in **Table 3**.

❑14. **Repeat** procedures 12 and 13, using angles of 80°, 70°, 60°, and 50°.

Conclude and Apply

1. **Explain** When you tested the effect of the angle of the drop of the pendulum on the swings per minute, which variables did you keep constant?

____

2. **Infer** which of the variables you tested affects the swing of a pendulum.

____

3. **Predict** Suppose you have a pendulum clock that indicates an earlier time than it really is. (This means it has too few swings per minute.) What could you do to the clock to make it keep better time?

____

Communicating Your Data

Graph the data from your tables. Title and label the graphs. Use different colored pencils for each graph. **Compare** your graphs with the graphs of other members of your class.

Name _______________ Date _______________ Class _______________

LAB Testing Variables of a Pendulum

LAB B

Lab Preview

Directions: *Answer these questions before you begin the Lab.*

1. What will you use to make a pendulum in this lab?

____

2. What will you use to determine the angle of release? _______________________

A pendulum is an old, but accurate, timekeeping device. It works because of two natural phenomena—gravity and inertia—that are important in the study of Earth science. Gravity makes all objects fall toward Earth's surface. Inertia makes matter remain at rest or in motion unless acted upon by an external force. In the following lab, you will test some variables that might affect the swing of a pendulum.

Real-World Question

How do the length of a pendulum, the attached mass, and the angle of the release of the mass affect the swing of a pendulum?

Materials

string (60 cm)
metal washers (5)
watch with a second hand
metric ruler
paper clip
protractor

Goals

- **Manipulate** variables of a pendulum.
- **Draw** conclusions from experimentation with pendulums.

Safety Precautions 

Procedure

- ❑ 1. **Study** the three data tables.
- ❑ 2. Bend the paperclip into an S shape and tie it to one end of the string.
- ❑ 3. Hang one washer from the paper clip.
- ❑ 4. **Measure** 10 cm of string from the washer and hold the string at that distance with one hand.

Table 1

The Length of the Pendulum

Length of String (cm)	Swings Per Minute		
	Trial 1	Trial 2	Average
10			
20			
30			
40			
50			

Table 2

Amount of Mass on the Pendulum

Units of Mass	Swings Per Minute		
	Trial 1	Trial 2	Average
1			
2			
3			
4			
5			

(continued)

Table 3

Angle of the Release of the Mass			
Angle of Release	Swings Per Minute		
	Trial 1	Trial 2	Average
90°			
80°			
70°			
60°			
50°			

❑ 5. **Use** your other hand to pull back the end of the pendulum with the washer so it is parallel with the ground. Let go of the washer.

❑ 6. **Count** the number of complete swings the pendulum makes in 1 min. Record this number in **Table 1**.

❑ 7. **Repeat** steps 5 and 6, and record the number of swings in **Table 1** under "Trial 2."

❑ 8. **Average** the results of steps 6 and 7 and record the average swings per minute in **Table 1**.

❑ 9. **Repeat** steps 4 through 8, using string lengths of 20 cm, 30 cm, 40 cm, and 50 cm. Record your data in **Table 1**.

❑ 10. **Copy** the data with the string length of 50 cm in **Table 2**.

❑ 11. **Repeat** steps 5 through 8 using two, three, four, and five washers. Record these data in **Table 2**.

❑ 12. **Use** 50 cm of string and one washer for the third set of tests.

❑ 13. **Use** the protractor to measure a 90° drop of the mass. Repeat this procedure, calculate the average, and record the data in **Table 3**.

❑ 14. **Repeat** procedures 12 and 13, using angles of 80°, 70°, 60°, and 50°.

Conclude and Apply

1. **Explain** When you tested the effect of the angle of the drop of the pendulum on the swings per minute, which variables did you keep constant?

____

____

2. **Infer** which of the variables you tested affects the swing of a pendulum.

____

____

3. **Predict** Suppose you have a pendulum clock that indicates an earlier time than it really is. (This means it has too few swings per minute.) What could you do to the clock to make it keep better time?

____

____

LAB (continued) **LAB B**

Challenge

1. **Hypothesize** How will the motion of the pendulum change if the angle of the drop is more than 90 degrees?

2. **Infer** What force is acting on the pendulum at the pivot point? What is the effect of this?

3. **Construct** Draw a diagram of a simple pendulum. Include in your diagram the length of the pendulum, the weight of the pendulum, the angle of the pendulum, and the pivot point. Also include the motion of the pendulum and the force of gravity.

Extension

Determine Using only a stopwatch and a pendulum, determine the length of a pendulum that will produce a period (one complete swing) of exactly one second.

Communicating Your Data

Graph the data from your tables. Title and label the graphs. Use different colored pencils for each graph. **Compare** your graphs with the graphs of other members of your class.

Name ______ Date ______ Class ______

The Nature of Science

I. Testing Concepts

Directions: *In the blank at the left, write the letter of the term that best completes each statement.*

______ **1.** Earth scientists study ______.
- **a.** plants and animals
- **b.** Earth and space
- **c.** Earth and people
- **d.** all life on Earth

______ **2.** A hypothesis is ______.
- **a.** an educated guess
- **b.** the end result of an experiment
- **c.** a variable in an experiment
- **d.** an opinion

______ **3.** Ethics deals with ______.
- **a.** scientific measurements
- **b.** science and technology
- **c.** factual information
- **d.** moral values about what is good or bad

______ **4.** ______ is a process of observing, studying, and thinking about things in your world.
- **a.** The scientific method
- **b.** Science
- **c.** Experimentation
- **d.** Ethics

______ **5.** Making up data and changing results are examples of ______.
- **a.** variables
- **b.** bias
- **c.** controls
- **d.** hypothesizing

______ **6.** ______ was the first American to suggest weather could be predicted.
- **a.** Sir Isaac Newton
- **b.** Ben Franklin
- **c.** Thomas Jefferson
- **d.** Joseph Henry

______ **7.** ______ makes all objects fall toward Earth's surface.
- **a.** Inertia
- **b.** Air resistance
- **c.** Gravity
- **d.** Wind speed

Directions: *Match each description on the left with the correct term on the right. Write the letter of the correct term in the blank at the left.*

______ **8.** problem-solving procedures

______ **9.** variable that does not change

______ **10.** an accurate time-keeping device

______ **11.** scientific discoveries put to practical uses

______ **12.** variable being measured

- **a.** dependent variable
- **b.** pendulum
- **c.** constant
- **d.** scientific method
- **e.** technology

Name ______ Date ______ Class ______

II. Understanding Concepts

Skill: Sequencing

Directions: *Number six likely steps of a scientific method in order.*

______ **1.** make a hypothesis

______ **2.** draw conclusions

______ **3.** identify a problem

______ **4.** analyze the results

______ **5.** gather information

______ **6.** test the hypothesis

Skill: Cause and Effect

Directions: *Place an* **X** *by each cause.*

7. ______ Scientific knowledge grows.

______ There is continuous research and improvement in technological instruments.

8. ______ There are reliable results.

______ Experiments are repeated many times.

9. ______ A force acts on an object.

______ The object changes speed, direction, or both.

10. ______ Observations and experiments can be inaccurate.

______ There is personal bias.

Skill: Classifying

Directions: *Read the experiment design below. Identify each element as an* **independent variable, dependent variable, constant,** *or* **control.**

A scientist wants to test the effectiveness of fertilizer in making plants grow taller. She places three seeds of the same kind in three different containers. Each container receives the same amount of light, water, and soil. One pot receives no fertilizer. Another plant receives 5 grams of fertilizer, and the last plant receives 15 grams of the same fertilizer.

______________ **11.** height of stem

______________ **12.** amount of sunlight

______________ **13.** plant with no fertilizer

______________ **14.** amount of water

______________ **15.** fertilizer

Chapter Test A (continued)

III. Applying Concepts

Writing Skills

Directions: *Respond to the following using complete sentences.*

1. **State** How is technology used in the study of Earth science? Give an example.

2. **Compare** How is a scientist similar to a detective?

3. **Apply** In 1912, a German scientist proposed the idea that millions of years ago, the Earth had one giant continent that eventually broke apart and formed seven different continents. There was research and data to support his idea. Is this is an example of scientific theory or scientific law? Why?

4. **List** Name five topics an Earth scientist might be interested in exploring.

5. **Explain** Why do scientists repeat their experiments?

Name _______________ Date _______________ Class _______________

The Nature of Science

I. Testing Concepts

Directions: *Match the description in the first column with the item in the second by writing the correct letter in the space provided. Some items in the second column may not be used.*

_____ **1.** variables that do not change in an experiment

_____ **2.** an educated guess that can be tested

_____ **3.** standard to which experimental results are compared

_____ **4.** rule that describes behavior of nature

_____ **5.** deals with morals and values

_____ **6.** the use of scientific discoveries to make products or tools

_____ **7.** a personal opinion

_____ **8.** an explanation backed by results from repeated testing

_____ **9.** a variable that can change in an experiment

_____ **10.** study of Earth and space

a. hypothesis
b. Earth science
c. variable
d. constant
e. control
f. technology
g. scientific theory
h. scientific law
i. independent
j. ethics
k. dependent
l. bias

Directions: *Identify each statement as* **true** *or* **false.** *Rewrite false statements to make them correct.*

_____ **11.** Ethics deals with morals and values and can be measured and tested using the scientific method.

____

____

_____ **12.** Until proven incorrect, there are no "wrong" hypotheses.

____

_____ **13.** The more variables you can test in an experiment, the better the results.

____

____

_____ **14.** Earth science is the study of rocks and trees only.

____

_____ **15.** Bias, or personal opinions, never influence scientific results.

____

Chapter Test B (continued)

Directions: *Fill in the blanks in the following statements with the correct terms.*

16. In 1970, in the United States, the Weather Bureau was renamed the ________________.

17. In 1850, Joseph Henry, secretary of the Smithsonian Institution, started drawing ________________.

18. Although many advances in meteorology were made in the United States in the 1800's, weather instruments such as the thermometer and the anemometer were invented in the ________________ in Italy.

19. Newton's observations about motion are examples of scientific ________________.

20. Gathering information and testing hypotheses are examples of problem-solving procedures called ________________.

21. The opposite of ethical behavior in science is ________________, which could include such things as making up data, changing results, or taking credit for the work of others.

22. The process of observing, studying, and thinking about things to gain knowledge is called ________________.

II. Understanding Concepts

Skill: Designing an Experiment

1. How could you use two beakers, distilled water, two hot plates, two thermometers, and salt to test if adding salt affects the boiling point of water?

____

____

____

____

____

2. Compare and **contrast** scientific methods with ethics and belief systems.

____

____

____

____

____

Chapter Test B (continued)

Skill: Concept Mapping

Directions: *Complete the following events chain for doing an experiment.*

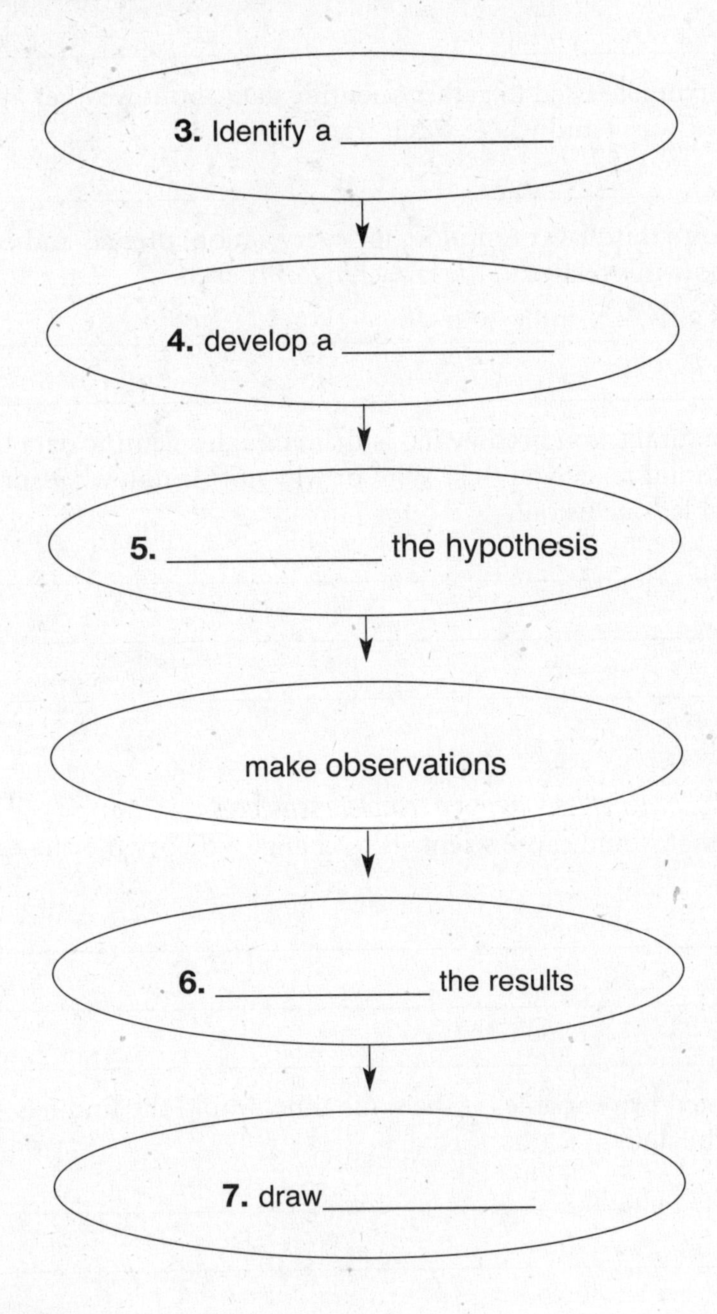

III. Applying Concepts

Directions: *Answer the following questions on the lines provided.*

1. What method did Benjamin Franklin use to draw conclusions about weather predictions and what were those conclusions?

Chapter Test B (continued)

2. How did the invention of the telegraph in 1837 affect the science of meteorology?

3. The first known instrument used to gather scientific data about weather appears in history around 300 B.C. What was it and where was it used?

4. According to Newton's third law of motion, for every action, there is and equal and opposite reaction. Explain how this relates to the launching of rockets.

5. After eating at a restaurant, you become ill. Is that enough scientific data to conclude that the food from the restaurant made you sick? Why, or why not? If not, what sort of data would you need to draw a reliable conclusion?

IV. Writing Skills

Directions: *Answer the following questions using complete sentences.*

1. Give some reasons that would cause scientists to change a theory they have believed in for a long time.

2. If an experiment tested two variables at the same time, would the findings of the experiment be accurate? Why or why not?

3. When testing new medicines on humans, some of the test subjects are given placebos, or "fake" pills, that look like the real drug, but actually contain some harmless substance that has no medical effect. What purpose do you think this might serve in the experiment? Explain.

Name ______________________ Date ______________ Class ______________

The Nature of Science

I. Testing Concepts

Directions: *Identify each statement as* **true** *or* **false**. *If the statement is false, change the underlined term to make it true.*

______ **1.** Controls are the variables that do not change in an experiment.

____

______ **2.** Scientists make hypotheses based on prior knowledge.

____

______ **3.** The invention of the satellite in 1837 made it possible to send weather observations across the country.

____

______ **4.** Technology is the use of scientific discoveries for practical purposes.

____

______ **5.** Scientific theories are backed up by many tests or experiments.

____

Directions: *Fill in the blank with the word or words that best complete the sentence.*

6. The goal of ______________ is to gain knowledge and better understand the world.

7. ______________, ______________, and ______________ are topics studied in Earth science.

8. Dr. Whipple's hypothesis that a(n) ______________ consists of ice and dust is now an accepted theory.

9. According to Newton's third law, for every action there is a(n) ______________ and ______________ reaction.

10. Scientists were able to know the causes of the great tsunami in 1700 by analyzing ______________.

11. Science is unable to answer ______________ and ______________ questions.

12. A(n) ______________ was probably the first weather instrument.

13. Unexpected results in an experiment can lead to new ______________.

14. In ancient times, people relied on ______________ to explain natural phenomena.

Name Date Class

Chapter Test C (continued)

II. Understanding Concepts

Skill: Sequencing

Directions: *List six likely steps of a scientific method in order.*

1. ______________________________
2. ______________________________
3. ______________________________
4. ______________________________
5. ______________________________
6. ______________________________

Skill: Cause and Effect

Directions: *Fill in the blanks to complete the cause-and-effect relationships.*

7. Scientific knowledge grows because ______________________________.
8. Objects fall toward Earth because ______________________________.
9. An object will change speed, direction, or both because ______________________________.
10. Early Germanic people thought lightning happened because ______________________________.
11. A tsunami hit the island of Honshu because ______________________________.
12. Scientists are like detectives because ______________________________.
13. The Egyptians developed a calendar because ______________________________.

Skill: Classifying

14. Write a paragraph describing an experiment. Identify the ***independent variables***, ***dependent variables***, ***constant***, and ***controls***.

____

____

____

____

____

____

____

Name Date Class

III. Applying Concepts

Writing Skills

Directions: *Respond to the following using complete sentences.*

1. **Analyze** Discuss the relationship between science and technology.

2. **Reason** How does society benefit from transferable technology?

3. **Debate** Do you support the statement "Science is limited and always changing"? Why or why not?

4. **Critique** A scientist performs an experiment to determine if music helps plants grow. He plants six lima-bean seeds in six different containers. Each plant receives an equal amount of soil, water, and sunlight. Two plants are exposed to classical music, two plants are exposed to rock music, and two plants are not exposed to any music. At the end of six weeks, the plants that were exposed to classical music were slightly bigger than the other plants. After this experiment, the scientist concluded that plants grow better when exposed to classical music. Is this a good experiment? Why or why not?

5. **Assess** Headrests are placed in cars to prevent whiplash injuries during rear-end collisions. To which of Newton's scientific laws does this relate?

Name Date Class

Design Your Own

Determining Density

LAB A

Lab Preview

Directions: *Answer these questions before you begin the Lab.*

1. Why does this lab include the sharp object safety symbol?

____

____

2. What equation is used to determine the density of an object?

____

Real-World Question

Which has a greater density—a rock or a piece of wood? Is cork more dense than clay? Density is the ratio of an object's mass to its volume.

Form a Hypothesis

State a hypothesis about what process you can use to measure and compare the densities of several materials.

Possible Materials

pan
triple-beam balance
100-mL beaker
250-mL graduated cylinder
water
chalk
piece of quartz
piece of clay
small wooden block
small metal block
small cork
rock
ruler

Goals

- **List** some ways that the density of an object can be measured.
- **Design** an experiment that compares the densities of several materials.

Safety Precautions

WARNING: *Be wary of sharp edges on some of the materials and take care not to break the beaker or graduated cylinder. Wash hands thoroughly with soap and water when finished.*

Test Your Hypothesis

Make a Plan

❏ 1. As a group, agree upon and write the hypothesis statement. Think about what you know about density.

❏ 2. As a group, list the steps that you need to take to test your hypothesis. Be specific, describing exactly what you will do at each step.

❏ **List** your materials.

❏ 3. Working as a group, use the equation: density = mass/volume. Devise a method of determining the mass and volume of each material to be tested. **Hint:** *You can use a triple beam to measure mass. You can measure volume by using a graduated cylinder.*

❏ 4. **Design** a data table like the one on the next page on a separate sheet of paper so that it is ready to use as your group collects data.

❏ 5. **Read** over your entire experiment to make sure that all steps are in a logical order.

❏ 6. Should you run the process more than once for any of the materials?

❏ 7. **Identify** any constants, variables, and controls of the experiment. **Hint:** *A constant is a variable that you do not change. Variables are things that you can change. The control is your standard for comparison.*

(continued)

LAB A

Follow Your Plan

- ❑ **1.** Make sure your teacher approves your plan before you start.
- ❑ **2.** Carry out the experiment as planned.
- ❑ **3.** While the experiment is going on, write any observations that you make and complete the data table you made.

Object	Mass	Volume	Density	Observations

Analyze Your Data

1. **Observe** Do you observe anything about the way objects with greater density feel compared with objects of lower density?

2. **Predict** Which of those objects you measured directly would float in water? Which would sink?

3. **Predict** how your volume measurements might be affected by using a tool to push a floating object under water. Explain how this error might increase or decrease the density you obtained.

Conclude and Apply

1. **Form Hypotheses** Based on your results, would you hypothesize that a cork is more dense, the same density, or less dense than water?

2. **Draw Conclusions** Without measuring the density of an object that floats, conclude how you know that it has a density of less than 1.0 g/cm^3.

3. **Predict** Would the density of the clay be affected if you were to break it into smaller pieces?

LAB (continued) **LAB A**

4. **Explain** why ships float, even though they are made mostly of steel that has a density much greater than that of water.

Communicating Your Data

Write an informational pamphlet on different methods for determining the density of objects. Include equations and a step-by-step procedure.

Name Date Class

Design Your Own

Determining Density

LAB B

Lab Preview

Directions: *Answer these questions before you begin the Lab.*

1. Why does this lab include the sharp object safety symbol?

____

____

2. What equation is used to determine the density of an object?

____

Real-World Question

Which has a greater density—a rock or a piece of wood? Is cork more dense than clay? Density is the ratio of an object's mass to its volume.

Form a Hypothesis

State a hypothesis about what process you can use to measure and compare the densities of several materials.

Possible Materials

pan
triple-beam balance
100-mL beaker
250-mL graduated cylinder
water
chalk
piece of quartz
piece of clay
small wooden block
small metal block
small cork
rock
ruler

Goals

- **List** some ways that the density of an object can be measured.
- **Design** an experiment that compares the densities of several materials.

Safety Precautions

WARNING: *Be wary of sharp edges on some of the materials and take care not to break the beaker or graduated cylinder. Wash hands thoroughly with soap and water when finished.*

Test Your Hypothesis

Make a Plan

- ❑ 1. As a group, agree upon and write the hypothesis statement.
- ❑ 2. As a group, list the steps that you need to take to test your hypothesis. Be specific, describing exactly what you will do at each step. List your materials.
- ❑ 3. Working as a group, use the equation: density = mass/volume. Devise a method of determining the mass and volume of each material to be tested.
- ❑ 4. **Design** a data table on a separate sheet of paper so that it is ready to use as your group collects data.
- ❑ 5. **Read** over your entire experiment to make sure that all steps are in a logical order.
- ❑ 6. Should you run the process more than once for any of the materials?
- ❑ 7. **Identify** any constants, variables, and controls of the experiment.

Follow Your Plan

- ❑ 1. Make sure your teacher approves your plan before you start.
- ❑ 2. Carry out the experiment as planned.
- ❑ 3. While the experiment is going on, write any observations that you make and complete the data table you made.

LAB (continued)

LAB B

Analyze Your Data

Put table here:

1. **Observe** Do you observe anything about the way objects with greater density feel compared with objects of lower density?

2. **Predict** Which of those objects you measured directly would float in water? Which would sink?

3. **Predict** how your volume measurements might be affected by using a tool to push a floating object under water. Explain how this error might increase or decrease the density you obtained.

Conclude and Apply

1. **Form Hypotheses** Based on your results, would you hypothesize that a cork is more dense, the same density, or less dense than water?

2. **Draw Conclusions** Without measuring the density of an object that floats, conclude how you know that it has a density of less than 1.0 g/cm^3.

3. **Predict** Would the density of the clay be affected if you were to break it into smaller pieces?

4. **Explain** why ships float, even though they are made mostly of steel that has a density much greater than that of water.

LAB (continued) **LAB B**

Challenge

1. **Evaluate** Why is aluminum often used in manufacturing airplane parts? Why is titanium used to make racing bicycles?

2. **Analyze** Which would be more dense: a sports bottle filled with water or a sports bottle filled with ice and water?

3. **Analyze** To make the fizzy bubbles in sparkling water, still water is injected with carbon dioxide gas. How would you expect the density of still water to compare to the same volume of water after carbonation?

Extension

Predict Which would be more dense: a diet drink or a nondiet version of the same drink? Design a lab to test your prediction.

Communicating Your Data

Write an informational pamphlet on different methods for determining the density of objects. Include equations and a step-by-step procedure.

Chapter Test A — Matter

I. Testing Concepts

Directions: *In the blank at the left, write the letter of the term that best completes each statement.*

______ **1.** A ______ of water is that it changes to hydrogen and oxygen gas when an electrical current passes through it.
a. physical property
b. chemical property
c. covalent bond
d. mixture

______ **2.** ______ is a physical property of a rock.
a. Density **b.** Rust **c.** Flammability **d.** Reactivity

______ **3.** Atoms of the same element that have different numbers of neutrons are called ______.
a. radioactive **b.** electrons **c.** periodic **d.** isotopes

______ **4.** The number of neutrons is determined by subtracting the ______ from the mass number.
a. atomic number **b.** isotopes **c.** electrons **d.** atoms

______ **5.** Matter is anything that has ______ and takes up space.
a. atoms **b.** minerals **c.** mass **d.** elements

Directions: *Match each phrase with the correct term.*

Matching Set 1

______ **6.** electrically charged atoms
______ **7.** particles with a negative charge
______ **8.** groups of atoms connected by covalent bonds
______ **9.** substances made of only one type of atom

a. molecules
b. ions
c. electrons
d. elements

Chapter Test A (continued)

Matching Set 2

_______ **10.** a mixture in which elements are not mixed evenly and each component retains its own properties

_______ **11.** a mixture in which components are evenly mixed throughout

_______ **12.** measure of the mass of an object divided by its volume

_______ **13.** another name for a homogeneous mixture

_______ **14.** atoms of more than one element combined

e. compound

f. heterogeneous

g. homogeneous

h. solution

i. density

II. Understanding Concepts

Skill: Making and Using Tables

Directions: *Use the sentences and phrases to complete the table. Then, use the table to compare and contrast compounds and mixtures.*

- **contain atoms of more than one type of element**
- **contain two or more substances**
- **not chemically combined**
- **chemically bonded together**
- **The properties are different from the properties of the elements that combine to form them.**
- **may be represented by a chemical formula**
- **may be separated**
- **may be heterogeneous or homogeneous**

Compounds	Mixtures
1.	5.
2.	6.
3.	7.
4.	8.

9. How are compounds and mixtures similar?

____

10. How are compounds and mixtures different?

____

____

Chapter Test A (continued)

Skill: Labeling a Diagram

Directions: *Label the internal structure of the atom using these terms:* **nucleus, electron cloud, proton,** *and* **neutron.**

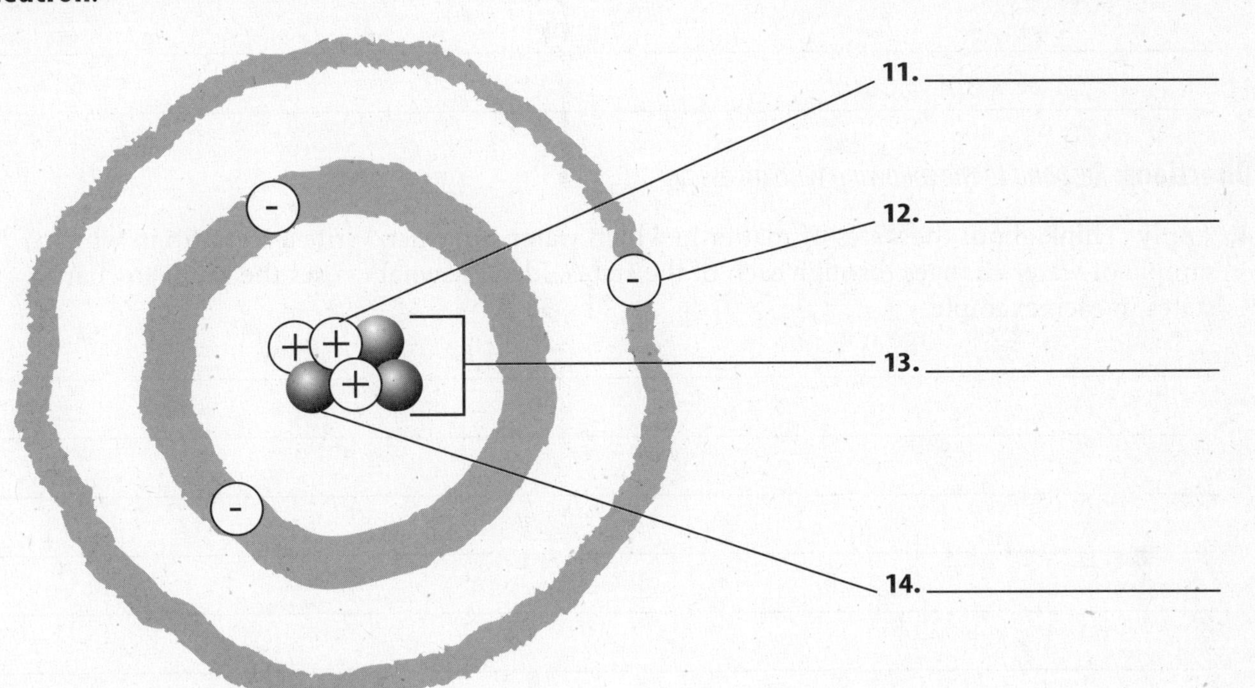

III. Applying Concepts

Writing Skills

Directions: *Answer the following questions on the lines or in the space provided.*

1. **Give Example** List the states of matter and give an example for each.

2. **Show** Make a drawing that shows how water forms a compound.

Chapter Test A (continued)

3. **Categorize** A student mixes water, lemon juice, and a sweetener to make lemonade. What kind of mixture was created? How do you know?

____

____

____

Directions: *Respond to the following with an essay.*

4. **Apply** Think about the states of matter in which water can exist. Write a scenario in which a sample of water changes through each of the states. Identify what causes the water to change states in each example.

____

____

____

____

____

____

Name Date Class

Matter

I. Testing Concepts

Directions: *In the blank at the left, write the letter of the term that best completes the sentence.*

______ **1.** A(n) ______ is the basic unit of matter.
a. electron **b.** molecule **c.** atom **d.** space

______ **2.** Properties of matter that do not change a substance into a new substance are ______ properties.
a. chemical **b.** atomic **c.** physical **d.** solid

______ **3.** ______ are particles without electric charge in the atom's nucleus.
a. Neutrons **b.** Electrons **c.** Ions **d.** Protons

______ **4.** Electrically charged atoms are called ______.
a. electrons **b.** isotopes **c.** molecules **d.** ions

______ **5.** Hydrogen-1 and hydrogen-2 are ______ of one another.
a. ions **b.** conductors **c.** isotopes **d.** compounds

______ **6.** The density of a substance is a ______ of the substance.
a. state of matter **c.** solution
b. physical property **d.** chemical property

______ **7.** Anything that takes up space and has mass is ______.
a. a compound **b.** an element **c.** matter **d.** plasma

______ **8.** Tea with sugar is an example of a(n) ______.
a. mixture **b.** gas **c.** compound **d.** element

______ **9.** A positively charged ______ has more protons than electrons.
a. ion **b.** isotope **c.** neutron **d.** molecule

______ **10.** Isotopes of carbon have different ______.
a. numbers of electrons **c.** atomic numbers
b. mass numbers **d.** numbers of protons

______ **11.** ______ are particles located in an atom's nucleus.
a. Electrons and neutrons **c.** Protons and electrons
b. Only electrons **d.** Protons and neutrons

______ **12.** On Earth, water is naturally found in all of these states except ______.
a. gas **b.** liquid **c.** solid **d.** plasma

______ **13.** At its boiling point, a liquid becomes a ______.
a. gas **b.** liquid **c.** solid **d.** plasma

______ **14.** State of matter can be changed by ______ or temperature.
a. weight **b.** density **c.** pressure **d.** observation

______ **15.** H_2O is a compound formed by sharing ______.
a. neutrons **b.** electrons **c.** ions **d.** protons

Name Date Class

Chapter Test B (continued)

Directions: *Identify each statement as* **true** *or* **false***. Rewrite false statements to make them correct.*

______ **16.** A substance with greater density than water will sink in water.

____

______ **17.** A compound is a group of substances in which each substance retains its own properties.

____

____

______ **18.** One chemical property of a substance is its density.

____

______ **19.** A substance that expands to completely fill a container is a liquid.

____

______ **20.** A proton is a positively charged particle in an atom's nucleus.

____

Directions: *If the statement or term identifies a compound, list its number under "Compound." If it identifies a mixture, list its number under "Mixture."*

Compound	Mixture
______	______
______	______
______	______
______	______
______	______

21. H_2O or NaCl

22. It has properties that differ from those of its separate elements.

23. a solution

24. Its components can be separated by physical means.

25. It can be formed by atoms sharing electrons or by negative and positive ions joining.

26. air or salt water

27. It is made up of two or more compounds.

28. Its components keep their own properties.

29. It requires a chemical change to be separated.

30. carbon dioxide

Chapter Test B (continued)

II. Understanding Concepts

Skill: Making and Using a Table

Directions: *Complete the table. Then use the table to answer the questions.*

Atom	Number of protons	Number of neutrons	Number of electrons	Atomic number	Mass number
1. a	6		6		12
2. b		0	1	1	
3. c	11		10		23
4. d		8	6	6	
5. e	17		18		35
6. f	12	12	12		
7. g		10	10	9	

8. Which two substances are isotopes of one another? Explain why they are isotopes.

9. Identify the particles that are ions and tell how you know they are ions.

10. Identify the positively charged ion and explain why its charge is positive.

11. Which atom could combine with atom e to form a compound? Explain why they could combine.

12. Can atoms e and g combine to form a compound? Explain.

Skill: Outlining

13. In an outline, the subtopics are neutron, proton, and electron. What would the main topic be?

Name Date Class

Skill: Concept Mapping

14. In a network-tree concept map, what word would complete the diagram?

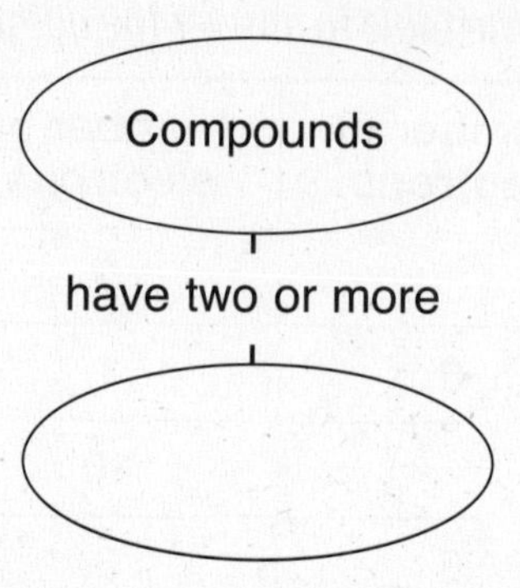

III. Applying Concepts

1. If you place 100 mL of water in a beaker and boil the water, will you have more or less liquid after the water has boiled for five minutes? Explain your answer.

2. **Identify** the state of matter of each of the following substances. Explain the relationship of the different atoms or molecules in the substances and tell how each substance would fit into a container.

   a. egg whites

   b. frozen juice bars

IV. Writing Skills

3. Use your knowledge of the state of matter and the other physical properties of matter to write an explanation for what may have caused the following situation.
   Situation: Although it hasn't rained in a week, every morning the grass and car windows are wet.

Name _______________ Date _______________ Class _______________

Matter

I. Testing Concepts

Directions: *Identify each statement as* **true** *or* **false**. *If the statement is false, change the underlined term to make it correct.*

______ **1.** There are four states of <u>matter</u>: solid, liquid, gas, and plasma.

____

______ **2.** Ice melts as thermal energy is added, causing the rate of movement of its molecules to <u>decrease</u>.

____

______ **3.** Changes in <u>state</u> can occur because of increases or decreases in pressure.

____

______ **4.** Density, temperature, and <u>reactivity to water</u> are all physical properties of matter.

____

______ **5.** Another name for a <u>heterogeneous</u> mixture is a solution.

____

______ **6.** Water molecules are polar molecules. The positive side of one molecule attracts the <u>positive side</u> of another molecule.

____

Directions: *Match each example on the left with the correct term.*

Matching Set 1

______ **7.** copper

______ **8.** salt

______ **9.** beach sand

______ **10.** Na^{+}

______ **11.** lemonade

a. homogeneous mixture

b. heterogeneous mixture

c. compound

d. element

e. ion

Name ____________________ Date ____________ Class ____________

II. Understanding Concepts

Skill: Making a Diagram

Directions: *Create a diagram showing the internal structure of an atom. Label the parts.*

1.

Skill: Using a Table

2. Complete the table. Then, use the table to answer the questions.

	Number of Protons	Number of Neutrons	Number of Electrons	Atomic Number	Mass Number
Hydrogen-1		0	1	1	1
Hydrogen-2		1	1	1	2
Hydrogen-3	1	2	1		3
Carbon-12	6		6		12
Carbon-13	6		6	6	14

3. What would be a good title for this table?

____

4. Are any of these ions? Why or why not?

____

____

____

5. Are these atoms likely to form bonds? If so, what type of bonds would they form?

____

____

____

____

Chapter Test C (continued)

III. Applying Concepts

Directions: *Answer the following questions on the lines provided.*

1. **Analyze** A chef makes a salad dressing by mixing vinegar and oil. Before she mixes it, the oil floats on top of the vinegar. Why does the oil float on top?

2. **Critique** A teacher uses a magnet to demonstrate how ionic bonds are formed. Is this a good model? Why or why not?

3. **Reason** A student fills a glass with water until it overflows. Then the student drops water from a dropper onto the top of the water in the glass. Predict what will happen to the water in the glass and explain your prediction.

4. **Judge** One student says water is a compound, so salt water must also be a compound. A second student disagrees. Who is right? Why?

Chapter Test C (continued)

Writing Skills

Directions: *Respond to the following with an essay.*

5. **Suggest** Plasma is the most common state of matter in the universe. Write a paragraph explaining plasma and suggesting why it is common throughout the universe, yet rare on Earth.

Name Date Class

Mineral Identification

LAB A

Lab Preview

Directions: *Answer these questions before you begin the Lab.*

1. What safety symbols are associated with this lab?

____

2. What are all the possible properties that minerals have that can be used to determine their identities?

____

____

Although certain minerals can be identified by observing only one property, others require testing several properties to identify them.

Real-World Question

How can you identify unknown minerals?

Goals

- **Hypothesize** which properties of each mineral are most useful for identification purposes.
- **Test** your hypothesis as you attempt to identify unknown mineral samples.

Materials

mineral samples
magnifying lens
pan balance
graduated cylinder
safety goggles
**Alternate materials*

**copper penny*
glass plate
small iron nail
steel file
water
piece of copper

5% HCl with dropper
Mohs scale of hardness
Minerals Appendix
**minerals field guide*
streak plate

Safety Precautions

WARNING: *If an HCl spill occurs, notify your teacher and rinse with cool water until you are told to stop. Do not taste, eat, or drink any lab materials.*

Procedure

❑ 1. Copy the data table from page 81 of the textbook into your Science Journal or onto a sheet of paper.

❑ 2. Obtain a set of unknown minerals.
- ❑ Each sample has a number on it. Record these numbers in the data table as a way to keep track of your samples.

❑ 3. Observe a numbered mineral specimen carefully.
- ❑ **Write** a star in the table entry that represents what you hypothesize is an important physical property.
- ❑ **Choose** one or two properties that you think will help most in identifying the sample.

(continued)

- ❑ **4.** Perform tests to observe your chosen properties first.
  - ❑ **a.** To estimate hardness:
    - ❑ Rub the sample firmly against objects of known hardness and observe whether it leaves a scratch on the objects.
    - ❑ Estimate a hardness range based on which items the mineral scratches.
  - ❑ **b.** To estimate specific gravity: Perform a density measurement.
    - ❑ Use the pan balance to determine the sample's mass, in grams.
    - ❑ Measure its volume using a graduated cylinder partially filled with water. The amount of water displaced by the immersed sample, in mL, is an estimate of its volume in cm^3.
    - ❑ Divide mass by volume to determine density. This number, without units, is comparable to specific gravity.
- ❑ **5.** With the help of the Mineral Appendix or a field guide, attempt to identify the sample using the properties from step 2. Perform more physical property observations until you can identify the sample. Repeat steps 2 through 4 for each unknown.

Analyze Your Data

1. Which properties were most useful in identifying your samples? Which properties were least useful?

____

2. **Compare** the properties that worked best for you with those that worked best for other students.

____

Conclude and Apply

1. **Determine** two properties that distinguish clear, transparent quartz from clear, transparent calcite. Explain your choice of properties.

____

2. Which physical properties would be easiest to determine if you found a mineral specimen in the field?

____

____

Communicating Your Data

For three minerals, list physical properties that were important for their identification. **For more help, refer to the Science Skill Handbook.**

____

Name Date Class

LAB Mineral Identification

LAB B

Lab Preview

Directions: *Answer these questions before you begin the Lab.*

1. What safety symbols are associated with this lab?

2. What are all the possible properties that minerals have that can be used to determine their identities?

Although certain minerals can be identified by observing only one property, others require testing several properties to identify them.

Real-World Question

How can you identify unknown minerals?

Goals

- **Hypothesize** which properties of each mineral are most useful for identification purposes.
- **Test** your hypothesis as you attempt to identify unknown mineral samples.

Materials

mineral samples
magnifying lens
pan balance
graduated cylinder
safety goggles
**Alternate materials*

**copper penny*
glass plate
small iron nail
steel file
water
piece of copper

5% HCl with dropper
Mohs scale of hardness
Minerals Appendix
**minerals field guide*
streak plate

Safety Precautions

WARNING: *If an HCl spill occurs, notify your teacher and rinse with cool water until you are told to stop. Do not taste, eat, or drink any lab materials.*

(continued)

LAB B

Procedure

❑ **1.** Copy the data table from page 81 of the textbook into your Science Journal or onto a sheet of paper.

❑ **2.** Obtain a set of unknown minerals.

❑ **3.** Observe a numbered mineral specimen carefully. Write a star in the table entry that represents what you hypothesize is an important physical property. Choose one or two properties that you think will help most in identifying the sample.

❑ **4.** Perform tests to observe your chosen properties first.

a. To estimate hardness:
Rub the sample firmly against objects of known hardness and observe whether it leaves a scratch on the objects.
Estimate a hardness range based on which items the mineral scratches.

b. To estimate specific gravity: Perform a density measurement.
Use the pan balance to determine the sample's mass, in grams.
Measure its volume using a graduated cylinder partially filled with water. The amount of water displaced by the immersed sample, in mL, is an estimate of its volume in cm^3.
Divide mass by volume to determine density. This number, without units, is comparable to specific gravity.

❑ **5.** With the help of the Mineral Appendix or a field guide, attempt to identify the sample using the properties from step 2. Perform more physical property observations until you can identify the sample. Repeat steps 2 through 4 for each unknown.

Analyze Your Data

1. Which properties were most useful in identifying your samples? Which properties were least useful?

____

2. **Compare** the properties that worked best for you with those that worked best for other students.

____

Conclude and Apply

1. **Determine** two properties that distinguish clear, transparent quartz from clear, transparent calcite. Explain your choice of properties.

____

2. Which physical properties would be easiest to determine if you found a mineral specimen in the field?

____

____

Challenge

1. **Reason** Why would geologists look at both the color of the rock and the color of the streak?

2. **Analyze** Physical properties that can be observed with the unaided eye are helpful in determining a mineral's identity. However, most scientists use an X-ray machine or optical microscope and a chemical test to arrive at a definite answer. What might these tools help determine?

3. **Analyze** Why might some geologists consider the density of a mineral one of the most reliable physical properties for identification?

Extension

Create Think about what you learned about the usefulness of various physical properties in identifying minerals. Create a diagram of steps that could be used to determine a mineral's identity. Be sure to include a description of how you would perform each step.

Communicating Your Data

For three minerals, list physical properties that were important for their identification. **For more help, refer to the Science Skill Handbook.**

Name _______________ Date _______________ Class _______________

Minerals

I. Testing Concepts

Directions: *In the blank at the left, write the letter of the term that best completes each statement.*

_____ 1. The Mohs scale measures the _____ of a mineral.
a. streak **b.** cut **c.** hardness **d.** luster

_____ 2. _____ is the way a mineral reflects light.
a. Streak **b.** Luster **c.** Cleavage **d.** Fracture

_____ 3. The specific gravity of a mineral compares the ratio of its weight to an equal volume of _____.
a. gold **b.** air **c.** talc **d.** water

_____ 4. Streak is the _____ of a mineral in its powdered form.
a. color **b.** texture **c.** luster **d.** cleavage

_____ 5. Minerals that break along smooth, flat surfaces have _____.
a. fractures **b.** cleavage **c.** streaks **d.** breakage

_____ 6. Quartz is a mineral with _____; it breaks with uneven, rough, or jagged surfaces.
a. texture **b.** luster **c.** fracture **d.** cleavage

Directions: *Match each description with the correct term.*

Column I	Column II
_____ 7. a highly prized mineral	**a.** crystal
_____ 8. a mineral or rock that contains a useful substance that can be mined for profit	**b.** gem
_____ 9. a solid in which the atoms are arranged in orderly, repeating patterns	**c.** silicates
_____ 10. minerals that contain silicon and oxygen	**d.** magma
_____ 11. hot, melted rock	**e.** ore

Chapter Test A (continued)

II. Understanding Concepts

Skill: Concept Mapping

Directions: *Complete the concept map by identifying the characteristics that all minerals share. Use the following terms:* **inorganic, natural, crystalline,** *and* **chemical**. *Write your answers on the lines below the map.*

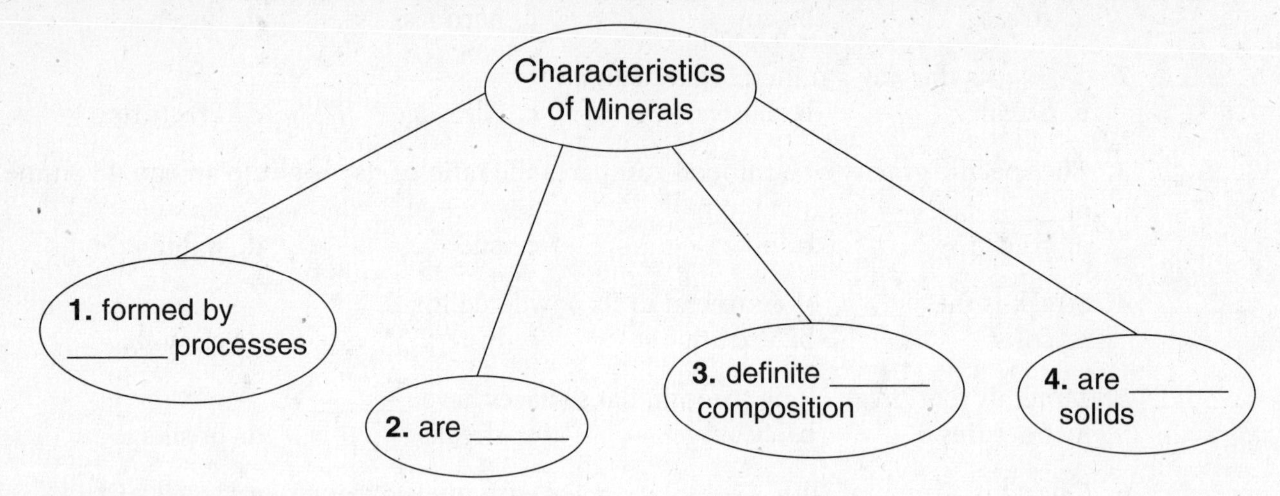

1. ______________________________
2. ______________________________
3. ______________________________
4. ______________________________

Skill: Classifying

Directions: *Write* **yes** *next to the substances that are minerals. Write* **no** *next to the substances that are not minerals.*

Are they minerals?

______ **5.** oil

______ **6.** quartz

______ **7.** titanium

______ **8.** oxygen

______ **9.** diamond

Chapter Test A (continued)

Skill: Sequencing

Directions: *For each series, number the events in the order that they occur.*

Crystals created from magma:

______ **10.** It combines into compounds arranged in orderly, repeating patterns.

______ **11.** Magma rises to the surface and cools.

Crystals created from solution:

______ **12.** The water evaporates.

______ **13.** Ions that are left behind form crystals.

______ **14.** Minerals dissolve in water.

III. Applying Concepts

Writing Skills

Directions: *Respond to the following using complete sentences.*

1. **Explain** A miner finds a mineral that looks like gold. Explain why the mineral cannot be identified based on appearance alone.

2. **Describe** How can you use streak to identify a mineral?

3. **Give an example** of a gem that is more valuable than other minerals.

4. **Give an example** of a gem that is not only beautiful, but also useful. Explain how it is used.

Chapter Test A (continued)

5. **Describe** Define *ore.* Describe how aluminum is refined from the ore bauxite.

Name ____________________ Date ____________ Class ____________

Minerals

I. Testing Concepts

Directions: *Determine whether the statements below are* **true** *or* **false.** *In each false statement, circle the word that makes the statement false and write the correct word on the line after the statement.*

______ **1.** A mineral is a crystalline liquid. ____________________

______ **2.** Some minerals form when magma cools. ____________________

______ **3.** The phrase "crystal structure" refers to the repeating patterns in which atoms are arranged in a crystal. ____________________

______ **4.** Some crystals are formed from minerals dissolved in liquids. ____________________

______ **5.** When liquid evaporates, mineral molecules may come together to form crystals. ____________________

______ **6.** Minerals that are different in other properties may be alike in color. ____________________

______ **7.** Tests for hardness and streak help identify minerals. ____________________

______ **8.** Two types of cleavage are metallic and glassy. ____________________

______ **9.** Fracture is the tendency of a mineral to break along a smooth, flat surface. ____________________

______ **10.** Minerals called ores are mined because they contain beautiful substances. ____________________

Directions: *Match the descriptions in Column I with the terms in Column II. Write the letter of the correct pair of words in the blank at the left.*

Column I	Column II
______ **11.** properties that make titanium useful for tennis rackets and wheelchairs	**a.** usefulness, profitability
______ **12.** minerals mined for titanium	**b.** lightness, durability
______ **13.** products in which titanium is used	**c.** ilmenite, rutile
______ **14.** qualities of a stone that make it a gemstone	**d.** automobiles, aircraft
______ **15.** qualities of a mineral that classify it as ore	**e.** beauty, rarity

Chapter Test B (continued)

Directions: *For each of the following, write the letter of the term or phrase that best completes the sentence.*

______ **16.** Most minerals are composed of ______ combined with other elements.
a. carbon and hydrogen
b. silicon and oxygen
c. calcium and oxygen
d. chlorine and sodium

______ **17.** A crystal is always ______.
a. a hexagon **b.** a cube **c.** a liquid **d.** none of these

______ **18.** One important use for titanium is ______.
a. soft drink cans
b. lawn furniture
c. automobile body parts
d. cooking equipment

______ **19.** A mineral is classified as an ore as long as ______.
a. it's rare and valuable
b. it can be used for jewelry
c. it's profitable and useful
d. it's solid and natural

______ **20.** Titanium ores can occur as ______.
a. vein mineral deposits
b. beach sands
c. magma-formed rocks
d. all of the above

______ **21.** Crystals may be ______.
a. cubic **b.** monoclinic **c.** tetragonal **d.** all of these

______ **22.** All of the following are minerals **EXCEPT** ______.
a. salt **b.** quartz **c.** sugar **d.** gold

______ **23.** Most common rock-forming minerals are ______.
a. gems **b.** ores **c.** silicates **d.** oxides

______ **24.** A salt crystal is ______ in shape.
a. cubic **b.** hexagonal **c.** tetragonal **d.** monoclinic

______ **25.** One of the softest minerals is ______.
a. graphite **b.** diamond **c.** corundum **d.** amethyst

II. Understanding Concepts

Directions: *Answer the following questions on the lines provided.*

1. **List** four characteristics all minerals share.

____

____

2. What partly determines the type of mineral formed by cooling magma?

____

____

Chapter Test B (continued)

3. How would a collector of minerals determine the hardness of an unknown mineral specimen?

____

____

4. What three qualities of titanium make it a good material for producing hip or knee replacements?

____

5. Coal, like graphite, is composed of carbon. Unlike graphite, coal is formed from decayed, once-living matter. Is it a mineral? Explain your answer.

____

____

6. **Explain** why most quartz is not considered a gemstone while amethyst, which is a kind of quartz, is a gemstone.

____

____

____

Skill: Comparing and Contrasting

7. Extracting minerals for human use can have both advantages and disadvantages. List two advantages and two disadvantages.

____

____

____

Skill: Concept Mapping

8. In the process of mining for bauxite ore, what is the first item: processing to get aluminum, locating the mineral, or mining the bauxite?

____

Skill: Classifying

Directions: *Classify the following materials by writing* **M** *for mineral,* **G** *for gem,* **O** *for ore, and* **N** *for none. Some may have more than one label.*

______ 9. diamond

______ 10. hematite

______ 11. sphalerite

______ 12. halite

______ 13. quartz

______ 14. pyrite

______ 15. magma

Chapter Test B (continued)

III. Applying Concepts

Writing Skills

Directions: *Answer the following questions using complete sentences.*

1. Why are ilmenite and rutile considered to be ores?

2. Today, most mining for ores involves digging beneath Earth's surface. Why is this necessary?

3. Why is sugar **NOT** a mineral?

4. What is the relationship between magma and minerals?

5. What are two ways in which the crystals of a mineral may form? Include an explanation of how the space where they form may affect the crystal.

6. Why are many minerals silicates?

Name ________________ Date ________________ Class ________________

Minerals

I. Testing Concepts

Directions: *Determine whether the statements below are* **true** *or* **false**. *If the statement is false, change the underlined word(s) to make it correct.*

______ **1.** There are five major crystal systems that have similar atomic arrangements and external crystal shapes.

____

______ **2.** Evaporites are most likely to form in moist climates.

____

______ **3.** Magma is hot melted minerals.

____

______ **4.** The specific gravity of a mineral is the ratio of its weight compared with the weight of an equal volume of water.

____

______ **5.** Streak is more useful than mineral color for mineral identification.

____

Directions: *Fill in the blank with the word or words that best complete the sentence.*

6. Most industrial diamonds and other gems are ____________________, which means that humans make them.

7. Most gems are special varieties of a particular ____________________.

8. ____________________ is a gem form of quartz that contains traces of iron in its structure.

9. Rubies are used to produce ____________________.

10. ____________________ crystals are used in watches to help keep time.

11. A mineral is a(n) ____________________ if it contains a useful substance that can be mined at a profit.

12. During ____________________, a substance is melted to separate it from any unwanted materials that may remain.

13. ____________________ is used to make soft-drink cans, foil, and car parts.

14. Mineral deposits that fill in open spaces created by weaknesses are called

____________________ deposits.

Chapter Test C (continued)

II. Understanding Concepts

Skill: Concept Mapping

Directions: *Create two maps illustrating two ways that minerals form.*

1. Crystals from Solution

2. Crystals from Magma

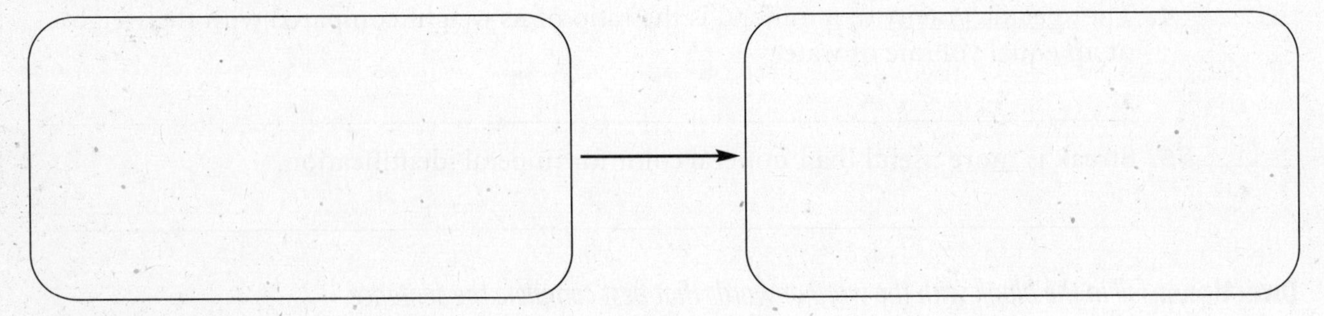

Skill: Classifying

Directions: *Create a diagram to sort the following into the categories* gem, mineral, *and* ore: **peridot, hematite, tanzanite, bauxite, amethyst,** *and* **sapphire.**

3–8.

Skill: Interpreting Scientific Illustrations

Directions: *Write the answer in the space provided.*

9. **Distinguish** If you were shown photographs of graphite and fluorite, how could you use luster to distinguish the two?

III. Applying Concepts

Writing Skills

Directions: *Answer the following questions using complete sentences.*

1. **Deduce** A miner finds a mineral that looks like gold. When he compares it to a similar-sized sample of gold that he found last week, the new sample feels lighter. Why is this so? How could the miner accurately determine the type of mineral he found?

2. **Defend** A friend argues that gems shouldn't be worth much since they are only used for jewelry and other decorations. Create an argument disagreeing with his assertion.

3. **Analyze** A geologist performs a streak test on a sample of corundum, but a streak does not appear. Why?

Chapter Test C (continued)

4. **Classify** The coal briquettes that are used in barbecue grills come from the ground. Decaying plant matter is transformed by extreme heat and pressure into coal, which is used for many purposes. Name the four characteristics of a mineral and use these to determine whether coal is a mineral.

5. **Analyze** Can a mineral have both cleavage and fracture? Why or why not?

6. **Infer** What can you infer from a mineral's cleavage patterns?

Name Date Class

LAB

Sedimentary Rocks

LAB A

Lab Preview

Directions: *Answer these questions before you begin the Lab.*

1. What warning does the eye safety symbol in this lab give you?

2. How do the materials for classifying sedimentary rocks differ from the materials you used for classifying igneous rocks?

Sedimentary rocks are formed by compaction and cementation of sediment. Because sediment is found in all shapes and sizes, do you think these characteristics could be used to classify detrital sedimentary rocks? Sedimentary rocks also can be classified as chemical, or organic.

Real-World Question

How are rock characteristics used to classify sedimentary rocks as detrital, chemical, or organic?

Goals

- **Observe** sedimentary rock characteristics.
- **Compare and contrast** sedimentary rock textures.
- **Classify** sedimentary rocks as detrital, chemical, or organic.

Materials

unknown sedimentary rock samples
marking pen
5% hydrochloric acid (HCl)
dropper
paper towels
water
magnifying lens
metric ruler

Safety Precautions

WARNING: *HCl is an acid and can cause burns. Wear goggles and a lab apron. Rinse spills with water and wash hands afterward.*

Procedure

❑ 1. **Complete** the procedure below and fill in the Sedimentary Rock Samples table in the Data and Observations section.

❑ 2. **Determine** the sizes of sediments in each sample, using a magnifying lens and a metric ruler.

❑ Using **Table 2,** in your textbook, classify any grains of sediment in the rocks as gravel, sand, silt, or clay. In general, the sediment is silt if it is gritty and just barely visible, and clay if it is smooth and if individual grains are not visible.

❑ 3. Put a few drops of 5% HCl solution on each rock sample. Bubbling on a rock indicates the presence of calcite.

❑ 4. **Examine** each sample for fossils and describe any that are present.

❑ 5. **Determine** whether each sample has a granular or nongranular texture.

Analyze Your Data

❑ 1. **Classify** your samples as detrital, chemical, or organic. **Hint:** *Look at the pictures of each rock type in your text.*

❑ 2. **Identify** each rock sample.

 (continued)

LAB A

Data and Observations

Sedimentary Rock Samples

Sample	Observations	Minerals or Fossils Present	Sediment Size	Detrital Chemical, or Organic	Rock Name
A					
B					
C					
D					
E					

Conclude and Apply

1. **Explain** why you tested the rocks with acid. What minerals react with acid?

2. **Compare and contrast** sedimentary rocks that have a granular texture with sedimentary rocks that have a nongranular texture.

Communicating Your Data

Compare your conclusions with those of other students in your class. **For more help, refer to the Science Skill Handbook.**

Name ______ Date ______ Class ______

Sedimentary Rocks

LAB B

Lab Preview

Directions: *Answer these questions before you begin the Lab.*

1. What warning does the eye safety symbol in this lab give you?

______

2. How do the materials for classifying sedimentary rocks differ from the materials you used for classifying igneous rocks?

______

______

Sedimentary rocks are formed by compaction and cementation of sediment. Because sediment is found in all shapes and sizes, do you think these characteristics could be used to classify detrital sedimentary rocks? Sedimentary rocks also can be classified as chemical, or organic.

Real-World Question

How are rock characteristics used to classify sedimentary rocks as detrital, chemical, or organic?

Goals

- **Observe** sedimentary rock characteristics.
- **Compare and contrast** sedimentary rock textures.
- **Classify** sedimentary rocks as detrital, chemical, or organic.

Materials

unknown sedimentary rock samples
marking pen
5% hydrochloric acid (HCl)
dropper
paper towels
water
magnifying lens
metric ruler

Safety Precautions

WARNING: *HCl is an acid and can cause burns. Wear goggles and a lab apron. Rinse spills with water and wash hands afterward.*

Procedure

❑ 1. **Complete** the procedure below and fill in the Sedimentary Rock Samples table in the Data and Observations section.

❑ 2. **Determine** the sizes of sediments in each sample, using a magnifying lens and a metric ruler. Using **Table 2,** in your textbook, classify any grains of sediment in the rocks as gravel, sand, silt, or clay. In general, the sediment is silt if it is gritty and just barely visible, and clay if it is smooth and if individual grains are not visible.

❑ 3. Put a few drops of 5% HCl solution on each rock sample. Bubbling on a rock indicates the presence of calcite.

❑ 4. **Examine** each sample for fossils and describe any that are present.

❑ 5. **Determine** whether each sample has a granular or nongranular texture.

Analyze Your Data

❑ 1. **Classify** your samples as detrital, chemical, or organic.

❑ 2. **Identify** each rock sample.

 (continued)

LAB B

Data and Observations

Sedimentary Rock Samples

Sample	Observations	Minerals or Fossils Present	Sediment Size	Detrital Chemical, or Organic	Rock Name
A					
B					
C					
D					
E					

Conclude and Apply

1. **Explain** why you tested the rocks with acid. What minerals react with acid?

2. **Compare and contrast** sedimentary rocks that have a granular texture with sedimentary rocks that have a nongranular texture.

Challenge

1. **Infer** What observations did you make about grain size? What can you infer from these observations?

(continued) **LAB B**

2. **Consider** What types of rocks do you think would most likely be found in your area? Why?

3. **Evaluate** Which of the characteristics was most helpful in evaluating the rock's identity? Which was least helpful? Why?

Extension

Create Make a chart that could be used to record observations about metamorphic and sedimentary rocks. What headings would the chart have? How would the columns for metamorphic rocks and sedimentary rocks be similar and different?

Communicating Your Data

Compare your conclusions with those of other students in your class. **For more help, refer to the Science Skill Handbook.**

Name _______________ Date _______________ Class _______________

Rocks

I. Testing Concepts

Directions: *In the blank at the left, write the letter of the term that best completes each statement.*

______ 1. ______ rock is formed when magma cools and hardens.
a. Sedimentary **b.** Igneous **c.** Metamorphic **d.** Crystal

______ 2. Magma that reaches Earth's surface and flows from volcanoes is called ______.
a. lava **b.** intrusive **c.** foliated **d.** stacked

______ 3. Rocks that have changed because of changes in temperature and pressure or the presence of hot, watery fluids are called ______ rock.
a. igneous **b.** sedimentary **c.** metamorphic **d.** mineral

______ 4. ______ such as rock fragments and shells may be moved by wind, water, ice, or gravity.
a. Sediments **b.** Minerals **c.** Crystals **d.** Rocks

______ 5. ______ forms when sediments are pressed and cemented together or when minerals form from solutions.
a. Igneous rock
b. Sedimentary rock
c. Metamorphic rock
d. Mineral

Directions: *Match the descriptions in Column I with the terms in Column II. Write the letter of the correct term in the blank at the left.*

Column I	Column II
______ 6. rocks that form as lava cools on the surface of Earth	**a.** intrusive
______ 7. rocks that form from magma below the surface	**b.** extrusive
______ 8. rocks with mineral grains lined up in parallel layers	**c.** foliated
______ 9. rocks with mineral grains that do not form layers	**d.** nonfoliated

Chapter Test A (continued)

II. Understanding Concepts

Skill: Outlining

Directions: *Complete the outline for metamorphic rocks.*

I. Metamorphic rocks

A. Source of material

1. ______________________________

2. ______________________________

3. ______________________________

B. Cause of change

4. ______________________________

5. ______________________________

II. Igneous rocks

III. Sedimentary rocks

Skill: Concept Mapping

Directions: *Complete the concept map below with the following terms:* **andesitic, basaltic, granitic, dense and dark, light-colored and low density, found around the rim of the Pacific Ocean,** *and* **magma type.**

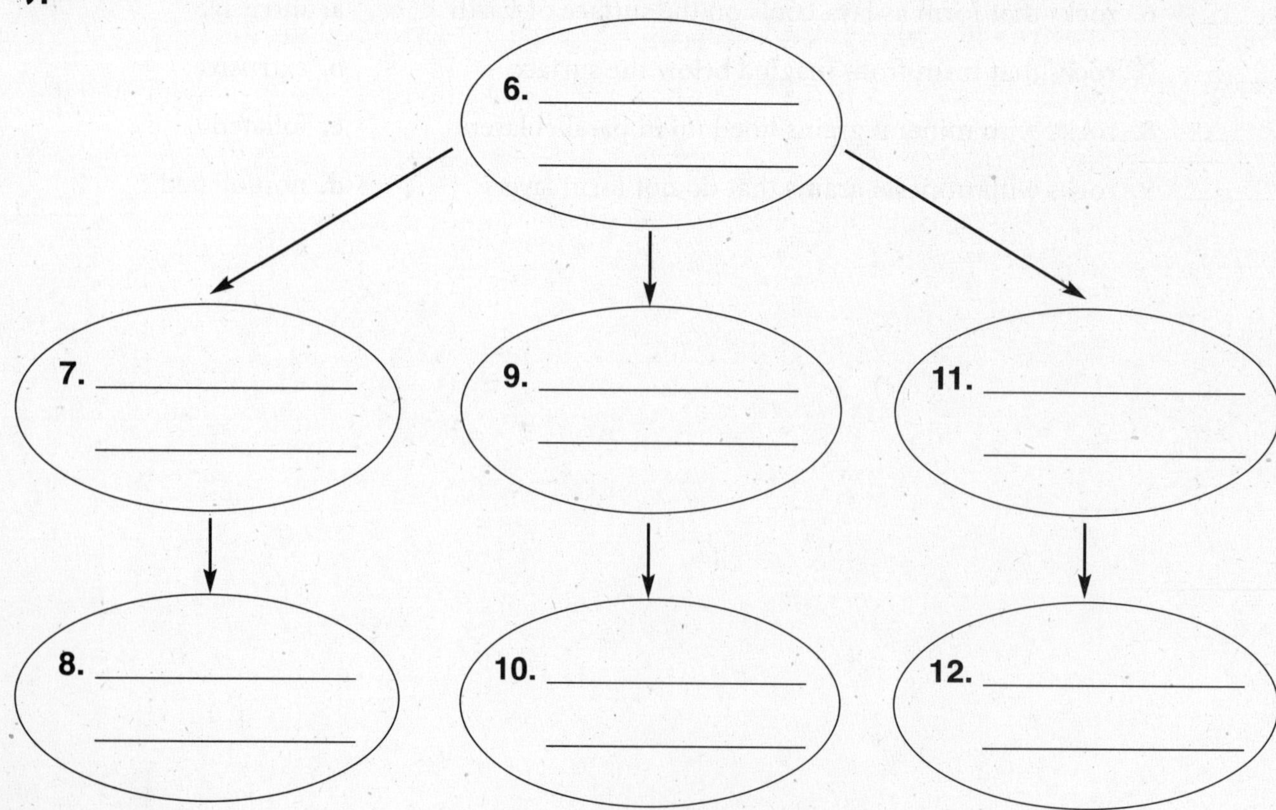

Name ____________________ Date ____________________ Class ____________________

Chapter Test A (continued)

Skill: Sequencing

Directions: *Place an* **X** *next to the event that occurs first.*

13. Heat and pressure cause rocks to melt and magma to form.

Shale turns into slate.

14. Rocks form as mineral grains grow together.

Magma cools, and atoms and compounds in the liquid rearrange to form mineral grains.

III. Applying Concepts

Directions: *Identify each description of rock as* **igneous, metamorphic,** *or* **sedimentary.**

____________________ **1.** intrusive or extrusive

____________________ **2.** detrital, chemical, or organic

____________________ **3.** foliated or nonfoliated

____________________ **4.** sandstone

____________________ **5.** slate

____________________ **6.** granite

Writing Skills

Directions: *Respond to the following using complete sentences.*

7. State How are rocks and minerals related?

____

____

____

8. Describe How can an igneous rock move through the rock cycle and help form a sedimentary rock?

____

____

____

____

Name _______________ Date _______________ Class _______________

Rocks

I. Testing Concepts

Directions: *For each of the following, write the letter of the term that best completes the statement.*

______ **1.** Magma that cools below Earth's surface forms _____ rock.
a. extrusive metamorphic
b. extrusive igneous
c. intrusive metamorphic
d. intrusive igneous

______ **2.** The processes involved in the rock cycle include all of the following **EXCEPT** ______.
a. condensation **b.** erosion **c.** weathering **d.** compaction

______ **3.** Foliated rocks are distinguished by ______.
a. large pores
b. layers
c. the enlargement of mineral grains
d. the shape and size of the sediments

______ **4.** Lava that cools quickly forms ______ rocks.
a. extrusive metamorphic
b. extrusive igneous
c. intrusive metamorphic
d. intrusive igneous

______ **5.** Metamorphic rocks can be formed from all of the following **EXCEPT** ______.
a. the formation of minerals from solutions
b. the presence of hot, watery fluids
c. temperature
d. pressure

______ **6.** Quartz is a mineral; granite is ______.
a. also a mineral **b.** a rock **c.** glass **d.** mica

______ **7.** A classification of metamorphic rocks would include whether they are ______.
a. chemical or organic
b. intrusive or extrusive
c. foliated or nonfoliated
d. basaltic or granitic

______ **8.** Sedimentary rocks are ______.
a. formed below Earth's surface as magma
b. a type of foliated igneous rock
c. formed by great heat
d. formed from already existing rocks that are weathered and eroded

______ **9.** Andesitic rocks have mineral compositions between those of ______ and basaltic rocks.
a. conglomerate
b. metamorphic
c. granitic
d. organic

______ **10.** The changes that take place in the rock cycle ______.
a. create matter
b. destroy matter
c. create and destroy matter
d. never create nor destroy matter

Chapter Test B (continued)

_____ 11. Detrital rocks are _____.
a. made of fragments of other rocks
b. formed from magma
c. precipitated from solution
d. all of these

_____ 12. The rock cycle indicates that each type of rock can _____.
a. provide materials to make other rocks
b. form other types of rocks
c. be changed by natural processes
d. all of the above

_____ 13. Pumice, obsidian, and scoria are kinds of _____.
a. granite
b. volcanic glass
c. intrusive rocks
d. andesitic rocks

_____ 14. A rock is _____.
a. always made of molten material
b. a mixture of minerals, organic matter, volcanic glass, or other materials
c. a pure mineral
d. either igneous or sedimentary

_____ 15. The crystals that form in slowly cooling magma are generally _____.
a. nonexistent
b. invisible
c. tiny
d. large

_____ 16. Detrital rocks are named according to _____.
a. their ages
b. their locations
c. the size and shape of the sediments
d. the color of the sediments

_____ 17. Sedimentary rocks are usually classified as _____.
a. intrusive or extrusive
b. foliated or nonfoliated
c. basaltic, granite, or andesitic
d. detrital, chemical, or organic

II. Understanding Concepts

Directions: *Identify each statement as* **true** *or* **false**. *Rewrite false statements to make them correct.*

_____ 1. The composition of a sedimentary rock depends upon the composition of the rocks and living things its sediments came from.

____

____

_____ 2. All igneous rocks have the same mineral compositions.

____

____

_____ 3. Nonfoliated rocks have very narrow layering.

____

____

Name ____________________ Date ____________________ Class ____________________

Chapter Test B (continued)

______ **4.** Sedimentary rock can be formed from changes in igneous rock, but igneous rock cannot be formed from changes in sedimentary rock.

____

____

____

______ **5.** Metamorphic rocks can form from other metamorphic rocks.

____

____

____

______ **6.** Metamorphic rocks can form from igneous but not from sedimentary rocks.

____

____

____

Skill: Interpreting Data

Directions: *Use the information about igneous rocks A–D to classify each one as* **intrusive** *or* **extrusive** *and* **basaltic** *or* **granitic**. *Fill in the chart with A, B, C, or D.*

Rock A–dark-colored large grains
Rock B–large crystals, high percentage of silica
Rock C–fine-grained texture, light-colored
Rock D–from Hawaiian volcano area, no visible crystals

	Extrusive	Intrusive
Basaltic	7.	8.
Granitic	9.	10.

Skill: Concept Mapping

Directions: *Write the answers in the space provided.*

11. In a concept map, would you list basaltic lava under high silica content or low silica content?

____

12. In a concept map, would you list intrusive rocks under rocks that form above the ground or below?

____

Chapter Test B (continued)

Skill: Interpreting Scientific Illustrations

Directions: *Write the answer in the space provided.*

13. If you were shown one photograph of pumice and one of granite, how could you distinguish between the two rocks?

____

Skill: Sequencing

Directions: *For each item, tell which event would occur first.*

14. Molten material cools and forms igneous rocks. Lava flows from a volcano.

____

15. Gneiss is formed. The mineral grains in granite are flattened under pressure.

____

III. Applying Concepts

Directions: *Identify each rock as* **igneous, metamorphic,** *or* **sedimentary.**

_______________ 1. sandstone

_______________ 2. granite

_______________ 3. rock salt

_______________ 4. obsidian

_______________ 5. gneiss

_______________ 6. slate

_______________ 7. limestone

IV. Writing Skills

Directions: *Answer the following questions using complete sentences.*

1. **Describe** the differences among detrital, chemical, and organic rocks.

____

____

____

____

____

2. Where does the rock cycle begin?

____

____

Name ______ Date ______ Class ______

Chapter Test C

Rocks

I. Testing Concepts

Directions: *Determine whether the statements below are* **true** *or* **false**. *If the statement is false, change the underlined term to make it correct.*

______ **1.** The rock cycle destroys and creates matter.

____

______ **2.** Processes that are part of the rock cycle change rocks slowly over time.

____

______ **3.** Lava is molten rock that flows under Earth's surface.

____

______ **4.** Because magma is denser than the surrounding rock, it is pushed toward the surface.

____

______ **5.** Because basalt is an intrusive rock, it forms beneath Earth's surface.

____

Directions: *Fill in the blanks to complete the sentences.*

6. When molten rock material, or ______________, cools and hardens, ______________ rock forms.

7. ______________ rocks form as magma cools and hardens beneath Earth's surface.

8. ______________ rocks form as lava cools and hardens on Earth's surface.

9. Changes in pressure, ______________, or the presence of ______________ can cause metamorphic rocks to form.

10. Hot fluids that move through and react with preexisting rock are composed mainly of ______________ and ______________.

11. Texture and ______________ determine how a metamorphic rock is classified.

12. Sedimentary rocks form as ______________, with older layers near the ______________ of an undisturbed stack.

13. ______________ come from weathered and eroded rocks.

14. During ______________, sediments can stick together and form solid rock.

15. ______________ occurs when minerals are deposited between the pieces of sediment.

Name Date Class

Chapter Test C (continued)

II. Understanding Concepts

Skill: Outlining

1. **Create** an outline showing the material source and causes of change for metamorphic rocks.

Skill: Concept Mapping

Directions: *Create a concept map about sedimentary rocks. Include how the rocks are classified and how they are formed.*

2.

Skill: Sequencing

Directions: *Number the sentences in each group 1, 2, or 3 to show the sequence of events. Then, on the line below, identify the process that is described.*

______ **3.** The sediments are covered by more layers.

______ **4.** The sediments are pressed and cemented together to form new rock.

______ **5.** Sediments from rock fragments and shells are moved by wind and water.

6. ______________________________

______ **7.** Heat and pressure build up around rocks.

______ **8.** Minerals exchange atoms with surrounding minerals, and new, bigger minerals form.

______ **9.** The rocks melt, and magma forms.

10. ______________________________

______ **11.** When the magma reaches the surface, it cools and solidifies.

______ **12.** Rock melts and forms magma.

______ **13.** Magma is forced upward toward the surface because it is less dense than the solid rock.

14. ______________________________

III. Applying Concepts

Writing Skills

Directions: *Categorize each rock as* **igneous, metamorphic,** *or* **sedimentary**.

______________ **1.** pumice

______________ **2.** shale

______________ **3.** obsidian

______________ **4.** conglomerate

______________ **5.** diorite

______________ **6.** quartzite

______________ **7.** marble

______________ **8.** coal

Chapter Test C (continued)

Directions: *Respond to the following using complete sentences.*

9. **Contrast** A friend places a sample of basaltic rock in one box and an equal-sized sample of granitic rock in another box. How might you tell the rocks apart without opening the boxes? How could you check your hypothesis once you opened the boxes?

____

____

10. **Appraise** A friend wants to enter his rock collection, which includes volcanic glass, quartz, chalk, feldspar, limestone, mica, and pumice, in the science fair. What advice would you offer your friend?

____

____

11. **Construct** Create a diagram to model the rock cycle.

Name Date Class

Model and Invent

Home Sweet Home

LAB A

Lab Preview

Directions: *Answer these questions before you begin the Lab.*

1. Where can you find information about home energy use?

____

2. What are some ways a home uses energy?

____

____

As fossil fuel supplies continue to be depleted, an increasing U.S. population has recognized the need for alternative energy sources. United States residents might be forced to consider using inexhaustible and other renewable energy resources to meet some of their energy needs. The need for energy-efficient housing is more relevant now than ever before. A designer of energy-efficient homes considers proper design and structure, a well chosen building site with wise material selection, and selection of efficient energy generation systems to power the home. Energy-efficient housing uses less energy and produces fewer pollutants.

Real-World Question

What does the floor plan, building plan, or a model of an energy efficient home look like? How and where should your house be designed and built to use the alternative energy resources you've chosen efficiently?

Goals

- **Research** various inexhaustible and other energy resources available to use in the home.
- **Design** blueprints for an energy-efficient home and/or design and build a model of an energy-efficient home.

Possible Materials

paper	cardboard
ruler	glue
pencils	aluminum foil

Make a Model

Plan

- ❑ 1. **Research** current information about energy-efficient homes.
- ❑ 2. **Research** inexhaustible energy resources such as wind, hydroelectric power, or solar power, as well as energy conservation.
  - ❑ **Decide** which energy resources are most efficient for your home design.
- ❑ 3. **Decide** where your house should be built to use energy efficiently.
- ❑ 4. **Decide** how your house will be laid out and draw mock blueprints for your home. Think about things such as where windows should be placed to take advantage of heat from the Sun.
  - ❑ **Highlight** energy issues such as where solar panels can be placed.
- ❑ 5. **Build** a model of your energy-efficient home.

(continued)

LAB A

Do

- ❑ **1.** Ask your peers for input on your home.
  - ❑ As you research, become an expert in one area of alternative energy generation and share your information with your classmates.
- ❑ **2.** **Compare** your home's design to energy-efficient homes you learn about through your research.

Test Your Model

- ❑ **1.** **Think** about how most of the energy in a home is used. Remember as you plan your home that energy-efficient homes not only generate energy—they also use it more efficiently.
- ❑ **2.** Carefully consider where your home should be built. For instance, if you plan to use wind power, will your house be built in an area that receives adequate wind?
- ❑ **3.** Be sure to plan for backup energy generation. For instance, if you plan to use mostly solar energy, what will you do if it's a cloudy day?

Analyze Your Data

Devise a budget for building your home. Could your energy-efficient home be built at a reasonable price? Could anyone afford to build it?

____

____

Conclude and Apply

Create a list of pro and con statements about the use of energy-efficient homes. Why aren't inexhaustible and other renewable energy sources widely used in homes today?

____

____

____

Communicating Your Data

Present your model to the class. Explain which energy resources you chose to use in your home and why. Have an open house. Take prospective home owners/classmates on a tour of your home and sell it.

Name Date Class

Model and Invent

Home Sweet Home

LAB B

Lab Preview

Directions: *Answer these questions before you begin the Lab.*

1. Where can you find information about home energy use?

2. What are some ways a home uses energy?

As fossil fuel supplies continue to be depleted, an increasing U.S. population has recognized the need for alternative energy sources. United States residents might be forced to consider using inexhaustible and other renewable energy resources to meet some of their energy needs. The need for energy-efficient housing is more relevant now than ever before. A designer of energy-efficient homes considers proper design and structure, a well chosen building site with wise material selection, and selection of efficient energy generation systems to power the home. Energy-efficient housing uses less energy and produces fewer pollutants.

Real-World Question

What does the floor plan, building plan, or a model of an energy efficient home look like? How and where should your house be designed and built to use the alternative energy resources you've chosen efficiently?

Goals

- **Research** various inexhaustible and other energy resources available to use in the home.
- **Design** blueprints for an energy-efficient home and/or design and build a model of an energy-efficient home.

Possible Materials

paper	cardboard
ruler	glue
pencils	aluminum foil

Make a Model

Plan

- ❑ 1. **Research** current information about energy-efficient homes.
- ❑ 2. **Research** inexhaustible energy resources such as wind, hydroelectric power, or solar power, as well as energy conservation. Decide which energy resources are most efficient for your home design.
- ❑ 3. **Decide** where your house should be built to use energy efficiently.
- ❑ 4. **Decide** how your house will be laid out and draw mock blueprints for your home. Highlight energy issues such as where solar panels can be placed.
- ❑ 5. **Build** a model of your energy-efficient home.

 (continued)

LAB B

Do

- ❑ 1. Ask your peers for input on your home. As you research, become an expert in one area of alternative energy generation and share your information with your classmates.
- ❑ 2. **Compare** your home's design to energy-efficient homes you learn about through your research.

Test Your Model

- ❑ 1. **Think** about how most of the energy in a home is used. Remember as you plan your home that energy-efficient homes not only generate energy—they also use it more efficiently.
- ❑ 2. Carefully consider where your home should be built. For instance, if you plan to use wind power, will your house be built in an area that receives adequate wind?
- ❑ 3. Be sure to plan for backup energy generation. For instance, if you plan to use mostly solar energy, what will you do if it's a cloudy day?

Analyze Your Data

Devise a budget for building your home. Could your energy-efficient home be built at a reasonable price? Could anyone afford to build it?

____

____

Conclude and Apply

Create a list of pro and con statements about the use of energy-efficient homes. Why aren't inexhaustible and other renewable energy sources widely used in homes today?

____

____

____

Challenge

1. **Analyze** What are some ways that a house uses energy inefficiently?

____

____

2. **Consider** What relationship does a home's location have to the resources that can be used? Give an example.

____

____

____

____

(continued) **LAB B**

3. **Evaluate** Based on your research, what would be the most practical alternative energy source for your community?

Extension

Assess Based on your research, create a home energy survey. Include possible sources of energy inefficiency as well as efficiency. Use this survey to rate the energy efficiency of your school. Create a set of recommendations for improving the school's energy efficiency.

Communicating Your Data

Present your model to the class. Explain which energy resources you chose to use in your home and why. Have an open house. Take prospective home owners/classmates on a tour of your home and sell it.

Name ______ Date ______ Class ______

Earth's Energy and Mineral Resources

I. Testing Concepts

Directions: *Determine whether the statements below are* **true** *or* **false**. *If the statement is false, change the underlined term to make it true.*

______ **1.** Coal, oil, and biomass are fossil fuels.

____

______ **2.** Synthetic fuels are human-made fuels that can be derived from coal.

____

______ **3.** The recycling process for aluminum uses more resources than it takes to obtain new material.

____

______ **4.** Bituminous coal is the cleanest-burning of all coals.

____

______ **5.** Oil is found in a solid state.

____

______ **6.** Oil and natural gas are made from the decay of ancient marine organisms.

____

Directions: *Match each description of a way energy is produced with the type of energy. Write the letter of the correct term in the blank at the left.*

______ **7.** Cells placed on a school-zone sign actively collect energy from the Sun to make the lights flash.

______ **8.** A large number of windmills are placed in an area to generate electricity.

______ **9.** Water is released from a dam and flows through turbines, generating electricity.

______ **10.** Hot, dry rocks produce steam, which turns a turbine and produces electricity.

______ **11.** Trash is burned to produce electricity.

______ **12.** Energy is released during a fission reaction.

a. hydroelectric energy

b. geothermal energy

c. biomass energy

d. solar energy

e. wind energy

f. nuclear energy

Name Date Class

Chapter Test A (continued)

II. Understanding Concepts

Skill: Using a Diagram

Directions: *Study the following diagram of an oil trap. Then label the diagram using the terms from the list.*

oil **roof rock** **gas** **reservoir rock**

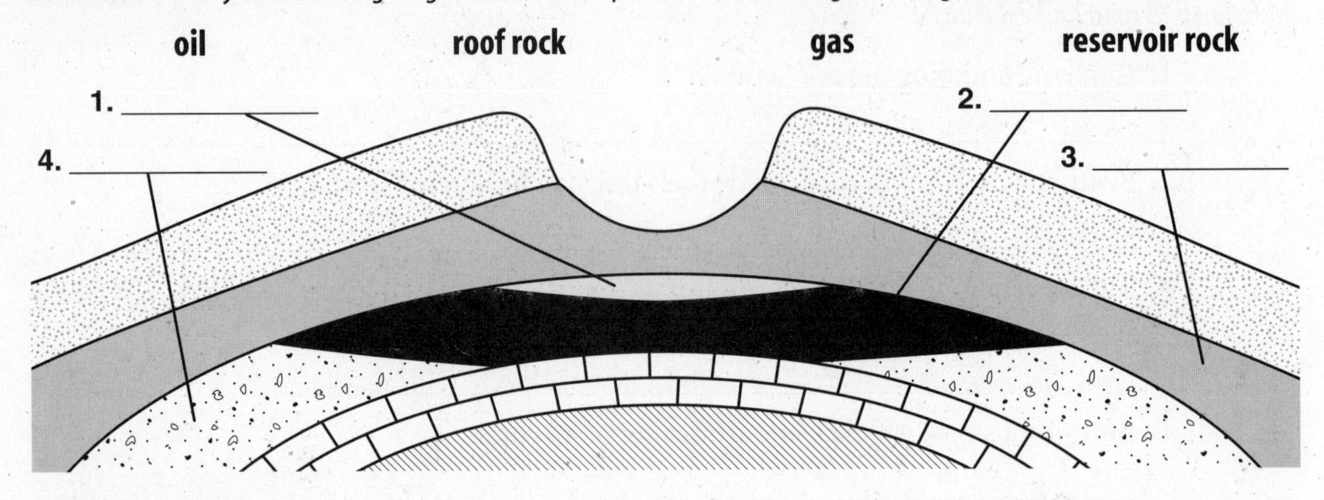

Skill: Using a Graph

Directions: *Study the following diagram of percentage of energy resources used in the United States. Use the diagram to answer the following questions.*

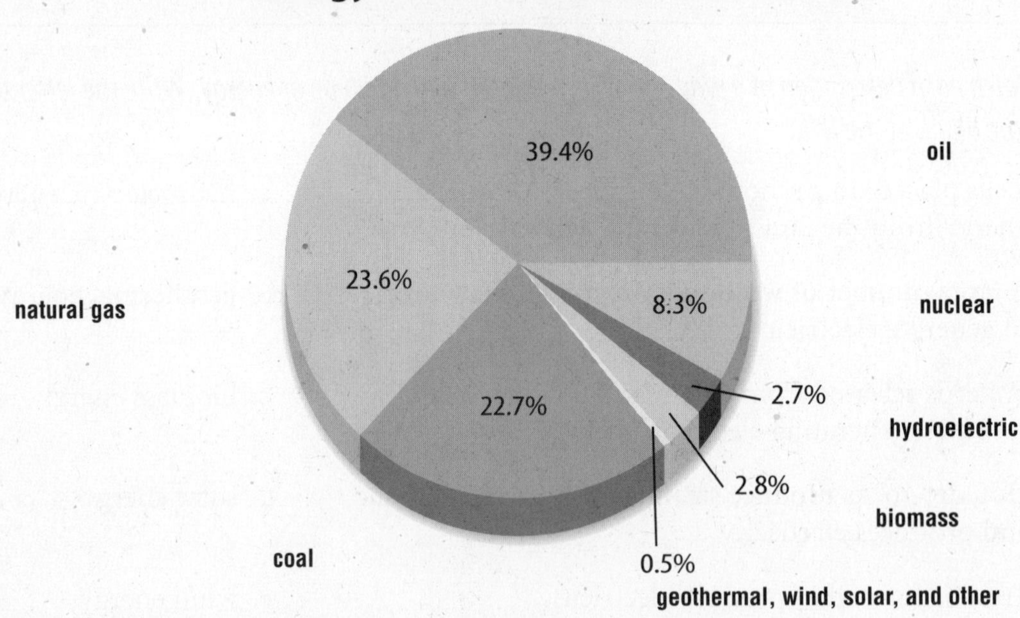

5. What are the three most used sources of energy in the United States?

____

6. Which resources are nonrenewable? ____

Chapter Test A (continued)

7. What percentage of energy used comes from nonrenewable resources?

____

8. Why do you think nonrenewable resources are used more than renewable resources?

____

____

Skill: Categorizing

Directions: *Identify each of these as an advantage* (**A**) *or disadvantage* (**D**).

______ **9.** It takes fossil fuels millions of years to form.

______ **10.** Coal is the most abundant fossil fuel in the world.

______ **11.** Nuclear fission produces radioactive waste.

______ **12.** Strip mining can destroy the habitat.

Directions: *Classify the following as inexhaustible* (**I**) *or renewable* (**R**).

______ **13.** the Sun

______ **14.** biomass

______ **15.** wind

______ **16.** water

______ **17.** geothermal

______ **18.** alcohol

______ **19.** garbage

______ **20.** wood

III. Applying Concepts

Writing Skills

Directions: *Respond to the following using complete sentences.*

1. List What are two metallic and two nonmetallic mineral resources?

____

____

____

2. Explain What makes an ore valuable?

____

____

____

Chapter Test A (continued)

3. **Consider** What determines if a mineral is an ore?

4. **Generalize** Why isn't wind power used more extensively?

Name _______________ Date _______________ Class _______________

Earth's Energy and Mineral Resources

I. Testing Concepts

Directions: *Match the description in the first column with the item in the second column by writing the correct letter in the space provided. Some items in the second column may not be used.*

_____ **1.** oil, natural gas, coal

_____ **2.** forms in a gaseous state under similar conditions as oil

_____ **3.** most abundant fossil fuel in the world

_____ **4.** energy from burning wood, alcohol, or garbage

_____ **5.** soft brown coal made from peat

_____ **6.** marine organisms that decay to make oil and natural gas

_____ **7.** electricity produced by waterpower

_____ **8.** large enough amount of a mineral that can be mined at a profit

_____ **9.** resources used faster than Earth can replace them

_____ **10.** using old materials to make new materials

_____ **11.** energy source produced from atomic reactions

_____ **12.** thick, black liquid

_____ **13.** energy from hot magma

_____ **14.** a large number of windmills generating electricity

_____ **15.** energy from the Sun

a. nonrenewable
b. fossil fuels
c. coal
d. oil
e. natural gas
f. reserve
g. nuclear
h. solar
i. wind farm
j. hydroelectric energy
k. geothermal
l. biomass
m. mineral resources
n. ore
o. recycling
p. lignite
q. plankton

Directions: *For each of the following, write the letter of the term or phrase that best completes the sentence.*

_____ **16.** Waste rock that must be removed before a mineral can be used is called _____
a. ore. **b.** methane. **c.** gangue. **d.** peat.

_____ **17.** Stable molecules that contain carbon and are formed below sea level under low temperatures and high pressures are called _____
a. hydroelectric energy.
b. methane hydrates.
c. industrial minerals.
d. mineral resources.

_____ **18.** _____ is composed of crushed stone or gravel and sand and has many uses in the building industry.
a. Aggregate **b.** Gangue **c.** Limestone **d.** Ore

Chapter Test B (continued)

_______ **19.** Materials of low mass are fused together to form a substance of higher mass during _______
a. smelting. **b.** fission. **c.** refining. **d.** fusion.

_______ **20.** _______ is a chemical process that removes unwanted elements from the metal being processed.
a. Fission **b.** Strip mining **c.** Recycling **d.** Smelting

_______ **21.** The removal of coal that is not close to Earth's surface through a horizontal opening in the side of a hill or mountain is called _______
a. slope mining. **b.** drift mining. **c.** drilling. **d.** strip mining.

_______ **22.** Coal, oil, and natural gas that formed from decaying plants and other organisms over millions of years are called _______
a. renewable resources.
b. mineral resources.
c. fossil fuels.
d. hydrocarbons.

_______ **23.** _______ is an example of inexhaustible energy.
a. Wind energy **b.** Reserve energy **c.** Nuclear energy **d.** Biomass energy

_______ **24.** Biomass energy is derived from burning organic material such as wood, garbage, and _______
a. coal. **b.** oil. **c.** alcohol. **d.** natural gas.

_______ **25.** _______ are compounds containing hydrogen and carbon atoms.
a. Ores
b. Hydrocarbons
c. Methane hydrates
d. Aggregates

II. Understanding Concepts

Skill: Using a Diagram

Directions: *Study the following diagram of an oil trap. Then label the diagram with the correct terms from the list.*

oil **roof rock** **gas** **reservoir rock**

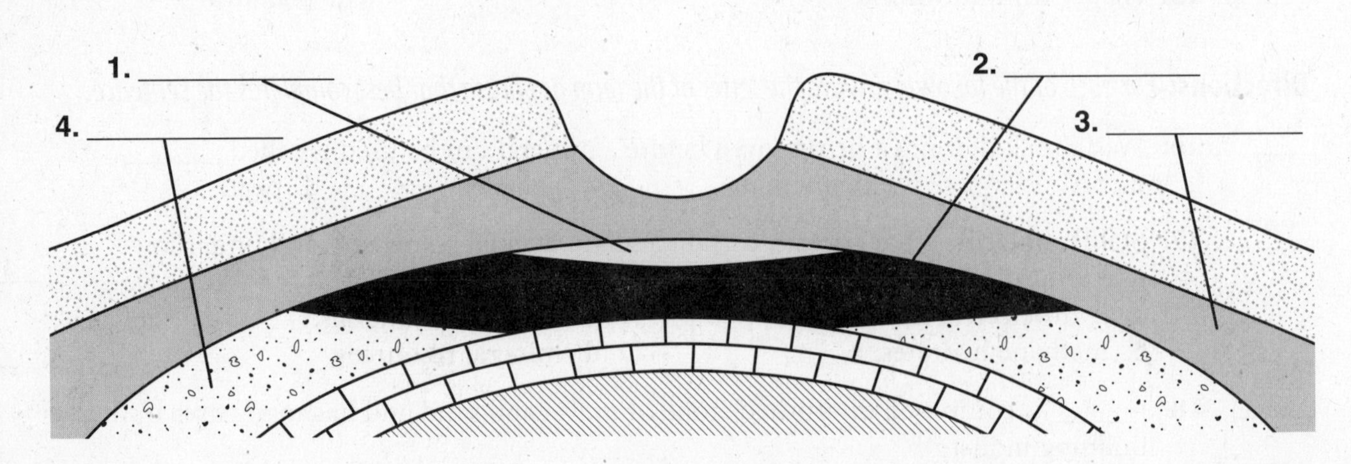

Name Date Class

Chapter Test B (continued)

Directions: *Study the following diagram of percentage of energy resources used in the United States. Then label the circle graph using the correct terms from the list.*

coal	natural gas	nuclear	oil
biomass	hydroelectric	geothermal, wind, solar, and other	

Energy Use in the United States, 2002

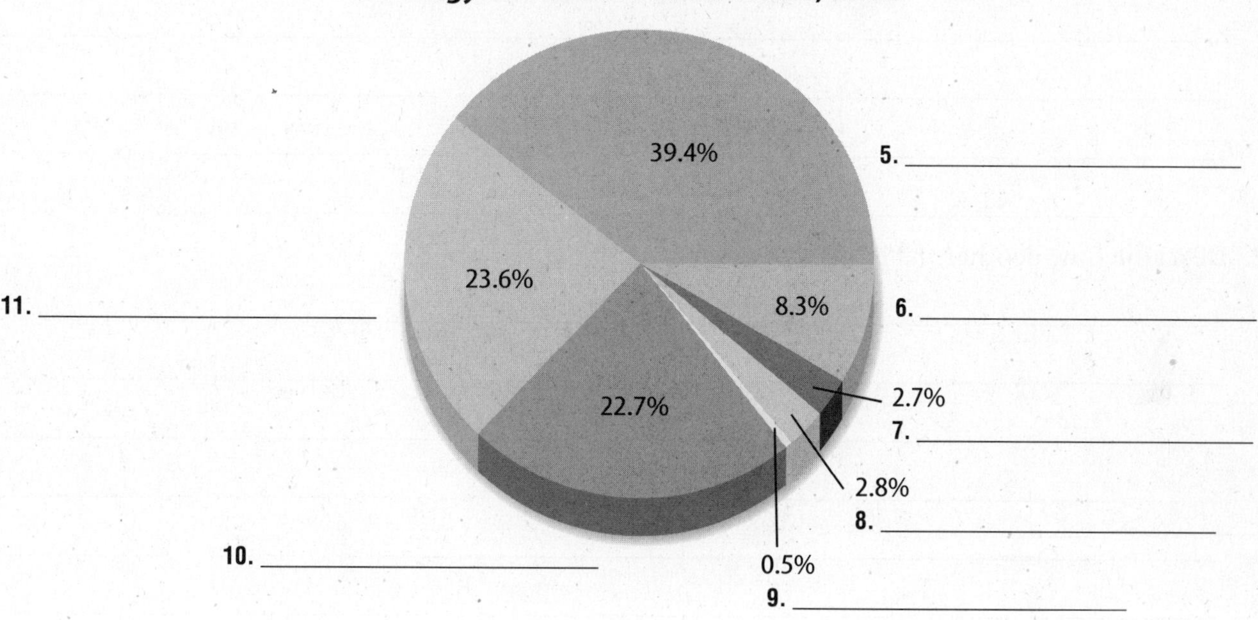

III. Applying Concepts

Directions: *Number the following steps of coal formation in the correct order.*

_____ **1.** Anthracite coal is formed.

_____ **2.** Peat is formed.

_____ **3.** Plants decay.

_____ **4.** Peat changes into lignite.

_____ **5.** Bituminous coal is formed.

Chapter Test B (continued)

IV. Writing Skills

Directions: *Answer the following questions using complete sentences.*

1. **Explain** some of the disadvantages of using nuclear energy.

2. **Describe** how geothermal energy works.

3. **Name** some materials that you can recycle.

4. **Explain** why inexhaustible and renewable resources are used less than nonrenewable resources.

Earth's Energy and Mineral Resources

I. Testing Concepts

Directions: *Determine whether the statements below are* **true** *or* **false**. *If the statement is false, change the underlined term to make it true.*

______ **1.** Oil and natural gas are often found in layers of rock that <u>are flat and thick</u>.

____

______ **2.** Biomass fuel, such as corn, is changed to an alcohol, such as <u>gasoline</u>.

____

______ **3.** Inexhaustible energy resources include the Sun, wind, water, and <u>nuclear</u> energy.

____

______ **4.** During fusion, materials of <u>low mass</u> are fused together to form a substance of <u>higher mass</u>.

____

______ **5.** <u>Natural gas</u> is often referred to as petroleum.

____

Directions: *Fill in the blanks to complete the sentences.*

6. The earliest stage of coal formation is ______________, followed by ______________, ______________, and finally ______________.

7. After coal is mined, the process of ______________, in which trees and grass are replaced, begins.

8. ______________ are stable molecules found hundreds of meters below sea level in ocean floor sediment.

9. ______________ occurs when the nucleus of a heavy element is split, forming lighter elements.

10. One method of refining is ______________.

11. The recycling process often uses less ______________ than it takes to obtain new material.

12. When wood is burned, it releases stored ______________ energy as heat energy.

13. When dams are built, upstream lakes fill with ______________, while downstream, ______________ increases.

14. Erupting volcanoes and geysers are examples of ______________ energy in action.

Chapter Test C (continued)

II. Understanding Concepts

Skill: Create a Diagram

1. Draw a diagram of an oil trap. Then label the diagram with the correct terms, showing the locations of the layers and fossil fuels.

Skill: Using a Graph

Directions: *Complete the following diagram of percentage of energy resources used in the United States. Use the graph to answer the following questions.*

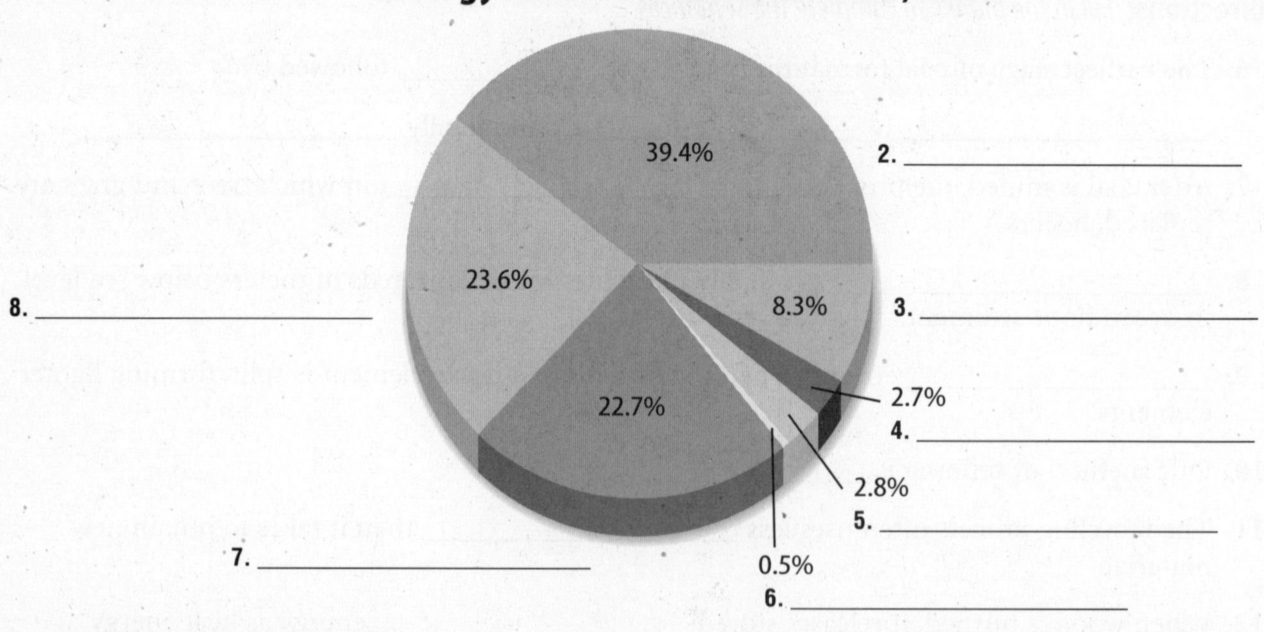

9. Which of these resources are nonrenewable? ____

10. What percentage of energy use comes from nonrenewable resources?

____

11. Why do you think nonrenewable resources are used more than renewable resources?

____

Skill: Classifying

Directions: *List three inexhaustible resources and three renewable resources.*

Inexhaustible

12. ____________________

13. ____________________

14. ____________________

Renewable

15. ____________________

16. ____________________

17. ____________________

Directions: *Classify the following as metallic mineral resources* (**M**) *or nonmetallic mineral resources* (**N**).

______ **18.** limestone

______ **19.** bauxite

______ **20.** halite

______ **21.** hematite

______ **22.** garnet

______ **23.** granite

III. Applying Concepts

Writing Skills

Directions: *Respond to the following using complete sentences.*

1. Consider A geologist discovers a bed of a metallic mineral that is in high demand. There is an abundance of the mineral, but it is deeply embedded in another rock and would be hard to separate. Does this meet the criteria to be classified as an ore? Explain.

____

____

____

2. Evaluate What are the advantages and disadvantages of using fossil fuels and nuclear power for energy?

____

____

____

____

3. Assess Would methane hydrates be considered a reserve?

____

____

____

Name Date Class

Model and Invent

Constructing Landforms

LAB A

Lab Preview

Directions: *Answer these questions before you begin the Lab.*

1. What is a topographic map?

____

2. How does a topographic map show a three dimensional landscape in two dimensions?

____

Most maps perform well in helping you get from place to place. A road map, for example, will allow you to choose the shortest route from one place to another. If you are hiking, though, distance might not be so important. You might want to choose a route that avoids steep terrain. In this case you need a map that shows the highs and lows of Earth's surface, called relief. Topographic maps use contour lines to show the landscape in three dimensions. Among their many uses, such maps allow hikers to choose routes that maximize the scenery and minimize the physical exertion.

Real-World Question

What does a landscape depicted on a two-dimensional topographic map look like in three dimensions?

Goals

- **Research** how contour lines show relief on a topographic map.
- **Determine** what scale you can best use to model a landscape of your choice.
- Working cooperatively with your classmates, model a landscape in three dimensions from the information given on a topographic map.

Possible Materials

U.S. Geological Survey 7.5 minute quadrangle maps
sandbox sand
rolls of brown paper towels
spray bottle filled with water
ruler

Make a Model

❏ **1. Choose** a topographic map showing a landscape easily modeled using sand.
- ❏ Check to see what contour interval is used on the map.
- ❏ Use the index contours to find the difference between the lowest and the highest elevations shown on the landscape. The index contours will be marked with their elevations.
- ❏ Check the distance scale to determine how much area the landscape covers.

❏ **2. Determine** the scale you will use to convert the elevations shown on your map to heights on your model.
- ❏ Make sure the scale is proportional to the distances on your map.

❏ **3. Plan** a model of the landscape in sand by sketching the main features and their scaled heights onto paper. Note the degree of steepness found on all sides of the features.

❑ 4. **Prepare** a document that shows the scale you plan to use for your model and the calculations you used to derive that scale.
  ❑ Remember to use the same scale for distance as you use for height. If your landscape is fairly flat, you can exaggerate the vertical scale by a factor of two or three.
  ❑ Be sure your paper is neat, is easy to follow, and includes all units. Present the document to your teacher for approval.

Test Your Model

❑ 1. Using the sand, spray bottle, and ruler, create a scale model of your landscape on the brown paper towels.

❑ 2. **Check** your topographic map to be sure your model includes the landscape features at their proper heights and proper degrees of steepness.

Analyze Your Data

1. **Determine** if your model accurately represents the landscape depicted on your topographic map. Discuss the strengths and weaknesses of your model.

2. **Explain** why it was important to use the same scale for height and distance. If you exaggerated the height, why was it important to indicate the exaggeration on your model?

Conclude and Apply

1. **Infer** why the mapmakers chose the contour interval used on your topographic map.

2. **Predict** the contour intervals mapmakers might choose for topographic maps of the world's tallest mountains—the Himalayas, and for topographic maps of Kansas, which is fairly flat.

Name Date Class

Model and Invent
Constructing Landforms

LAB B

Lab Preview

Directions: *Answer these questions before you begin the Lab.*

1. What is a topographic map?

____

2. How does a topographic map show a three dimensional landscape in two dimensions?

____

Most maps perform well in helping you get from place to place. A road map, for example, will allow you to choose the shortest route from one place to another. If you are hiking, though, distance might not be so important. You might want to choose a route that avoids steep terrain. In this case you need a map that shows the highs and lows of Earth's surface, called relief. Topographic maps use contour lines to show the landscape in three dimensions. Among their many uses, such maps allow hikers to choose routes that maximize the scenery and minimize the physical exertion.

Real-World Question

What does a landscape depicted on a two-dimensional topographic map look like in three dimensions?

Goals

- **Research** how contour lines show relief on a topographic map.
- **Determine** what scale you can best use to model a landscape of your choice.
- Working cooperatively with your classmates, model a landscape in three dimensions from the information given on a topographic map.

Possible Materials

U.S. Geological Survey 7.5 minute quadrangle maps
sandbox sand
rolls of brown paper towels
spray bottle filled with water
ruler

Make a Model

❑ **1. Choose** a topographic map showing a landscape easily modeled using sand. Check to see what contour interval is used on the map. Use the index contours to find the difference between the lowest and the highest elevations shown on the landscape. Check the distance scale to determine how much area the landscape covers.

❑ **2. Determine** the scale you will use to convert the elevations shown on your map to heights on your model. Make sure the scale is proportional to the distances on your map.

❑ **3. Plan** a model of the landscape in sand by sketching the main features and their scaled heights onto paper. Note the degree of steepness found on all sides of the features.

(continued)

❑ 4. **Prepare** a document that shows the scale you plan to use for your model and the calculations you used to derive that scale. Remember to use the same scale for distance as you use for height. If your landscape is fairly flat, you can exaggerate the vertical scale by a factor of two or three. Be sure your paper is neat, is easy to follow, and includes all units. Present the document to your teacher for approval.

Test Your Model

❑ 1. Using the sand, spray bottle, and ruler, create a scale model of your landscape on the brown paper towels.

❑ 2. **Check** your topographic map to be sure your model includes the landscape features at their proper heights and proper degrees of steepness.

Analyze Your Data

1. **Determine** if your model accurately represents the landscape depicted on your topographic map. Discuss the strengths and weaknesses of your model.

____

____

____

____

2. **Explain** why it was important to use the same scale for height and distance. If you exaggerated the height, why was it important to indicate the exaggeration on your model?

____

____

____

____

Conclude and Apply

1. **Infer** why the mapmakers chose the contour interval used on your topographic map.

____

____

____

2. **Predict** the contour intervals mapmakers might choose for topographic maps of the world's tallest mountains—the Himalayas, and for topographic maps of Kansas, which is fairly flat.

____

____

(continued)

Challenge

1. **Analyze** Why is accuracy important in mapmaking?

2. **Compare and Contrast** How are an aerial photograph and a topographic map alike and different? Why might an aerial photograph be useful in constructing a topographical map?

3. **Predict** Benchmarks are markers. They are used to show actual locations that match those on specifically made maps. A benchmark might appear on a large boulder at the beginning of a hiking trail. Why would the boulder make a good location for a benchmark?

Extension

Diagram Create a new landform using the lab materials. Create a topographic map with contour lines to map this new landform. Remember to keep a consistent scale. Review the three rules for contour lines in your text.

Name _______________ Date _______________ Class _______________

Views of Earth

I. Testing Concepts

Directions: *In the blank at the left, write the letter of the term that best completes each statement.*

______ **1.** The ______ is an imaginary line that runs from the north pole through Greenwich to the south pole.
a. equator **b.** prime meridian **c.** longitude **d.** latitude

______ **2.** Earth is divided into ______ time zones.
a. 24 **b.** 15 **c.** 10 **d.** 3

______ **3.** The map's ______ tells the relationship between the distance on the map and the distances on Earth's surface.
a. title **b.** projection **c.** legend **d.** scale

______ **4.** To understand the symbols used on the map, look at the ______.
a. title **b.** projection **c.** legend **d.** scale

______ **5.** On a topographic map, a ______ connects points of equal elevation.
a. projection **b.** scale **c.** contour line **d.** contour interval

______ **6.** The ______ divides Earth into a northern hemisphere and a southern hemisphere.
a. longitude **b.** latitude **c.** equator **d.** prime meridian

______ **7.** A series of imaginary lines that run from the north pole to the south pole are called ______.
a. latitude lines **b.** longitude lines **c.** primes **d.** contour lines

Directions: *Match each use with the correct map type. Write the letter of the correct map type in the blank at the left.*

Column I	Column II
______ **8.** finding out the height of a mountain trail	**a.** conic projection
______ **9.** determining the path of a hurricane	**b.** topographic map
______ **10.** charting a course for a ship	**c.** Mercator projection
______ **11.** finding a deposit of natural gas	**d.** geologic map
______ **12.** choosing the route for a road trip	**e.** remote sensing

Chapter Test A (continued)

II. Understanding Concepts

Skill: Interpreting Scientific Illustrations

Directions: *Use the map to answer questions 1–4.*

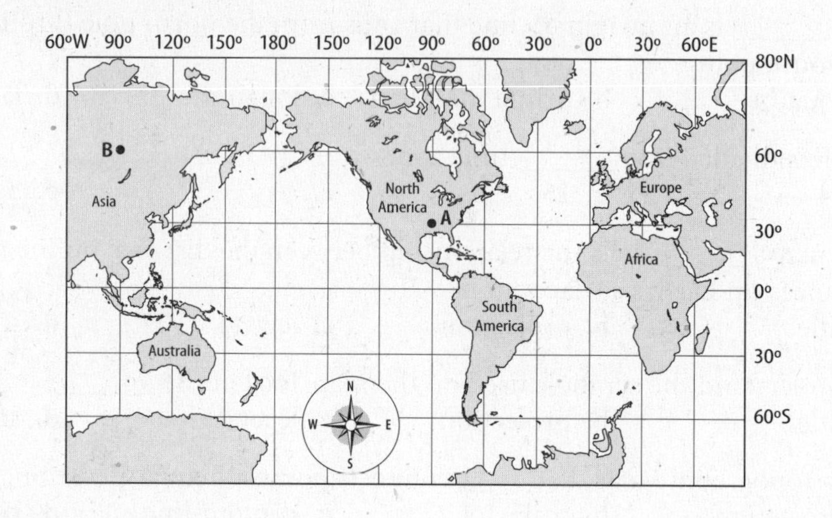

1. What is the latitude of Point B? ______
2. What is the longitude of Point B? ______
3. Which point is closer to the equator? ______
4. If it is 1:30 at point A, would it be earlier or later at Point B? ______

Skill: Making Tables

Directions: *Complete the table using the following phrases.*

found in interior regions **flat raised areas**
large, flat area **edges rise steeply**
made up of uplifted rocks **thick, fertile soil**

Interior Plain	Plateau
5.	8.
6.	9.
7.	10.

Chapter Test A (continued)

Skill: Classifying

Directions: *Use these terms to classify the following according to their mountain type:* **folded, upwarped, fault-block,** *and* **volcanic.**

__________________ **11.** huge, tilted blocks of rock that are separated by faults

__________________ **12.** horizontal layers are squeezed from opposite sides

__________________ **13.** molten rock forms cone-shaped structures at Earth's surface

__________________ **14.** blocks of Earth's crust are pushed up by forces inside Earth

Skill: Measuring in SI

Directions: *Answer the following questions on the lines provided.*

15. A topographic map has a contour interval of 10 m. You are on a trail that begins at 200 m. The trail goes up one contour interval. What is the new elevation?

____

16. The scale on a map indicates that 1 cm = 10 km. The bike path you want to take is 2 cm long on the map. How long is the path?

____

III. Applying Concepts

Directions: *Answer the following questions using complete sentences.*

1. Describe Write about the appearance of upwarped mountains, fault-block mountains, and volcanic mountains.

____

____

____

____

2. Explain A Chicago, IL, resident has a friend who lives in Boston, MA. The two agree to talk on the telephone at 4:00 P.M. When the friend in Chicago calls at 4:00, the second friend is angry that he called so late. Explain what has happened.

____

____

Chapter Test A (continued)

3. **Locate** What continent could you go to if you wanted to be at the equator? What continent could you go to if you wanted to be at the prime meridian?

____

____

4. **Apply** A hiker is trying to choose between two paths. He wants to take a hike on a steep trail. What should the hiker look for on the topographic map?

____

____

5. **Give an Example** How might a computer be useful in creating maps?

____

____

6. **Explain** Why does the size of a coastal plain vary over time?

____

____

Name Date Class

Views of Earth

I. Testing Concepts

Directions: *Match the description in Column I with the term in Column II. Write the letter of the correct term in the blank at the left.*

Column I	Column II
______ 1. distances in degrees east or west of the prime meridian	a. plains
______ 2. large, flat landforms	b. plateaus
______ 3. a way of collecting information about Earth from a distance	c. folded mountains
______ 4. landforms formed when horizontal rock layers are squeezed together and buckle	d. upwarped mountains
______ 5. map projection that shows correct shapes of continents but distorts their areas	e. fault-block mountains
______ 6. landforms made of layers of molten rock	f. volcanic mountains
______ 7. shows the changes in elevation of Earth's surface	g. latitude
______ 8. explains what the symbols used on the map mean	h. prime meridian
______ 9. landforms formed by forces pushing up Earth's crust	i. longitude
______ 10. flat, raised areas of land	j. International Date Line
______ 11. imaginary line that represents 0° longitude	k. Mercator projection
______ 12. map projection showing fairly accurate shapes and land areas of continents	l. Robinson projection
______ 13. the distance in degrees either north or south of the equator	m. conic projection
______ 14. the transition line for calendar days	n. topographic map
______ 15. projection useful for producing maps of small areas	o. contour line
______ 16. the difference in elevation between two side-by-side contour lines	p. contour interval
______ 17. the relationship between the distances on the map and actual distances on Earth	q. map scale
______ 18. imaginary line that circles Earth exactly halfway between the north and south poles	r. remote sensing
______ 19. line on a map that connects points of equal elevation	s. map legend
______ 20. landforms made of huge, tilted blocks of rocks that are separated from surrounding rocks by faults	t. equator

Name _______________ Date _______________ Class _______________

Chapter Test B (continued)

Directions: *Write in the blank at the left the letter of the term or phrase that best completes each item.*

______ **21.** Coastal plains are also referred to as ______.
a. marshes **b.** lowlands **c.** interior plains **d.** plateaus

______ **22.** Since New York time is three hours ahead of Los Angeles time, it's ______ in Los Angeles when it is noon in New York.
a. 3 A.M. **b.** 3 P.M. **c.** 9. A.M. **d.** 9 P.M.

______ **23.** To show distances, a ______ is used on maps.
a. map scale
b. contour line
c. Robinson projection
d. contour interval

______ **24.** Landsat satellites use ______ to make detailed images of Earth's surface.
a. radar
b. different wavelengths of light
c. sound waves
d. radio signals

______ **25.** The Global Positioning System sends ______ to give users their precise locations.
a. sound waves
b. radio signals
c. Doppler radar
d. shadows cast by landforms

______ **26.** To determine distance east and west, you would use ______.
a. lines of latitude **b.** the equator **c.** contour lines **d.** lines of longitude

______ **27.** Landforms formed by molted materials are ______ mountains.
a. volcanic **b.** upwarped **c.** folded **d.** fault-block

______ **28.** Areas of equal elevation are connected by ______ lines.
a. meridian **b.** contour **c.** longitude **d.** latitude

______ **29.** To determine exact location on a map, you can use ______.
a. latitude
b. the International Date Line
c. latitude and longitude together
d. longitude

______ **30.** If you travel ______ across the International Date Line, you lose one day.
a. west **b.** east **c.** north **d.** south

______ **31.** An example of a raised, flat area is/are the ______.
a. Grand Teton Mountains
b. Coastal Plains
c. Colorado Plateau
d. Appalachian Mountains

______ **32.** Because New York time is five hours west of the prime meridian, it's 11:00 P.M. on Friday in New York when it's ______ at the prime meridian.
a. 8:00 P.M. on Saturday
b. 6:00 P.M. on Friday
c. 4:00 A.M. on Saturday
d. 4:00 A.M. on Friday

______ **33.** A road map is drawn to a ______ projection.
a. Mercator **b.** Robinson **c.** conic **d.** contour

______ **34.** Meridians ______ the poles.
a. represent **b.** parallel **c.** are unrelated to **d.** run through

II. Understanding Concepts

Directions: *Answer the following questions on the lines provided.*

Skill: Measuring in SI

1. A store is 10 km from a school, and a map of the area has a scale of 1 cm = 1 km. How many centimeters on the map is the distance between the store and the school?

2. A topographic map has a contour interval of 10 m. The map has 5 contour lines, and the lowest elevation is shown as 15 m. What is the elevation of the highest contour line?

3. A topographic map has a contour interval of 1 m. The map has six contour lines, and the highest elevation is shown as 15 m. What is the elevation of the lowest contour line?

4. If a map has a scale of 1 cm = 50,000 cm, how many kilometers apart on Earth's surface would two cities be if they were 3 cm apart on the map?

Skill: Interpreting Scientific Illustrations

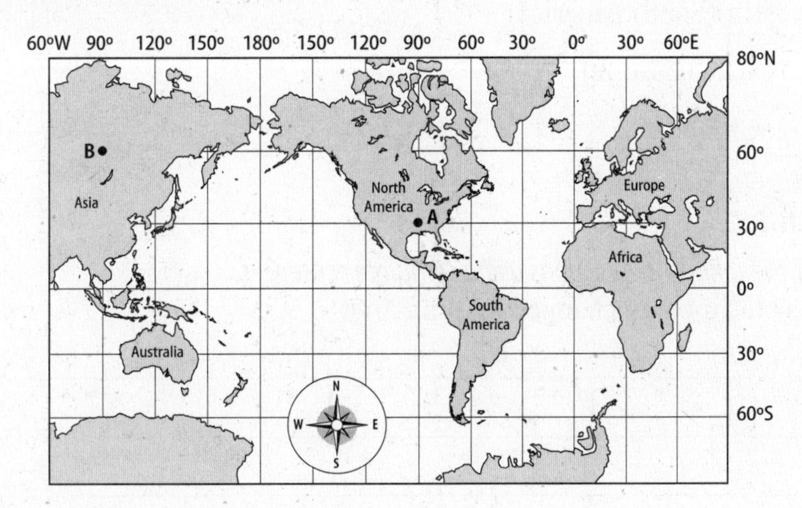

5. What are the latitude and longitude of Point A?

6. What are the latitude and longitude of Point B?

7. What does 0 represent on a topographic map?

8. Which imaginary lines on a globe or map run parallel to the equator?

9. Would Greenland appear smaller on a Mercator or a Robinson map projection?

Chapter Test B (continued)

III. Applying Concepts

Directions: *Answer the following questions on the lines provided.*

1. Compare and contrast plains and plateaus.

2. A plane flew along 20° latitude north between 20°E and 30°W. How many degrees of longitude did the plane cover?

3. At 2:00 A.M. in New York on Saturday, what time and day is it in Los Angeles, where it is three hours earlier?

Directions: *Using a globe and your knowledge of latitude and longitude, match the cities below with their locations.*

_____ 4. San Francisco, California (North America)   **a.** 40°N, 116°E

_____ 5. Lima, Peru (South America)   **b.** 12°S, 77°W

_____ 6. Paris, France (Europe)   **c.** 38°N, 122°W

_____ 7. Beijing, China (Asia)   **d.** 49°N, 2°E

IV. Writing Skills

Directions: *Answer the following questions using complete sentences.*

1. In what ways has technology changed mapmaking?

2. Would a topographic map of the Rocky Mountains have a large or small contour interval? Explain.

3. Compare a Mercator projection map to a Robinson projection map.

Name ______ Date ______ Class ______

Views of Earth

I. Testing Concepts

Directions: *Identify the best map type for each situation.*

______ **1.** A geologist is looking for coal beds.

______ **2.** A meteorologist wants to measure the depth of snow on a mountaintop.

______ **3.** A geologist wants to determine the elevation of a river across states.

______ **4.** A meteorologist wants to display local weather.

______ **5.** A geologist wants to model the layers of rock under a rock bed.

Directions: *Fill in the blanks to complete each sentence.*

6. A map ______ shows the relationship between the distance on the map and distances on Earth's surface.

7. A map ______ explains what the symbols used on the map mean.

8. A map ______ includes maps that have the same dimensions of latitude and longitude.

9. The ______ is the transition line for calendar days.

10. Earth is divided into 24 ______.

11. A(n) ______ is a line on a map that connects points of equal elevation.

12. A map ______ is made when points and lines on a globe's surface are transferred onto paper.

Directions: *Determine whether the statements below are* **true** *or* **false**. *Rewrite the underlined word(s) in the false statements to make them correct.*

______ **13.** The world's highest peak is in the <u>Rocky Mountains</u>.

______

______ **14.** Fault fractures create the majestic peaks and steep slopes of <u>upwarped</u> mountains.

______

______ **15.** The southern Rocky Mountains were created when <u>crust</u> was pushed up by forces inside Earth. ______

______ **16.** <u>Mount Shasta</u> is a volcanic mountain made up of layers of lava flows and ash.

______

Chapter Test C (continued)

II. Understanding Concepts

Skill: Interpreting Scientific Illustrations

Directions: *Use the map to answer questions 1–5.*

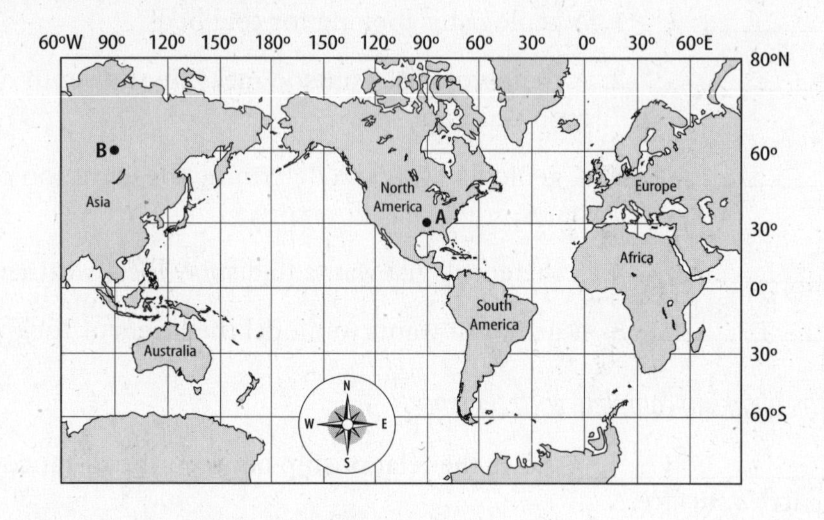

1. What type of map is shown? How do you know?

____

2. What is one flaw of this map?

____

3. Some travelers experience jet lag, or feeling tired after flying great distances. Why might a traveler flying from Point A to Point B experience jet lag?

____

4. Would you cross the prime meridian or the equator when traveling from Point A to Point B?

____

5. What is the difference in latitude between Point A and Point B? _______________

Skill: Comparing and Contrasting

6. **Write** a paragraph comparing and contrasting interior plains and plateaus.

____

____

____

____

Chapter Test C (continued)

Skill: Creating a Chart

7. **Directions:** *Create a chart describing each of the mountain types.*

Skill: Measuring in SI

Directions: *Answer the following questions on the lines provided.*

8. **Analyze** A map has a scale of 0.5 cm = 100 km. How many kilometers on Earth's surface are represented by 4 cm?

9. You traveled from 45°N latitude to 15°S latitude. How many degrees of latitude did you cover?

III. Applying Concepts

Writing Skills

Directions: *Answer the following questions using complete sentences.*

1. **Compare and Contrast** How are Mercator projection and conic projection maps alike and different?

Chapter Test C (continued)

2. **Decide** A hiker plans a trip to the mountains. She checks a weather map to see if it will rain. She maps driving directions to the hiking trails. She wants a challenging trail with a steep elevation, and she consults a map to help her choose the trail. As she travels, a built-in mapping system in her car gives her driving directions. What types of maps and mapping systems did the hiker use for each task?

3. **Evaluate** How suitable for agriculture are plains and plateaus?

4. **Compare and Contrast** How are longitude and latitude lines alike and different?

5. **Determine** What types of landforms are present in your area? What evidence helped you decide?

Name Date Class

Design Your Own

Weathering Chalk

LAB A

Lab Preview

Directions: *Answer these questions before you begin the Lab.*

1. Look at the chalk samples for this lab. What do you think could change these rocks?

____

2. What effects could these factors have on the chalk?

____

Chalk is a type of limestone made of the shells of microscopic organisms. The famous White Cliffs of Dover, England, are made up of chalk. This lab will help you understand how chalk can be chemically weathered.

Real-World Question

How can you simulate the chemical weathering of chalk?

Form a Hypothesis

How do you think acidity, surface area, and temperature affect the rate of chemical weathering of chalk? What happens to chalk in water? What happens to chalk in acid (vinegar)? How will the size of the chalk pieces affect the rate of weathering? What will happen if you heat the acid? Make hypotheses to support your ideas.

Possible Materials

equal-sized pieces of chalk (6)
small beakers (2)
metric ruler
water
white vinegar (100 mL)
hot plate
computer probe for temperature
**thermometer*

**alternate materials*

Goals

- **Design** experiments to evaluate the effects of acidity, surface area, and temperature on the rate of chemical weathering of chalk.
- **Describe** factors that affect chemical weathering.
- **Explain** how the chemical weathering of chalk is similar to the chemical weathering of rocks.

Safety Precautions

Wear safety goggles when pouring vinegar. Be careful when using a hot plate and heated solutions. **WARNING:** *If mixing liquids, always add acid to water.*

Test Your Hypothesis

Make a Plan

❑ 1. **Develop** hypotheses about the 1) effects of acidity, 2) surface area, and 3) temperature on the rate of chemical weathering.

❑ 2. **Decide** how to test your first hypothesis. List the steps needed to test the hypothesis.

❑ 3. **Repeat** step 2 for your other two hypotheses.

❑ 4. **Copy** the data table on the next page on separate sheets of paper. Make one for acidity, one for surface area, and one for temperature.

(continued)

LAB A

❑ 5. **Identify** what remains constant in your experiment and what varies.
  ❑ Change only one variable in each procedure.

❑ 6. **Summarize** your data in a graph. Use one color for water and another color for acid.

Type of Test			
Material	**Before**	**After**	**Observations**

Follow Your Plan

❑ 1. Make sure your teacher approves your plan before you start.

❑ 2. Carry out the three experiments as planned.

❑ 3. While you are conducting the experiments, record your observations on separate sheets of paper and complete the data tables.

❑ 4. **Graph** your data to show how each variable affected the rate of weathering.

Analyze Your Data

1. **Analyze** your graph to find out which substance—water or acid—weathered the chalk more quickly. Was your hypothesis supported by your data?

____

2. **Infer** from your data whether the amount of surface area makes a difference in the rate of chemical weathering. Explain.

____

____

Conclude and Apply

1. **Explain** how the chalk was chemically weathered.

____

2. How does heat affect the rate of chemical weathering?

____

3. What does this imply about weathering in the tropics and in polar regions?

____

Communicating Your Data

Compare your results with those of your classmates. How were your data similar? How were they different? **For more help, refer to the Science Skill Handbook.**

Name Date Class

Design Your Own

Weathering Chalk

LAB B

Lab Preview

Directions: *Answer these questions before you begin the Lab.*

1. Look at the chalk samples for this lab. What do you think could change these rocks?

____

2. What effects could these factors have on the chalk?

____

Chalk is a type of limestone made of the shells of microscopic organisms. The famous White Cliffs of Dover, England, are made up of chalk. This lab will help you understand how chalk can be chemically weathered.

Real-World Question

How can you simulate the chemical weathering of chalk?

Form a Hypothesis

How do you think acidity, surface area, and temperature affect the rate of chemical weathering of chalk? What happens to chalk in water? What happens to chalk in acid (vinegar)? How will the size of the chalk pieces affect the rate of weathering? What will happen if you heat the acid? Make hypotheses to support your ideas.

Possible Materials

equal-sized pieces of chalk (6)
small beakers (2)
metric ruler
water
white vinegar (100 mL)
hot plate
computer probe for temperature
**thermometer*

**alternate materials*

Goals

- **Design** experiments to evaluate the effects of acidity, surface area, and temperature on the rate of chemical weathering of chalk.
- **Describe** factors that affect chemical weathering.
- **Explain** how the chemical weathering of chalk is similar to the chemical weathering of rocks.

Safety Precautions

Wear safety goggles when pouring vinegar. Be careful when using a hot plate and heated solutions. **WARNING:** *If mixing liquids, always add acid to water.*

Test Your Hypothesis

Make a Plan

- ❑ **1. Develop** hypotheses about the effects of acidity, surface area, and temperature on the rate of chemical weathering.
- ❑ **2. Decide** how to test your first hypothesis. List the steps needed to test the hypothesis.
- ❑ **3. Repeat** step 2 for your other two hypotheses.
- ❑ **4. Design** data tables on separate sheets of paper. Make one for acidity, one for surface area, and one for temperature.

 (continued)

- ❑ **5. Identify** what remains constant in your experiment and what varies. Change only one variable in each procedure.
- ❑ **6. Summarize** your data in a graph. Decide from reading the **Science Skill Handbook** which type of graph to use.

Put table here:

Follow Your Plan

- ❑ **1.** Make sure your teacher approves your plan before you start.
- ❑ **2.** Carry out the three experiments as planned.
- ❑ **3.** While you are conducting the experiments, record your observations on separate sheets of paper and complete the data tables.
- ❑ **4. Graph** your data to show how each variable affected the rate of weathering.

Analyze Your Data

1. **Analyze** your graph to find out which substance—water or acid—weathered the chalk more quickly. Was your hypothesis supported by your data?

___

2. **Infer** from your data whether the amount of surface area makes a difference in the rate of chemical weathering. Explain.

___

___

Conclude and Apply

1. **Explain** how the chalk was chemically weathered.

___

___

2. How does heat affect the rate of chemical weathering?

___

___

3. What does this imply about weathering in the tropics and in polar regions?

Challenge

1. **Infer** An artist has been given a block of stone. She wants to use the stone to create a sculpture or two for an outdoor garden. However, she wants the sculpture or sculptures to weather as little as possible. Based on your investigation, what would you recommend?

2. **Rank** Create a list to show which factors had the most effect and which factors had the least effect on weathering.

3. **Analyze** When you first placed the chalk into the container, small flakes sank to the bottom of the container. Were these a result of chemical weathering? Why?

Extension

Apply Some scientists are concerned about acid rain. It occurs when gases such as sulfur dioxide and nitrogen dioxide are emitted into the air. These gases lower the pH of rain, making rainwater acidic. Acid rain can be produced naturally, by volcanic eruptions, or by humans, from such things as car emissions and power generation. Research acid rain. How does your lab support why acid rain is a concern? Write a paragraph explaining the problem.

Communicating Your Data

Compare your results with those of your classmates. How were your data similar? How were they different? **For more help, refer to the Science Skill Handbook.**

Name ______________________ Date ______________ Class ______________

Weathering and Soil

I. Testing Concepts

Directions: *In the blank at the left, write the letter of the term that best completes each statement.*

______ **1.** When water enters cracks in rocks and freezes, ______ can occur.
a. soil formation
b. acids
c. chemical weathering
d. ice wedging

______ **2.** The ______ of an area is the pattern of weather in that area over many years.
a. climate **b.** horizon **c.** humus **d.** terracing

______ **3.** ______ is a mixture of weathered rock, decayed organic matter, mineral fragments, water, and air.
a. Litter **b.** Slope **c.** Soil **d.** Horizon

______ **4.** In the topsoil layer you can find ______, a dark-colored material made from decayed organic matter.
a. humus **b.** horizon **c.** terracing **d.** wedging

______ **5.** Soil is divided into ______, or layers.
a. contours **b.** humus **c.** erosion **d.** horizons

______ **6.** ______ occurs when rocks are broken apart by physical processes.
a. Ice wedging
b. Terracing
c. Mechanical weathering
d. Chemical weathering

Directions: *Identify each statement as* **true** *or* **false**. *If a statement is false, change the underlined term to make it true.*

______ **7.** In soil, water reacts with humus and carbon dioxide to form <u>leaching</u>.

____

______ **8.** In some places, land is covered by a thick layer of sediment that was deposited by <u>glaciers</u>.

____

______ **9.** Soils in deserts contain little <u>organic</u> material and are thinner than soils in wetter climates.

____

______ **10.** Soil erosion is harmful because plants do not grow as well when <u>rocks</u> have been removed.

____

______ **11.** <u>Contour farming</u> helps stop erosion by creating level areas on steep slopes.

____

Chapter Test A (continued)

II. Understanding Concepts

Directions: *Match each description on the left with the correct term.*

Column I	Column II
______ 1. surface processes that work to break down rock	a. litter
______ 2. happens when some materials are exposed to water and to the oxygen in air	b. leaching
______ 3. consists of leaves, twigs, and other organic material	c. oxidation
______ 4. removal of minerals that have been dissolved in water	d. weathering

Skill: Classifying

Directions: *Place an **X** next to the factors that affect soil formation.*

______ 5. climate

______ 6. elevation

______ 7. types of rock

______ 8. slope of land

______ 9. shade

______ 10. types of vegetation

______ 11. amount of time rock has been weathering

Directions: *Classify each cause of weathering as* **chemical** *or* **mechanical.**

____________________ 12. roots of growing plants

____________________ 13. ice wedging

____________________ 14. carbonic acid

____________________ 15. burrowing animals

____________________ 16. plant acids

____________________ 17. oxidation

Skill: Cause and Effect

Directions: *Place an **X** by the cause in each pair.*

18. ______ Weathering of rock occurs over a short time period.

______ The soil resembles the parent rock.

19. ______ Rust forms.

______ Minerals containing iron are exposed to water and to the oxygen in air.

III. Applying Concepts

Writing Skills

Directions: *Respond to the following using complete sentences.*

1. **Describe** What are two strategies that farmers can use to conserve soil?

____

____

____

____

____

____

2. **Explain** Two friends go hiking and find a cave, where they see limestone. Explain how this cave could have formed.

____

____

____

3. **Analyze** In some areas, forests are burned down so that farmers can plant crops. Why is this a serious problem for tropical rain forests?

____

____

____

____

____

Chapter Test A (continued)

4. **Analyze** Would you expect chemical weathering to occur more quickly in a tropical rain forest or a desert? Why?

____

____

5. **Describe** Discuss each of the three soil horizons.

____

____

____

____

____

____

____

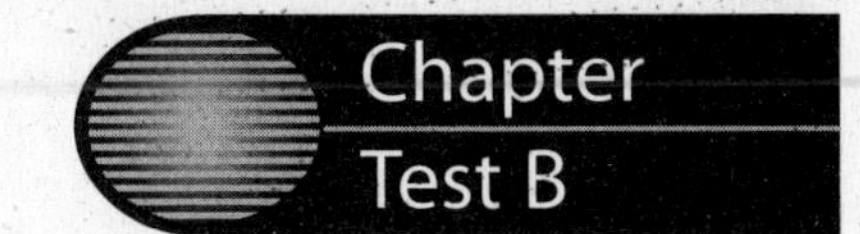

Weathering and Soil

I. Testing Concepts

Directions: *Write the letter of the term or phrase in the blanks at the left that best completes the following sentences.*

______ **1.** Soil is a mixture of weathered rock and _____.
a. water and air
b. decayed organic matter
c. mineral fragments
d. all of these

______ **2.** The layer of soil that contains the most humus and smaller rock and mineral particles than the other layers is the _____ horizon.
a. *A* **b.** *B* **c.** *C* **d.** *D*

______ **3.** All of the following are direct causes of mechanical weathering except _____.
a. ice **b.** tree roots **c.** water **d.** oxygen

______ **4.** Over thousands of years, _____ has chemically weathered limestone, creating caves.
a. caolinite clay **b.** carbonic acid **c.** oxidation **d.** sediment

______ **5.** Chemical weathering is more rapid in a _____ climate.
a. dry **b.** tropical **c.** cold **d.** moderate

______ **6.** Mechanical weathering is more rapid in a _____ climate.
a. dry **b.** tropical **c.** cold **d.** moderate

______ **7.** When livestock eat all the grass on the land, the land is said to be _____.
a. overgrazed **b.** leached **c.** weathered **d.** all of these

______ **8.** The organic material in humus includes _____.
a. plant leaves and stems
b. weathered rocks
c. sand
d. air

______ **9.** How fast weathering occurs depends on the _____ of an area.
a. oxygen **b.** climate **c.** water **d.** vegetation

______ **10.** In no-till farming, plant stalks are _____.
a. destroyed
b. covered with water
c. left in the field
d. plowed under

______ **11.** Compared to the *A* horizon in a soil profile, the *B* horizon _____.
a. is lighter in color
b. contains material leached from the *A* horizon
c. contains less humus
d. all of these

______ **12.** The difference between mechanical and chemical weathering is _____.
a. the length of time each takes to break up rock
b. that each occurs in different parts of the world
c. only one changes the chemical composition of a rock
d. that only chemical weathering involves water

______ **13.** Soil horizons in deserts are _____ than soil horizons in wetter climates.
a. thicker **b.** thinner **c.** darker **d.** more fertile

______ **14.** Forest harvesting creates the most severe problems in _____ regions.
a. desert **b.** tropical **c.** urban **d.** mountain

______ **15.** Agricultural practices that slow soil erosion include _____.
a. planting shelter belts of trees
b. plowing
c. allowing livestock to graze wherever they want
d. leaving soil open to rain

______ **16.** Causes of soil erosion include _____.
a. wind
b. water
c. removal of vegetation
d. all of these

______ **17.** Ice wedging is caused by _____.
a. acid freezing on rocks
b. water and oxygen reacting
c. water freezing and thawing
d. all of these

______ **18.** The minerals found in the *B* and *C* horizons were dissolved in water and carried down to those soil layers by a process called _____.
a. oxidation **b.** leaching **c.** weathering **d.** precipitation

______ **19.** Oxidation requires a combination of three things: _____.
a. iron, oxygen, and water
b. iron, carbon dioxide, and water
c. rock, oxygen, and water
d. acid, iron, and oxygen

______ **20.** An area's climate is its _____.
a. high and low temperatures
b. annual rainfall
c. pattern of weather over many years
d. daily weather over the last year

II. Understanding Concepts

Directions: *Complete the following sentences by writing the letter of the correct term in the blank at the left. Questions 1–6 are based on a soil profile.*

______ **1.** The *B* horizon is _____.
a. darker than *A*
b. darker than *C*
c. lighter than *A*
d. lighter than *C*

______ **2.** The *A* horizon is high in _____.
a. clay
b. organic materials
c. rocks
d. leached materials

______ **3.** Leaching occurs mainly in the _____ horizon.
a. *A* **b.** *B* **c.** *C* **d.** *D*

______ **4.** Weathering occurs most rapidly in the _____ horizon.
a. *A* **b.** *B* **c.** *C* **d.** *D*

Chapter Test B (continued)

_____ 5. Below the *C* horizon is _____.
a. humus b. rock c. clay d. more soil

_____ 6. The _____ horizon consists mostly of parent rock.
a. *A* b. *B* c. *C* d. *D*

Skill: Recognizing Cause and Effect

Directions: *Write* **Cause** *or* **Effect** *in the blanks before each pair of sentences below. Then rewrite the two sentences to make one sentence that shows the cause-and-effect relationship.*

__________ 7. Wedges form and the rock breaks apart.

__________ 8. Plants grow into cracks in rocks.

__________ 9. Wind and water are able to carry away the topsoil.

__________ 10. Cattle eat all the grass on the land.

__________ 11. The area has a rainy climate and a lot of plants.

__________ 12. The soil is rich with humus.

Directions: *Answer the following questions on the lines provided.*

13. **List** the steps in soil development.

14. **Explain** two ways to reduce soil erosion on slopes.

Chapter Test B (continued)

III. Applying Concepts

Directions: *Use the following words to fill in the blanks below. Not all the terms are used.*

soil **leaching** **terracing** **mechanical weathering**
carbonic acid **horizon** **no-till farming** **ice wedging**
soil profile **shelter belts** **chemical weathering**
oxidation **overgrazing** **humus** **contour farming**

1. When unpainted iron lawn furniture sits outside in the rain and begins to rust, ____________________ has occurred.
2. ____________________ has occurred when chemical reactions dissolve the minerals in rocks or change them into different minerals.
3. ____________________ is the process by which water moves minerals down from one soil layer to another.
4. Water freezing and cracking rock and tree roots spreading through rock are examples of ____________________.
5. When weathered rock, decayed organic matter, mineral fragments, water, and air are combined, ____________________ is formed.
6. Mountain peaks, where water freezes and thaws often, are often weathered by ____________________.
7. ____________________ is organic matter made of decayed plants and animals.
8. You can see the different layers of soil that make up a ____________________ on a hillside where the soil and rock have been exposed.
9. Planting along the natural contours of the land on gentle slopes is called ____________________.
10. Leaving plant stalks undisturbed in the field to cover the soil is known as ____________________.
11. Wind erosion of the land can be reduced by planting ____________________ of trees.

IV. Writing Skills

Directions: *Write a paragraph using complete sentences to answer the following question.*

12. Why is weathering important?

____

____

____

Name ______________________ Date ______________________ Class ______________________

Weathering and Soil

I. Testing Concepts

Directions: *Identify each statement as* **true** *or* **false**. *If a statement is false, change the underlined term to make it true.*

______ **1.** Soil erosion is harmful because plants don't grow well when the litter has been removed.

____

______ **2.** In mechanical weathering, the overall chemical makeup of the rock is unchanged.

____

______ **3.** Oxidation occurs when materials are exposed to oxygen and carbon.

____

______ **4.** No-till farming provides cover for the soil year-round, which reduces water retention and soil weathering.

____

______ **5.** Planting crops along the natural contours facilitates the flow of water down the slope and increases the formation of gullies.

____

______ **6.** Climate is the pattern of weather that occurs in a particular area over many years.

____

Directions: *Fill in the blanks to complete the sentences.*

7. ______________________ is a mixture of weathered rock, decayed organic matter, mineral fragments, water, and air.

8. Decaying plant matter turns into ______________________ which serves as source of ______________________ for the plants.

9. A layer called ______________________, consisting of leaves, twigs, and other ______________________ materials, is found in forests.

10. Leaching is the removal of minerals that have been dissolved in ______________________. These minerals seep from the ______________________ horizon to the ______________________ horizon.

11. Most soils have three ______________________ labeled A, B, and C.

12. All of the different layers of soil form a soil ______________________.

Name ______ Date ______ Class ______

Chapter Test C (continued)

13. Soil formation is affected by climate, slope of land, types of ____________, types of ____________, and amount of time rock has been weathering.

II. Understanding Concepts

Skill: Outlining

Directions: *Create an outline showing ways to reduce soil erosion.*

1.

Skill: Sequencing

Directions: *For each series, number the events in the order that they occur. Then, identify the type of weathering that is explained as either* **mechanical** *or* **chemical**.

______ 2. The roots wedge the rock apart.

______ 3. Water and nutrients that collect in the cracks allow plants to grow.

4. ____________

______ 5. Water reacts with carbon dioxide in the air, forming carbonic acid.

______ 6. Carbonic acid reacts with the minerals, causing them to dissolve.

7. ____________

______ 8. Weathering processes act on the sediment.

______ 9. Burrowing animals loosen sediment and push it to the surface.

10. ____________

Chapter Test C (continued)

Skill: Make a Diagram

Directions: *Create a diagram showing the levels of the soil horizon. Include attributes of each level.*

11.

III. Applying Concepts

Directions: *Answer the following questions using complete sentences.*

1. **Hypothesize** There are many trees and plants at the bottoms of mountains, but very few trees and plants at the tops of steep mountains. What might explain this?

2. **Support** In a region of a tropical rain forest, farmers are burning trees to create new farmland. You are in charge of raising money for a group to travel to the area, where they will train the farmers in new agricultural processes. Write an essay explaining why it is important for farmers to change their agricultural practices.

Chapter Test C (continued)

3. **Contrast** How would you expect soil and weathering to be different in the desert and a tropical rain forest? Why?

4. **Predict** A scientist compares a sample of pure water and a sample of groundwater. What might she observe?

5. **Defend** A city official in the Northeast compares the amount of money that his city pays to fill potholes in roads to the amount a city in the Southwest pays. The city in the Southwest pays less. The official wants to cut the budget for potholes. Explain why a city in the Northeast might need more money for pothole repair.

Name Date Class

Design Your Own

Blowing in the Wind

LAB A

Lab Preview

Directions: *Answer these questions before you begin the Lab.*

1. Why is it important to wear safety goggles during this lab?

2. Would you expect increased speeds of wind to increase the amount of erosion? Why or why not?

Have you ever played a sport outside and suddenly had the wind blow dust into your eyes? What did you do? Turn your back? Cover your eyes? How does wind pick up sediment? Why does wind pick up some sediments and leave others on the ground?

Real-World Question

What factors affect wind erosion?

Form a Hypothesis

How does moisture in sediment affect the ability of wind to erode sediments? Does the speed of the wind limit the size of sediments it can transport? Form a hypothesis about how sediment moisture affects wind erosion. Form another hypothesis about how wind speed affects the size of the sediment the wind can transport.

Goals

- **Observe** the effects of soil moisture and wind speed on wind erosion.
- **Design** and carry out experiments that test the effects of soil moisture and wind speed on wind erosion.

Possible Materials

flat pans (4)
fine sand (400 mL)
gravel (400 mL)
hair dryer
sprinkling can
water
28-cm × 35cm cardboard sheets (4)
tape
mixing bowl
metric ruler
wind speed indicator

Safety Precautions

Wear your safety goggles at all times when using the hair dryer on sediments. Make sure the dryer is plugged into a GFI electrical outlet.

Test Your Hypothesis

Make a Plan

❑ 1. As a group, agree upon and write your hypothesis statements.

❑ 2. **List** the steps needed to test your first hypothesis. Plan specific steps and vary only one factor at a time.
 ❑ Then, list the steps needed to test your second hypothesis. Test only one factor at a time.

❑ 3. **Mix** the sediments in the pans.
 ❑ **Plan** how you will fold cardboard sheets and attach them to the pans to keep sediments contained.

❑ 4. **Copy** the data table on the next page to record your data in the Data and Observations section.

(continued)

LAB A

- ❑ 5. **Identify** all constants, variables, and controls of the experiment. The constant will not change. Your control is your standard of comparison. One example of a control is a pan of sediment not subjected to any wind.

Follow Your Plan

- ❑ 1. Make sure your teacher approves your plan before you start.
- ❑ 2. Carry out the experiments as planned.
- ❑ 3. While doing the experiments, write any observations that you or other members of your group make. Summarize your data in the data tables.

Data and Observations

Sediment Movement		
Sediment	low	
	high	

Analyze Your Data

1. **Compare** your results with those of other groups. Explain what might have caused any differences among the groups.

2. **Explain** the relationship that exists between the speed of the wind and the size of the sediments it transports.

Conclude and Apply

1. How does energy of motion of the wind influence sediment transport? What is the general relationship between wind speed and erosion?

(continued)

2. **Explain** the relationship between the sediment moisture and the amount of sediment moved by the wind.

Communicating Your Data

Design a table that summarizes the results of your experiment, and use it to explain your interpretations to others in the class.

Name ____________________ Date ____________ Class ____________

Design Your Own

Blowing in the Wind

LAB B

Lab Preview

Directions: *Answer these questions before you begin the Lab.*

1. Why is it important to wear safety goggles during this lab?

____

2. Would you expect increased speeds of wind to increase the amount of erosion? Why or why not?

____

____

Have you ever played a sport outside and suddenly had the wind blow dust into your eyes? What did you do? Turn your back? Cover your eyes? How does wind pick up sediment? Why does wind pick up some sediments and leave others on the ground?

Real-World Question

What factors affect wind erosion?

Form a Hypothesis

How does moisture in sediment affect the ability of wind to erode sediments? Does the speed of the wind limit the size of sediments it can transport? Form a hypothesis about how sediment moisture affects wind erosion. Form another hypothesis about how wind speed affects the size of the sediment the wind can transport.

Goals

- **Observe** the effects of soil moisture and wind speed on wind erosion.
- **Design** and carry out experiments that test the effects of soil moisture and wind speed on wind erosion.

Possible Materials

flat pans (4)
fine sand (400 mL)
gravel (400 mL)
hair dryer
sprinkling can
water
28-cm × 35cm cardboard sheets (4)
tape
mixing bowl
metric ruler
wind speed indicator

Safety Precautions

Wear your safety goggles at all times when using the hair dryer on sediments. Make sure the dryer is plugged into a GFI electrical outlet.

Test Your Hypothesis

Make a Plan

❑ 1. As a group, agree upon and write your hypothesis statements.

❑ 2. **List** the steps needed to test your first hypothesis. Plan specific steps and vary only one factor at a time. Then, list the steps needed to test your second hypothesis. Test only one factor at a time.

❑ 3. **Mix** the sediments in the pans. Plan how you will fold cardboard sheets and attach them to the pans to keep sediments contained.

❑ 4. **Design** data tables to record your data in the Data and Observations section.

(continued)

LAB B

❏ 5. **Identify** all constants, variables, and controls of the experiment. One example of a control is a pan of sediment not subjected to any wind.

Put table here:

Follow Your Plan

❏ 1. Make sure your teacher approves your plan before you start.
❏ 2. Carry out the experiments as planned.
❏ 3. While doing the experiments, write any observations that you or other members of your group make. Summarize your data in the data tables.

Data and Observations

Analyze Your Data

1. **Compare** your results with those of other groups. Explain what might have caused any differences among the groups.

____

____

2. **Explain** the relationship that exists between the speed of the wind and the size of the sediments it transports.

____

Conclude and Apply

1. How does energy of motion of the wind influence sediment transport? What is the general relationship between wind speed and erosion?

____

____

2. **Explain** the relationship between the sediment moisture and the amount of sediment moved by the wind.

____

____

Challenge

1. **Analyze** Why was it important to have the dryer at a consistent angle and distance?

2. **Infer** Both beaches and deserts are susceptible to wind erosion. Based on your findings, which location has the higher amount of erosion?

3. **Suggest** Based on your findings and the chapter, what would you recommend to a construction company that wanted to reduce erosion while building a site?

Extension

Construct In some areas, communities place dead trees on beaches to provide a windbreak. Revise your lab to explore the effectiveness of plant matter in providing a windbreak. What materials will you use? How would your procedures need to be revised? What would you expect to find?

Communicating Your Data

Design a table that summarizes the results of your experiment, and use it to explain your interpretations to others in the class.

Name Date Class

Erosional Forces

I. Testing Concepts

Directions: *Match the descriptions in Column I with the terms in Column II. Write the letter of the correct term in the blank at the left.*

Column I	Column II
______ 1. large deposits of fine-grained windblown sediments	a. plucking
______ 2. mound of sediment blown by the wind formed around an obstacle	b. loess
______ 3. process by which rock pieces are lifted out by ice	c. moraine
______ 4. ridge of sediment deposited by a glacier	d. dune
______ 5. large mass of ice and snow moving on land under its own weight	e. glacier

Directions: *In the blank at the left, write the letter of the term that best completes each statement.*

______ 6. ______ is the process that wears away surface materials and moves them from one place to another.
a. Weathering b. Erosion c. Slump d. Creep

______ 7. When agents of erosion drop sediment they are carrying, ______ occurs.
a. glacier b. abrasion c. deposition d. sediment

______ 8. ______ is a type of erosion occurring when wind blows across loose sediment, carrying small pieces of sediment away with it.
a. Deflation b. Abrasion c. Moraine d. Glacier

______ 9. Rock gets scraped and worn away by a process called ______.
a. till b. deposition c. deflation d. abrasion

______ 10. One type of outwash, called ______, looks like a long, winding ridge.
a. an esker b. till c. retreat d. a cirque

______ 11. ______ are thicker than some mountain ranges.
a. Eskers
b. Continental glaciers
c. Valley glaciers
d. Cirques

______ 12. Water and wind erode materials only when they have enough energy of ______ to do work.
a. force b. light c. gravity d. motion

Chapter Test A (continued)

II. Understanding Concepts

Skill: Completing and Using Charts

Directions: *Complete the chart below using these terms:* **slump**, **creep**, **rockfall**, **rock slide**, *and* **mudflow**.

Mass Movement	Description
1.	Blocks of rock break loose from a steep slope and tumble through the air.
2.	Layers of rock slip down slope suddenly.
3.	A mass of material slips down along a curved surface.
4.	Sediments slowly shift their positions downhill.
5.	A thick mixture of sediment and water flows down a slope.

Skill: Comparing and Contrasting

Directions: *Use the chart to answer the questions that follow.*

6. How are rockfalls and rock slides different?

____

____

7. How are creep and slump different?

____

____

8. How are all of these mass movements the same?

____

____

Skill: Sequencing

Directions: *Number the following events to show the formation and movement of a glacier.*

______ **9.** The ice becomes plasticlike.

______ **10.** Snow accumulates.

______ **11.** The weight of the snow compresses the lower layers into ice.

______ **12.** The glacier moves slowly away from its source.

______ **13.** The ice flows slowly on a thick, plasticlike lower layer.

Chapter Test A (continued)

III. Applying Concepts

Skill: Outlining

1. *Complete the outline of erosion and deposition by glaciers using the following phrases:* **scouring, outwash deposits, plucking,** *and* **till.**

I. Glacial Erosion

A. ______

B. ______

II. Glacial Deposition

A. ______

1. moraine deposits

B. ______

1. eskers

Writing Skills

Directions: *Respond to the following using complete sentences.*

2. **Define** What do the terms *till* and *outwash* mean? How are they the same?

______

______

______

3. **Explain** A family visits a beach and sees a sand dune with some scrub brush sticking out. Explain how the dune may have formed.

______

______

______

______

4. **Apply** Tell why it might be unwise to build a home on a steep slope.

______

______

______

______

______

Name Date Class

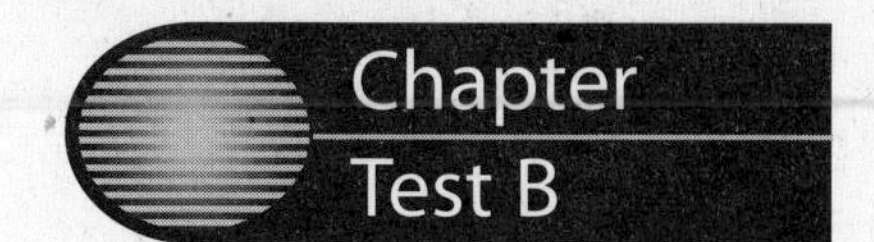

Erosional Forces

I. Testing Concepts

Directions: *Write the letter of each statement on the lines following the gravity erosion it describes. Items may be used more than once.*

a. This erosion is a mass movement.
b. This erosion usually occurs after a heavy rain in a normally dry area where there are thick layers of dry sediments.
c. This erosion occurs because underlying materials are weakened and can no longer hold the eroding materials.
d. This erosion happens most often after heavy rains or during earthquakes.
e. Large blocks of rocks break loose from a steep slope and start tumbling.
f. Loose materials or rock layers slip downslope as a large mass.
g. The deposits from this erosion are usually fan-shaped masses.
h. This kind of erosion is common in areas where freezing and thawing occur.
i. This erosion happens when sediments move slowly down a slope.

1. Mudflows: ________, ________, ________

2. Slump: ________, ________, ________

3. Creep: ________, ________, ________

4. Rockfalls: ________, ________, ________, ________

Directions: *Match the descriptions in Column I with the terms in Column II. Write the letter of the correct term in the blank at the left.*

Column I

______ **5.** the dropping of eroded sediments

______ **6.** large blocks of rock tumbling down a steep slope

______ **7.** mass movement when sediments slowly inch their way down a slope

______ **8.** deposits formed when windblown sediments settle and build up behind an obstacle

______ **9.** wind erosion of loose sediments

______ **10.** a process that wears away surface materials and moves them to a different location

______ **11.** material deposited by the meltwater from a glacier

______ **12.** a mixture of different-sized sediments deposited by a glacier

______ **13.** one way to reduce erosion on steep slopes

______ **14.** wind deposits of fine-grained sediments

______ **15.** an activity that can increase erosion on steep slopes

Column II

a. erosion
b. deposition
c. building
d. outwash
e. dunes
f. loess
g. deflation
h. planting
i. rockfall
j. till
k. creep

Name Date Class

Chapter Test B (continued)

Directions: *Circle the word in parentheses that makes each statement correct.*

16. The four agents of erosion and deposition are wind, (heat, water), gravity, and glaciers.

17. (Transverse, Star) dunes tend to form in regions where wind direction changes.

18. Today, continental glaciers cover about (28, 10) percent of Earth.

19. To protect their fields, farmers may plant belts of trees that act as (drains, windbreaks).

20. (Cirques, Grooves) occur when bedrock is gouged by rock fragments dragged by a glacier.

Directions: *Rewrite the following statements changing the italicized words to make the statements correct.*

21. *Deflation* is similar to sandblasting.

____

____

22. Much farmland of the midwestern United States is on fertile soil that developed from *creep* deposits.

____

____

23. Agents of erosion *pick up* sediments when they lose their energy of motion.

____

____

24. *Eskers* are bowl-shaped basins resulting from glacial erosion in the sides of a mountain.

____

____

25. *Erecting buildings* is one of the best ways to reduce erosion.

____

____

II. Understanding Concepts

Skill: Sequencing

Directions: *For each series, number the events in the order that they could occur.*

1. Creep erosion

_____ The soil thaws.

_____ The ground freezes.

_____ The sediment slowly inches downslope.

_____ Expanding ice in the soil pushes up fine-grained sediment particles.

Name ______ Date ______ Class ______

Chapter Test B (continued)

2. Glacial erosion

_____ The glacier loses its energy of motion.

_____ A glacier is formed.

_____ Till is deposited in front of the glacier that has stopped moving.

_____ Striations are gouged into bedrock.

_____ Plucking occurs as the glacier moves.

Skill: Concept Mapping

Directions: *Complete the concept map by identifying four types of mass movements caused by gravity.*

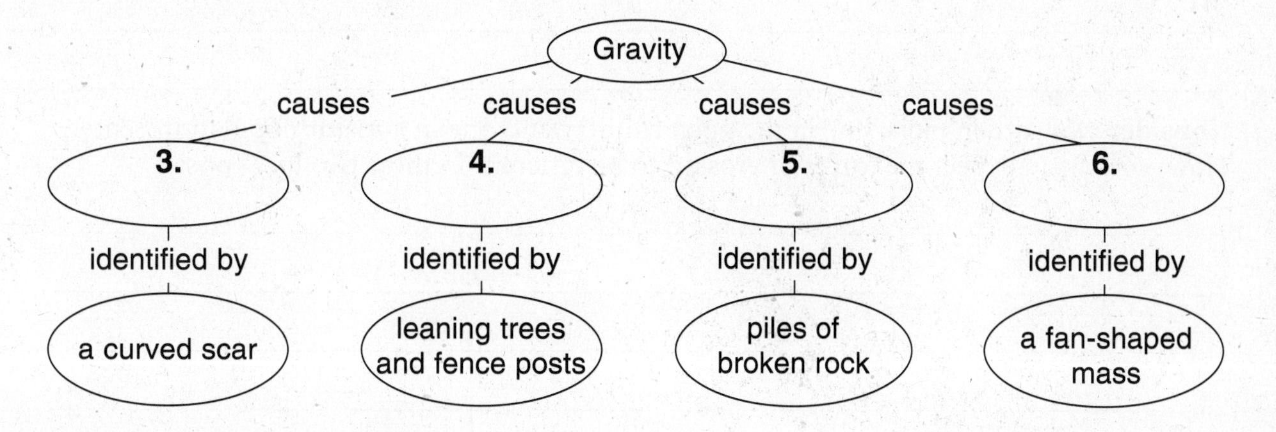

Skill: Comparing and Contrasting

7. Compare and contrast slump and creep.

____

____

Skill: Outlining

8. **Complete** the outline of erosion and deposition by glaciers.

I. Glacial Erosion

A. ______________________________

B. ______________________________

II. Glacial Deposition

A. ______________________________

1. Moraine deposits

B. ______________________________

1. Eskers

Name _________________________ Date _________________________ Class _________________________

Chapter Test B (continued)

III. Applying Concepts

Writing Skills

Directions: *Answer the following questions in complete sentences.*

1. Sand dunes are found on the eastern and southeastern shores of Lake Michigan. However, they are not found on the western shore of the lake. Why?

____
____
____
____
____
____

2. **Consider** two garden plots, one in the open country and one in a major population center. How would you expect the forces of erosion to be different in these two locations?

____
____
____
____
____
____
____

3. The roots of wheat are not very strong or deep. The roots of prairie grass are strong. Plowing up a field of prairie grass and planting wheat could lead to erosion. Write a short paragraph telling why the erosion might occur and suggest what might be done to help stop the erosion.

____
____
____
____
____
____

Name ______________________ Date ______________________ Class ______________________

Erosional Forces

I. Testing Concepts

Directions: *Fill in the blanks to complete the sentences.*

1. Erosion occurs when sediments ____________________ and ____________________ from one place to another.
2. Deposition occurs when agents of erosion ____________________ the sediments they are carrying as they ____________________ energy.
3. A mass movement is any type of erosion that happens as ____________________ moves materials ____________________.
4. Valley glaciers erode bowl-shaped basins, called ____________________, into the sides of mountains.
5. A long ridge called a(n) ____________________ forms when two valley glaciers erode a mountain side by side.
6. If valley glaciers erode a mountain from several directions, a sharpened peak called a(n) ____________________ may form.
7. The two types of glaciers are ____________________ and ____________________.
8. A glacier is said to ____________________ when it melts and begins to shrink back.
9. Some farmers plant ____________________, or rows of trees, to block the wind and prevent soil erosion.
10. Plants with fibrous root systems such as ____________________ work best at stopping wind erosion.

Directions: *Explain how the sets of words are related.*

11. glacier, plucking

____

____

12. till, moraine, outwash

____

____

13. deflation, abrasion

____

____

14. loess, dune

____

____

II. Understanding Concepts

Skill: Completing and Using Charts

1. **Directions:** *Create a concept map describing the types of mass movement.*

Skill: Comparing and Contrasting

Directions: *Think about the traits of mass movement to answer these questions.*

2. If you were looking at the aftermath of a mass movement, how would you know that slump had occurred and not creep?

____

____

3. If you were looking at the aftermath of a mass movement, how would you know that a rockfall had occurred and not a rock slide?

____

____

Skill: Interpreting Scientific Illustrations

Directions: *Write the answer on the lines provided.*

4. If you saw a photograph of rock with long striations or grooves, what conclusions could you draw?

____

____

5. If you saw a photograph of two valleys, one U-shaped and one V-shaped, what conclusions could you draw?

____

____

Chapter Test C (continued)

III. Applying Concepts

Skill: Outlining

1. **Create** an outline about erosion and deposition by glaciers.

Writing Skills

Directions: *Answer the following questions using complete sentences.*

2. **Suggest** A family wants to build a home on a beautiful, sloped lot. Identify the main concerns and make recommendations to make the home safer.

3. **Infer** A class looks for photographs showing evidence of deflation and abrasion. They find many pictures of beaches and deserts, but very few of prairies and grasslands. Explain abrasion and deflation. Infer why there are fewer examples in prairies and grasslands.

Chapter Test C (continued)

4. **Infer** A family just bought a beach house, but piles of sand were blocking their ocean view. They shoveled away piles of sand and found scrub brushes underneath. When they came back to the beach house the next weekend, the sand piles were back. Infer what has happened. Suggest a way to prevent it.

____

____

____

____

5. **Infer** Why do some communities build walls at the edges of their beaches?

____

____

Name Date Class

Water Speed and Erosion

LAB A

Lab Preview

Directions: *Answer these questions before you begin the Lab.*

1. Why is it important to clean up immediately any water that spills on the floor?

____

2. Why do you need to set one end of the pan on the wood block?

____

What would it be like to make a raft and use it to float on a river? Would it be easy? Would you feel like Tom Sawyer? Probably not. You'd be at the mercy of the current. Strong currents create fast rivers. But does fast moving water affect more than just floating rafts and other objects?

Real-World Question

How does the speed of a stream or river affect its ability to erode?

Materials

fine-mesh screen
sand
paint roller pan
**disposable wallpaper trays*
wood block
rubber tubing (20 cm)
water
1-L beaker
stopwatch
metric ruler
**Alternate materials*

Goals

- **Assemble** an apparatus for measuring the effect of water speed on erosion.
- **Observe and measure** the ability of water traveling at different speeds to erode sand.

Safety Precautions

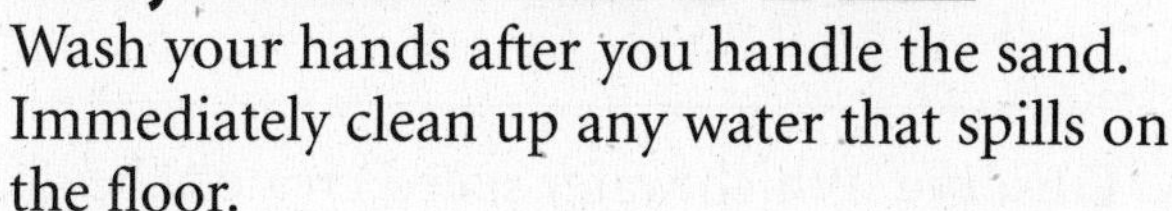

Wash your hands after you handle the sand. Immediately clean up any water that spills on the floor.

Procedure

❏ 1. Place the screen in the sink. Pour moist sand into your pan and smooth out the sand.

❏ Set one end of the pan on the wood block and hang the other end over the screen in the sink as shown in Figure 1. Excess water will flow onto the screen in the sink.

❏ 2. Attach one end of the hose to the faucet and place the other end in the beaker. Turn on the water so that it trickles into the beaker.

❏ Time how long it takes for the trickle of water to fill the beaker to the 1-L mark.

Figure 1

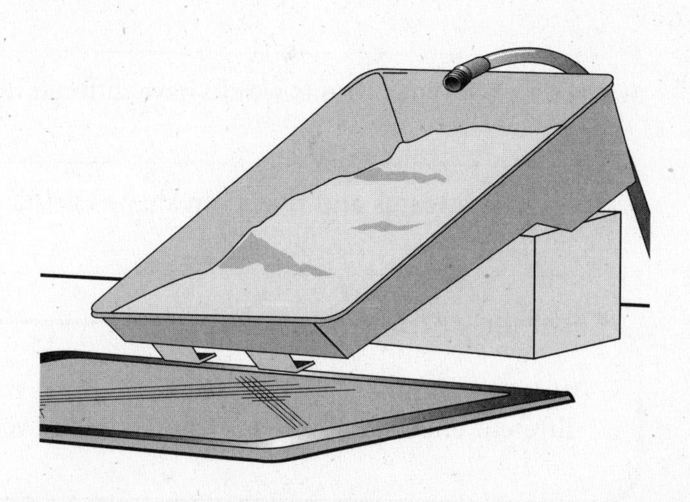

(continued)

- ❏ Divide 1 L by your time in seconds to calculate the water speed. Record the speed in your data table in the Data and Observations section.
- ❏ 3. Without altering the water speed, hold the hose over the end of the pan that is resting on the wood block. Allow the water to flow into the sand for 2 min. At the end of 2 min, turn off the water.
- ❏ 4. **Measure** the depth and length of the eroded channel formed by the water. Count the number of branches formed on the channel. Record your measurements and observations in your table.
- ❏ 5. Empty the excess water from the tray and smooth out the sand. Repeat steps 2 through 4 two more times increasing your water speed each time.

Data and Observations

Water Speed and Erosion

Water Speed (liters per second)	Depth of Channel	Length of Channel	Number of Channel Branches

Conclude and Apply

1. **Identify** the constants and variables in your experiment.

____

2. **Observe** Which water speed created the deepest and longest channel?

____

3. **Observe** Which water speed created the greatest number of branches?

____

4. **Infer** the effect that water speed has on erosion.

____

5. **Predict** how your results would have differed if one end of the pan had been raised higher.

____

6. **Infer** how streams and rivers can shape Earth's surface.

____

Communicating Your Data

Write a pamphlet for people buying homes near rivers or streams that outlines the different effects that water erosion could have on their property.

Name Date Class

Water Speed and Erosion

LAB B

Lab Preview

Directions: *Answer these questions before you begin the Lab.*

1. Why is it important to clean up immediately any water that spills on the floor?

2. Why do you need to set one end of the pan on the wood block?

What would it be like to make a raft and use it to float on a river? Would it be easy? Would you feel like Tom Sawyer? Probably not. You'd be at the mercy of the current. Strong currents create fast rivers. But does fast moving water affect more than just floating rafts and other objects?

Real-World Question

How does the speed of a stream or river affect its ability to erode?

Materials

fine-mesh screen
sand
paint roller pan
**disposable wallpaper trays*
wood block
rubber tubing (20 cm)
water
1-L beaker
stopwatch
metric ruler
**Alternate materials*

Goals

- **Assemble** an apparatus for measuring the effect of water speed on erosion.
- **Observe and measure** the ability of water traveling at different speeds to erode sand.

Safety Precautions

Wash your hands after you handle the sand. Immediately clean up any water that spills on the floor.

Procedure

❑ 1. Place the screen in the sink. Pour moist sand into your pan and smooth out the sand. Set one end of the pan on the wood block and hang the other end over the screen in the sink as shown in Figure 1. Excess water will flow onto the screen in the sink.

❑ 2. Attach one end of the hose to the faucet and place the other end in the beaker. Turn on the water so that it trickles into the beaker. Time how long it takes for the trickle of water to fill the beaker to the 1-L mark. Divide 1 L by your time in seconds to calculate the water speed. Record the speed in your data table in the Data and Observations section.

Figure 1

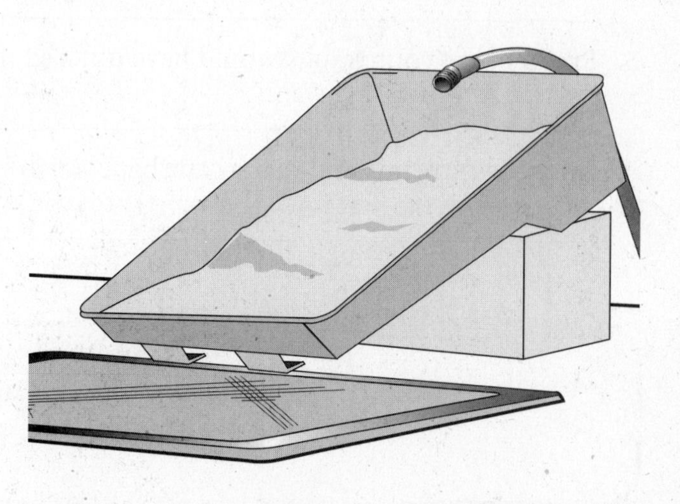

(continued)

❑ 3. Without altering the water speed, hold the hose over the end of the pan that is resting on the wood block. Allow the water to flow into the sand for 2 min. At the end of 2 min, turn off the water.

❑ 4. **Measure** the depth and length of the eroded channel formed by the water. Count the number of branches formed on the channel. Record your measurements and observations in your data table.

❑ 5. Empty the excess water from the tray and smooth out the sand. Repeat steps 2 through 4 two more times increasing your water speed each time.

Data and Observations

Water Speed and Erosion

Water Speed (liters per second)	Depth of Channel	Length of Channel	Number of Channel Branches

Conclude and Apply

1. **Identify** the constants and variables in your experiment.

2. **Observe** Which water speed created the deepest and longest channel?

3. **Observe** Which water speed created the greatest number of branches?

4. **Infer** the effect that water speed has on erosion.

5. **Predict** how your results would have differed if one end of the pan had been raised higher.

6. **Infer** how streams and rivers can shape Earth's surface.

Challenge

1. **Predict** What would have happened if you had not smoothed out the sand in step 5 before repeating the procedures?

2. **Hypothesize** What would happen if you repeated this experiment with the tray flat?

3. **Revise** If you wanted to increase the amount of water absorbed by the sand, how would you revise the lab setup? Why?

Extension

Construct Imagine that a house was being built on the slope. What could be done to prevent water erosion from undermining the house's foundation? Revise your lab to test your hypothesis. How will your materials and procedures change?

Communicating Your Data

Write a pamphlet for people buying homes near rivers or streams that outlines the different effects that water erosion could have on their property.

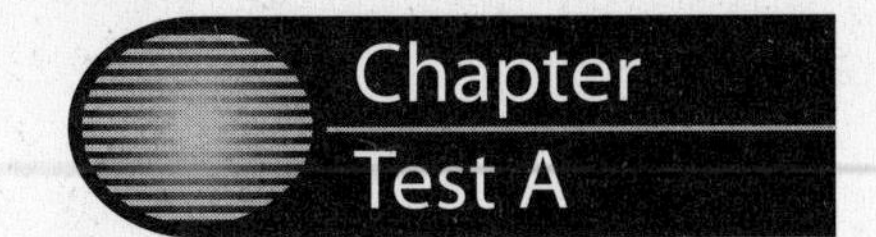

Water Erosion and Deposition

I. Testing Concepts

Directions: *Circle the term in parentheses that makes each statement correct.*

1. Water mixes with carbon dioxide gas to form a weak acid called (carbonic acid, limestone).
2. Carbon dioxide is absorbed from the air by (rainwater, groundwater) or surface water.
3. Most carbon dioxide is (blocked, absorbed) by groundwater moving through soil.
4. Acidic groundwater moves through natural (fibers, cracks) and holes, dissolving rock.
5. Gradually, the cracks can enlarge enough to create a (cave, geyser).

Directions: *Match the descriptions on the left with the terms on the right. Write the letter of the correct term in the blank at the left.*

Matching Set I

_______ 6. an area of land from which a stream collects runoff

_______ 7. a groove on a slope where water flows

_______ 8. an underground opening

_______ 9. a curve in a stream that grows to become a broad arc

_______ 10. water that does not soak in or evaporate but flows across Earth's surface

a. meander
b. drainage basin
c. channel
d. runoff
e. cave

Matching Set II

_______ 11. the upper surface of the zone of saturation

_______ 12. water that has collected in soil's pores and empty spaces

_______ 13. water that runs parallel to the shoreline

_______ 14. deposits of sediment that are parallel to the shore

_______ 15. layer of permeable rock that lets water move freely

a. beaches
b. longshore current
c. water table
d. aquifer
e. groundwater

Chapter Test A (continued)

II. Understanding Concepts

Skill: Interpreting Illustrations

Directions: *Look at the water in each illustration. Identify each stage of stream development as a* **young stream,** *a* **mature stream,** *or an* **old stream.**

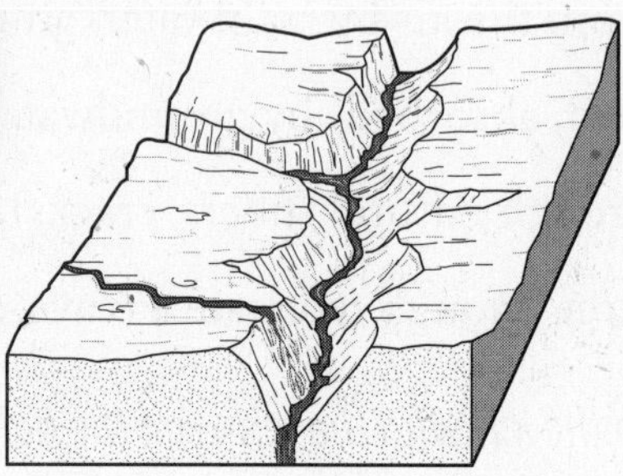

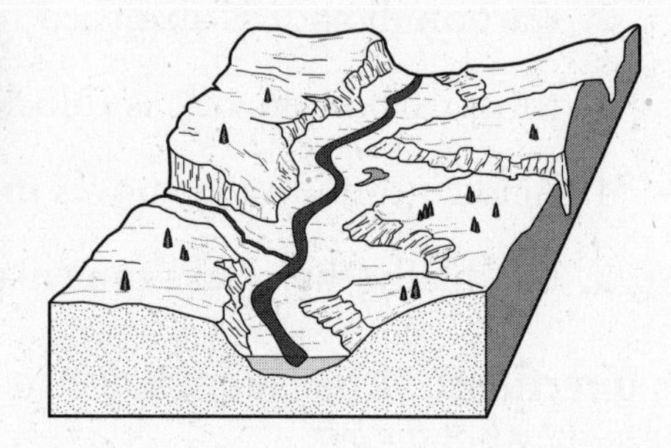

1. ______________________ 2. ______________________ 3. ______________________

Skill: Sequencing

Directions: *Number the events to show the sequence of events for filling an aquifer.*

______ **4.** fills up pores

______ **5.** soaks into the ground

______ **6.** reaches impermeable rock

Skill: Cause and Effect

Directions: *Place an* **X** *by the cause in each pair.*

7. ______ The groundwater system has connecting pores.

______ The soil is permeable.

8. ______ The soil is impermeable.

______ The soil has few pore spaces and is not well connected.

9. ______ Water reaches a layer of impermeable rock.

______ The water begins filling up the pores in the rocks above.

Chapter Test A (continued)

Skill: Compare and Contrast

10. Directions: *Complete the Venn diagram using the terms* **smooth, rocks, beaches, wind erosion, water erosion, gently sloping,** *and* **cliffs.**

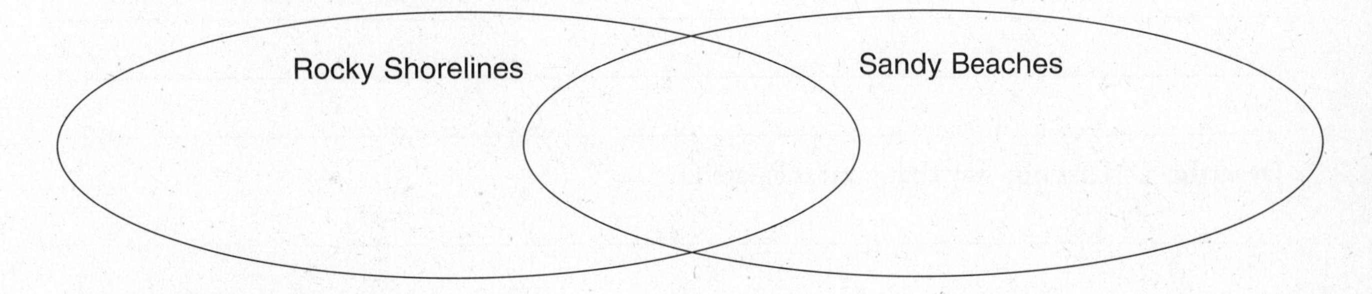

III. Applying Concepts

Skill: Interpreting Photographs

Directions: *Circle the term that identifies what you would be looking at if you saw a photograph of the following.*

1. water forming a triangular shape as it empties into a lake (geyser, delta)
2. water emptying from a mountain valley into an open plain (alluvial fan, delta)
3. water flowing out of the ground and collecting in pools (spring, geyser)
4. water shooting high in the air (geyser, spring)

Writing Skills

Directions: *Answer the following questions using complete sentences.*

5. **Summarize** Discuss the factors that cause runoff.

Chapter Test A (continued)

6. **Explain** How does rill erosion lead to gully erosion?

7. **Describe** Discuss one way that sand is created.

8. **Infer** There has been a drought, and it has not rained in awhile. What will happen to water in wells? Why?

Name ______ Date ______ Class ______

Water Erosion and Deposition

I. Testing Concepts

Directions: *Match the terms in Column II with the definitions or descriptions in Column I. Write the letter of the correct term in the blank at the left.*

Column I

______ 1. the land area from which a stream gets its water
______ 2. deposits of sediment that run along the shore
______ 3. cool water forced to the surface by pressure
______ 4. calcite formation on the floor of a cave
______ 5. the broad, flat valley floor carved by a meandering stream
______ 6. a curve in a stream's channel caused by erosion
______ 7. water that soaks into the ground
______ 8. coastal land with rocks and cliffs but little sand
______ 9. upper surface of the zone of saturation
______ 10. a hot spring that erupts periodically
______ 11. layer of rock that lets water move freely
______ 12. calcite formation hanging from the ceiling of a cave
______ 13. water that flows out across the ground
______ 14. underground opening formed in rock
______ 15. quality of rocks with connected pores through which water can pass
______ 16. formed when the water table meets Earth's surface
______ 17. results when a rill channel becomes broader and deeper
______ 18. the area where all of the pores in the rock are filled with water
______ 19. begins when a small stream forms during a heavy rain
______ 20. sand deposits that parallel the shore but are separated from the mainland
______ 21. the deposit formed when river waters empty onto a flat, open plain
______ 22. acts like a river of sand in the ocean
______ 23. quality of rocks with few connected pores through which water cannot pass

Column II

a. aquifer
b. artesian well
c. cave
d. rocky shoreline
e. floodplain
f. geyser
g. groundwater
h. barrier islands
i. impermeable
j. meander
k. permeable
l. gully erosion
m. spring
n. rill erosion
o. beaches
p. longshore current
q. zone of saturation
r. stalactite
s. alluvial fan
t. drainage basin
u. runoff
v. water table
w. stalagmite

Chapter Test B (continued)

Directions: *Identify each statement as* **true** *or* **false.** *Rewrite false statements to make them correct.*

______ **24.** The amount of vegetation affects the amount of runoff.

______ **25.** A cave is a layer of permeable rock containing water.

______ **26.** In dry seasons, some wells go dry because the water table drops.

______ **27.** A mature stream flows less swiftly through its valley.

______ **28.** Bays shape shorelines by eroding and redepositing sediments.

Directions: *For each of the following, write the letter of the term or phrase that best completes each sentence.*

______ **29.** In a city or town where groundwater is the main source of drinking water, the number of ______ becomes important.
a. springs **b.** geysers **c.** sinkholes **d.** wells

______ **30.** A(n) ______ forms where rivers empty into a lake or ocean.
a. aquifer **b.** delta **c.** spring **d.** longshore current

______ **31.** Green sands may be made of ______.
a. basalt fragments **b.** olivine **c.** quartz **d.** coral and shell

______ **32.** Groundwater travels through ______ in sediments.
a. springs **b.** pores **c.** layers **d.** caves

______ **33.** Runoff water ______.
a. supplies water for artesian wells
b. forms streams
c. forms precipitation
d. all of these

Chapter Test B (continued)

II. Understanding Concepts

Skill: Sequencing

Directions: *Number the illustrations in the order in which they occur.*

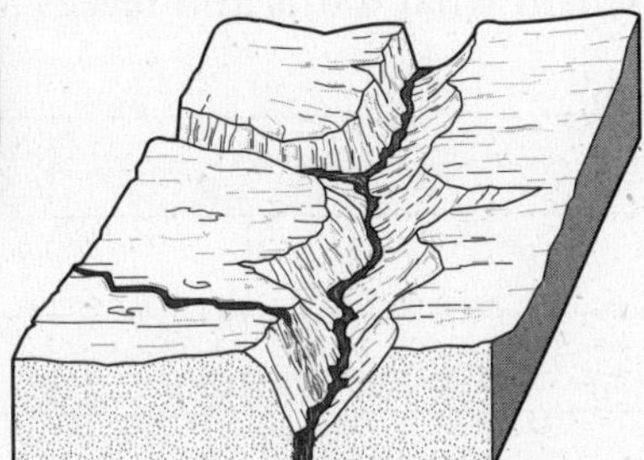

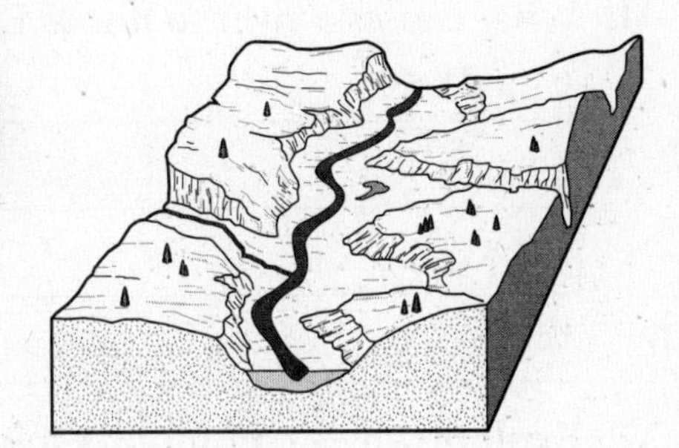

1. ____________ 2. ____________ 3. ____________

Skill: Concept Mapping

Directions: *Fill in the letter of the correct event in the events-chain map of an aquifer.*

a. Fills up pores
b. Soaks into the ground
c. Reaches impermeable rock

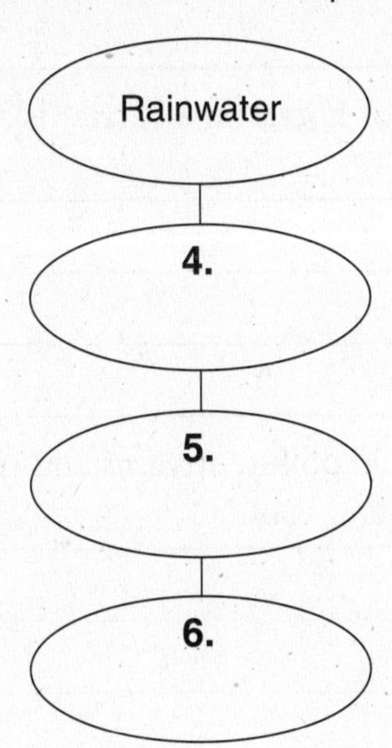

Skill: Comparing and Contrasting

Directions: *A river system is like a tree. In the blank at the left, write the letter of the tree part that is similar to the part in the river system.*

______	**7.** river	**a.** branches
______	**8.** large streams	**b.** twigs
______	**9.** small streams	**c.** trunk

III. Applying Concepts

Writing Skills

Directions: *Answer the following questions using complete sentences.*

1. What causes a river to flood? Explain what dams and levees are and how they relate to flooding.

2. **Explain** why a community might want to use stream or river water in addition to groundwater.

3. **Discuss** why building homes or hotels on a barrier island might be a problem.

4. **Explain** how runoff water could pollute streams and rivers.

5. **Explain** why some shorelines are rocky and others have sandy beaches.

Name ______ Date ______ Class ______

Water Erosion and Deposition

I. Testing Concepts

Directions: *Identify each statement as* **true** *or* **false**. *If a statement is false, change the underlined word(s) to make it true.*

______ 1. Rocks and cliffs are the most common features along <u>sandy beaches</u>.

____

______ 2. The amount of rain and the <u>type of precipitation</u> are two factors that affect runoff.

____

______ 3. A <u>drainage basin</u> is the area of land from which a stream or river collects runoff.

____

______ 4. Over time, a curve in a river can grow to become a broad arc called a <u>meander</u>.

____

______ 5. A layer of <u>impermeable rock</u> that lets water move freely is an aquifer.

____

Directions: *Fill in the blanks to complete the sentences.*

6. ______________ begins with a small stream that forms during a heavy rain.
7. Water moving down the same path creates a groove, called a(n) ______________.
8. During ______________, a rill channel becomes broader and deeper.
9. ______________ occurs when water that is flowing as sheets picks up and carries away sediment.
10. As water from a stream moves along, it picks up sediment from the bottom and sides of its channel, causing ______________.
11. In a cave, a(n) ______________ forms where drops of water fall to the floor.
12. Water dripping in a cave evaporates, leaving behind ______________ deposits.
13. A(n) ______________ is a well that does not need a pump to bring water to the surface.
14. The lightweight sediment in a stream is in the ______________ load.
15. The larger, heavy particles, called the ______________ load, roll along the bottom of a stream.

Name ________________ Date ________________ Class ________________

Chapter Test C (continued)

II. Understanding Concepts

Skill: Concept Mapping

1. Directions: *Create an events-chain map of an aquifer.*

Skill: Interpreting Illustrations

Directions: *Look at the water in each illustration. Identify each stage of stream development.*

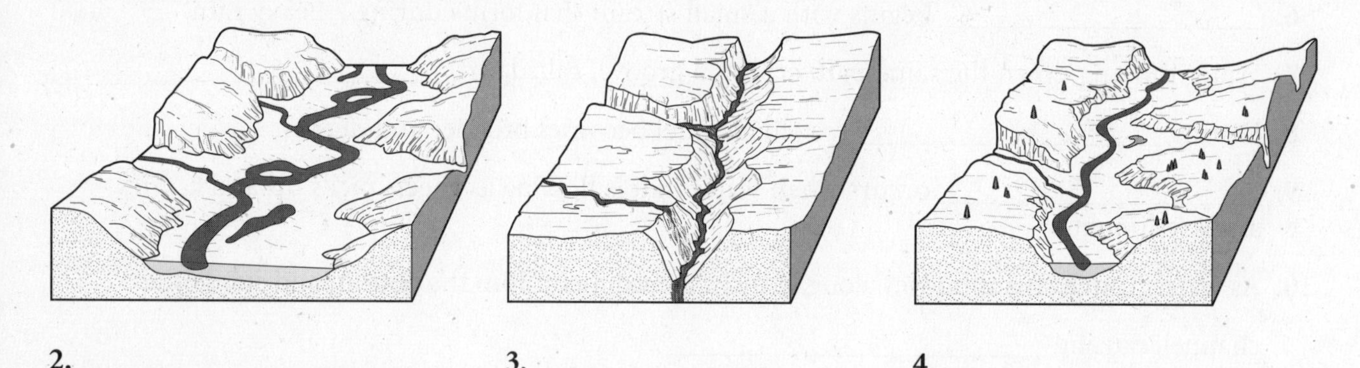

2. ________________ 3. ________________ 4. ________________

Skill: Compare and Contrast

Directions: *Fill in the blanks to complete the sentences.*

5. Rocks and cliffs are the most common features along ________________.
6. Smooth, sloping shorelines are the most common features along ________________.
7. At rocky shorelines, water erosion from the waves causes the rocks to ________________.
8. At sandy beaches, ________________ create ________________, by breaking down rocks.

III. Applying Concepts

Skill: Interpreting Photographs

Directions: *Describe what you would see in a photograph of each of the following.*

1. delta

2. alluvial fan

3. spring

4. geyser

Writing Skills

Directions: *Answer the following questions using complete sentences.*

5. Analyze Beaches may be tan, white, black, or even green. Why are different beaches different colors?

6. Analyze Explain groundwater movement. What would happen to groundwater if all rock were permeable?

7. Infer A scientist compares two samples of water. One is neutral and the other is acidic. Given what you've learned, where do you think the acidic sample came from? Why?

Use the Internet

Predicting Tectonic Activity

LAB A

The movement of plates on Earth causes forces that build up energy in rocks. The release of this energy can produce vibrations in Earth that you know as earthquakes. Earthquakes occur every day. Many of them are too small to be felt by humans, but each event tells scientists something more about the planet. Active volcanoes can do the same, and volcanoes often form at plate boundaries.

Think about where earthquakes and volcanoes have occurred in the past. Make a hypothesis about whether the locations of earthquake epicenters and active volcanoes can be used to predict tectonically active areas.

Real-World Question

Can you predict tectonically active areas by plotting locations of earthquake epicenters and volcanic eruptions?

Goals

- **Research** the locations of earthquakes and volcanic eruptions around the world.
- **Plot** earthquake epicenters and the locations of volcanic eruptions obtained from **msscience.com** site.
- **Predict** locations that are tectonically active based on a plot of the locations of earthquake epicenters and active volcanoes.

Data Sources

Science Online Visit **msscience.com/internet_lab** for more information about earthquake and volcano sites and data from other students.

Make a Plan

❑ **1.** Study the data table shown below. Use it to record your data.

❑ **2.** Collect data for earthquake epicenters and volcanic eruptions for at least the past two weeks. Your data should include the longitude and latitude for each location. For help, refer to the data sources given above.

Locations of Epicenters and Eruptions

Earthquake Epicenter/Volcanic Eruption	Longitude	Latitude

Name Date Class

LAB (continued)

LAB A

Follow Your Plan

- ❑ **1.** Make sure your teacher approves your plan before you start.
- ❑ **2.** **Plot** the locations of earthquake epicenters and volcanic eruptions on a map of the world. Use an overlay of tissue paper or plastic.
- ❑ **3.** After you have collected the necessary data, predict where the tectonically active areas on Earth are.
- ❑ **4.** **Compare** and **contrast** the areas that you predicted to be tectonically active with the plate boundary map shown in **Figure 9** in your textbook.

Analyze Your Data

1. What areas on Earth do you predict to be the locations of tectonic activity?

____

2. How close did your prediction come to the actual location of tectonically active areas?

____

Conclude and Apply

1. How could you make your predictions closer to the locations of actual tectonic activity?

____

____

2. Would data from a longer period of time help? Explain.

____

____

3. What types of plate boundaries were close to your locations of earthquake epicenters? Volcanic eruptions?

____

____

4. **Explain** which types of plate boundaries produce volcanic eruptions. Be specific.

____

____

Communicating Your Data

Find this lab using the link below. Post your data in the table provided. **Compare** your data with those of other students. Combine your data with those of other students, and **plot** these combined data on map to **recognize** the relationship between plate coundaries, volcanic eruptions, and earthquake epicenters.

Science Online **msscience.com/internet_lab**

Name Date Class

Use the Internet

Predicting Tectonic Activity

LAB B

The movement of plates on Earth causes forces that build up energy in rocks. The release of this energy can produce vibrations in Earth that you know as earthquakes. Earthquakes occur every day. Many of them are too small to be felt by humans, but each event tells scientists something more about the planet. Active volcanoes can do the same, and volcanoes often form at plate boundaries.

Think about where earthquakes and volcanoes have occurred in the past. Make a hypothesis about whether the locations of earthquake epicenters and active volcanoes can be used to predict tectonically active areas.

Real-World Question

Can you predict tectonically active areas by plotting locations of earthquake epicenters and volcanic eruptions?

Goals

- **Research** the locations of earthquakes and volcanic eruptions around the world.
- **Plot** earthquake epicenters and the locations of volcanic eruptions obtained from **msscience.com** site.
- **Predict** locations that are tectonically active based on a plot of the locations of earthquake epicenters and active volcanoes.

Data Sources

Science Online Visit **msscience.com/internet_lab** for more information about earthquake and volcano sites and data from other students.

Make a Plan

❑ **1.** Study the data table shown below. Use it to record your data.

❑ **2.** Collect data for earthquake epicenters and volcanic eruptions for at least the past two weeks. Your data should include the longitude and latitude for each location. For help, refer to the data sources given above.

Locations of Epicenters and Eruptions

Earthquake Epicenter/Volcanic Eruption	Longitude	Latitude

(continued)

LAB B

Follow Your Plan

- ❑ 1. Make sure your teacher approves your plan before you start.
- ❑ 2. **Plot** the locations of earthquake epicenters and volcanic eruptions on a map of the world. Use an overlay of tissue paper or plastic.
- ❑ 3. After you have collected the necessary data, predict where the tectonically active areas on Earth are.
- ❑ 4. **Compare** and **contrast** the areas that you predicted to be tectonically active with the plate boundary map shown in **Figure 9** in your textbook.

Analyze Your Data

1. What areas on Earth do you predict to be the locations of tectonic activity?

____

2. How close did your prediction come to the actual location of tectonically active areas?

____

Conclude and Apply

1. How could you make your predictions closer to the locations of actual tectonic activity?

____

____

2. Would data from a longer period of time help? Explain.

____

____

3. What types of plate boundaries were close to your locations of earthquake epicenters? Volcanic eruptions?

____

____

4. **Explain** which types of plate boundaries produce volcanic eruptions. Be specific.

____

____

Challenge

1. **Analyze** If you were looking for earthquake activity, what type or types of boundaries would you investigate? Why?

____

____

____

(continued)

2. **Analyze** What land features might you observe along plate boundaries?

____

____

3. **Analyze** Why are reverse faults common locations for mountains and volcanoes?

____

____

____

____

Extension

Create Use classroom materials to develop a model of a strike-slip fault along a transform boundary. What motion will the plates have? How will you show this motion?

Communicating Your Data

Find this lab using the link below. Post your data in the table provided. **Compare** your data with those of other students. Combine your data with those of other students, and **plot** these combined data on map to **recognize** the relationship between plate coundaries, volcanic eruptions, and earthquake epicenters.

Science Online **msscience.com/internet_lab**

Name Date Class

Plate Tectonics

I. Testing Concepts

Directions: *Identify each statement as* **true** *or* **false**. *If a statement is false, change the underlined word(s) to make it true.*

______ **1.** Iron-bearing minerals found in the rocks of the seafloor can record the direction of Earth's magnetic field.

____

______ **2.** Scientists found that the oldest rocks are located at the mid-ocean ridges.

____

______ **3.** As the seafloor spreads apart at a mid-ocean ridge, seafloor is destroyed.

____

______ **4.** Tension forces can stretch Earth's crust.

____

______ **5.** Most of the movement along a strike-slip fault is perpendicular to Earth's surface.

____

Directions: *Circle the term in parentheses that makes each statement correct.*

6. German meteorologist (Alfred Wegner, Harry Hess) formed the hypothesis of continental drift.

7. According to the theory of continental drift, the continents were all part of one land mass called (Glossopteris, Pangaea).

8. (Alfred Wegner, Harry Hess) proposed the theory of seafloor spreading.

9. According to the theory of seafloor spreading, hot, less dense material below Earth's crust rises toward the surface at (mid-ocean ridges, magnetic poles).

10. Earth's crust and part of the upper mantle are broken into sections called (plates, divergent boundaries).

11. According to the theory of plate tectonics, plates move on a (rigid, plasticlike) layer of the mantle.

12. The upper rigid part of Earth that contains the crust and part of the upper mantle is called the (lithosphere, continental crust).

13. The cycle of heating, rising, cooling, and sinking is called a (convection current, tension force).

Chapter Test A (continued)

II. Understanding Concepts

Skill: Concept Mapping

Directions: *Complete the concept map by contrasting the different types of plate boundaries. Use the following terms:* **convergent**, **transform**, *and* **divergent**.

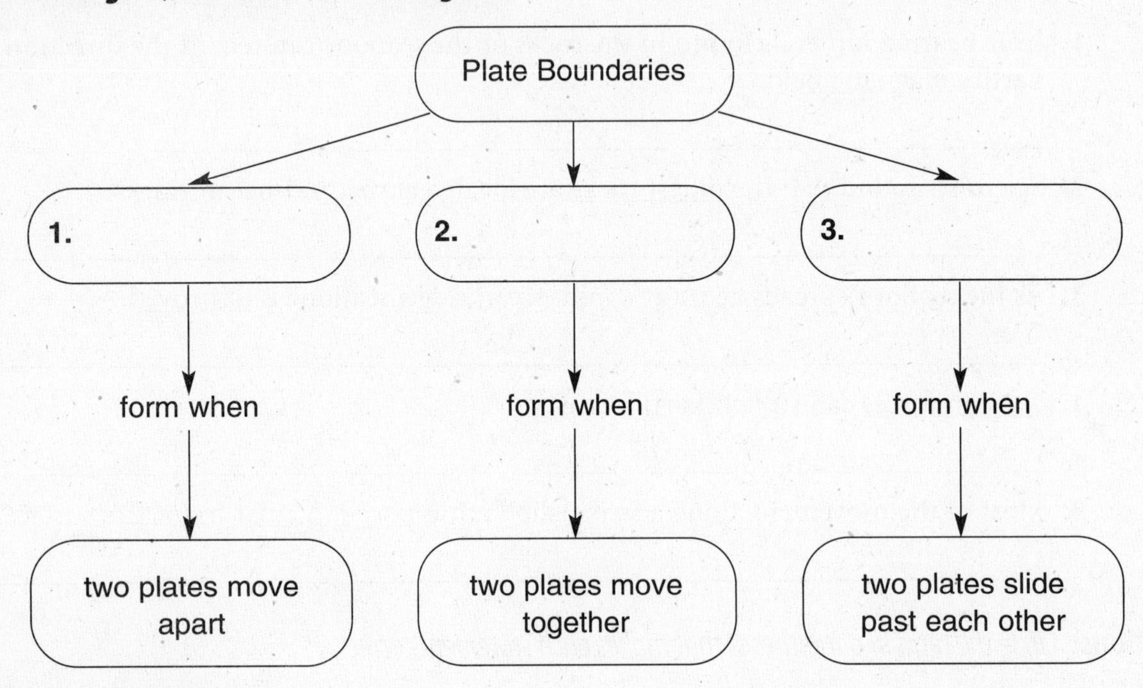

Skill: Cause and Effect

Directions: *Fill in the blanks to show the effect for each cause. Use the following sentences.*

A mid-ocean ridge forms.
An earthquake occurs.
Chains of volcanic islands form.
Fault-block mountains form.
Mountains form.

4. Cause: In a normal fault, rock layers above the fault move down when compared with rock layers below the fault.

   Effect: ______________________________

5. Cause: Two oceanic plates separate.

   Effect: ______________________________

6. Cause: Along a reverse fault, the rock layers above the fault surface move up relative to the rock layers beneath.

   Effect: ______________________________

7. Cause: Two oceanic plates converge, and the denser plate is forced beneath the other plate.

   Effect: ______________________________

8. Cause: At a transform boundary, two plates slide past each other.

   Effect: ______________________________

III. Applying Concepts

Skill: Sequencing

Directions: *Write numbers in the blanks at the left to sequence the process for seafloor spreading.*

_____ 1. The material flows sideways, carrying the seafloor away from the ridge.

_____ 2. The magma cools, contracts, and becomes denser.

_____ 3. Hot, less dense material below Earth's crust rises toward the surface at the mid-ocean ridge.

_____ 4. As the seafloor spreads apart, magma is forced upward and flows from the cracks.

_____ 5. The denser, colder seafloor sinks, helping to form the ridge.

Writing Skills

Directions: *Answer the following questions using complete sentences.*

6. **Restate** What is the hypothesis of continental drift?

7. **Give an Example** For each type of clue below, give an example and tell how it supports the theory of continental drift.
   a. animal fossil clues:

   b. plant fossil clues:

   c. climate clues:

   d. rock clues:

Name ______ Date ______ Class ______

Plate Tectonics

I. Testing Concepts

Directions: *For each of the following, write the letter of the term or phrase that best completes the sentence.*

______ **1.** The seafloor spreading theory was proposed by ______
a. Alfred Wegener. **b.** Harry Hess. **c.** Abraham Ortelius. **d.** Carl Sagan.

______ **2.** As Earth's plates move apart at some boundaries, they collide at others, forming ______
a. mountains and volcanoes. **b.** ocean basins. **c.** strike-slip faults. **d.** both a and b.

______ **3.** The youngest rocks in the ocean floor are located at the mid-ocean ______
a. volcanoes. **b.** basins. **c.** trenches. **d.** ridges.

______ **4.** The results of plate movement can be seen at ______
a. rift valleys. **b.** plate boundaries. **c.** plate centers. **d.** both a and b.

______ **5.** The ______ are forming where the Indo-Australian plate collides into the Eurasian plate.
a. Andes mountain range **b.** Rocky Mountains **c.** Himalayas **d.** Appalachian Mountains

______ **6.** The presence of the same ______ on several continents supports the idea of continental drift.
a. fossils **b.** rocks **c.** neither a nor b **d.** both a and b

______ **7.** Continental drift occurs because of ______
a. seafloor spreading. **b.** Pangaea. **c.** magnetic reversal. **d.** earthquakes.

______ **8.** The cycle of heating, rising, cooling, and sinking is called a ______
a. subduction zone. **b.** convergent boundary. **c.** convection current. **d.** conduction current.

______ **9.** Oceanic plates are pushed down into the upper mantle in ______
a. convection currents. **b.** subduction zones. **c.** strike-slip faults. **d.** divergent boundaries.

______ **10.** The hypothesis that continents have moved slowly to their current locations is called ______
a. continental drift. **b.** continental slope. **c.** magnetism. **d.** convection.

______ **11.** Plates move apart at ______ boundaries.
a. convergent **b.** transform **c.** divergent **d.** magnetic

______ **12.** Ocean floor rocks are ______ continental rocks.
a. more eroded than **b.** older than **c.** younger than **d.** the same age as

Chapter Test B (continued)

______ 13. The alignment of iron-bearing minerals in rocks when they formed reflects the fact that Earth's ______ has reversed itself several times in its past.
a. magnetic field b. core c. asthenosphere d. gravity

______ 14. The lack of an explanation for continental drift prevented many scientists from believing a single supercontinent called ______ once existed.
a. *Glomar* b. *Glossopteris* c. *Pangaea* d. *Mesosaurus*

______ 15. Scientists aboard the *Glomar Challenger* added to the evidence for the theory of seafloor spreading by providing ______
a. high altitude photos of existing continents.
b. samples of plant life from different locations.
c. samples of rock from different locations.
d. direct measurements of the movement of continents.

______ 16. Where plates slide past one another, ______ occur.
a. volcanoes b. earthquakes c. island arcs d. ocean trenches

______ 17. The places between plates moving together are called ______
a. divergent boundaries. c. strike-slip faults.
b. convergent boundaries. d. lithospheres.

______ 18. Seafloor spreading occurs because ______
a. new material is being added to the asthenosphere.
b. earthquakes break apart the ocean floor.
c. sediments accumulate on the ocean floor.
d. hot, less-dense material below Earth's crust is forced upward toward the surface.

______ 19. Studying the ocean floor, scientists found rocks showing magnetic ______
a. weakening. b. reversal. c. bonds. d. poles.

Directions: *Complete the following sentences using the correct terms.*

20. The theory that describes Earth's crust and upper mantle as being broken into sections is called ____________________.

21. The theory of ____________________ was shown to be correct by age evidence and magnetic clues.

22. ____________________, occurring in the mantle, are thought to be the force behind plate tectonics.

23. Earth's plasticlike layer is the ____________________.

24. Earth's ____________________ move around on a special layer of the mantle.

25. The main lines of evidence for ____________________ are fossil, rock, and climate clues, and the theory of seafloor spreading.

26. The rigid part of the plates of the ____________________ are made of oceanic crust or continental crust and upper mantle.

27. The name ____________________ means "all land."

Chapter Test B (continued)

II. Understanding Concepts

Directions: *Answer the following questions on the lines provided.*

1. What is the difference between a convergent and a divergent plate boundary?

2. What happens to warmer material in a convection current?

3. What observation led Albert Wegener to develop the hypothesis of continental drift?

4. Which part of Earth's structure is about 100 km thick?

5. How were the Andes mountain range, the Himalayas, and the islands of Japan formed alike?

6. How were the Andes mountain range, the Himalayas, and the islands of Japan formed differently?

Skill: Recognizing Cause and Effect

7. What causes new material to form at a mid-ocean ridge on the ocean floor?

Chapter Test B (continued)

III. Applying Concepts

Directions: *Answer the following questions on the lines provided.*

1. Why are there few volcanoes in the Himalayas?

2. Glacial deposits often form at a high latitude near the poles. Explain why glacial deposits have been found in Africa.

3. Why would the fossil of an ocean fish found on two different continents **NOT** be good evidence of continental drift?

IV. Writing Skills

Directions: *Answer the following questions using complete sentences.*

1. **Explain** how research from the *Glomar Challenger* helped scientists support the theory of seafloor spreading.

2. Since new crust is constantly being added, why does Earth's surface not keep expanding?

Name ______________ Date ______________ Class ______________

Plate Tectonics

I. Testing Concepts

Directions: *Fill in the blanks to complete the sentences.*

1. The meteorologist ______________ developed the hypothesis of continental drift.
2. Continental drift is a theory that the continents were all part of one land mass called ______________.
3. Harry Hess developed the theory of ______________.
4. Scientists have found that the youngest rocks in the ocean are at the ______________.
5. During a(n) ______________, the lines of magnetic force run the opposite way.
6. A device called a(n) ______________ is used to detect magnetic fields.
7. Earth's plates move on a(n) ______________ layer of the mantle.
8. Earth's plates are made up of the ______________ and a part of the ______________.
9. The plasticlike layer below the lithosphere is the ______________.
10. The area where an oceanic plate goes down into the mantle is called a(n) ______________.
11. According to one hypothesis, ______________ cause the movements of plates.
12. When ______________ form, they interrupt rock layers by moving them out of place.
13. Rift valleys and mid-ocean ridges can form where Earth's crust ______________.
14. Curved chains of volcanic islands called ______________ form above sinking plates.
15. When using the ______________, scientists on the ground aim laser pulses at a satellite to determine precise locations of plates.

Chapter Test C (continued)

II. Understanding Concepts

Skill: Concept Mapping

Directions: *Create a concept map to compare and contrast the types of plate boundaries.*

1.

Skill: Cause and Effect

Directions: *Write an effect to go with each cause.*

2. Cause: In a normal fault, rock layers above the fault move down when compared with rock layers below the fault.

   Effect: ______________________________

3. Cause: Two oceanic plates separate.

   Effect: ______________________________

4. Cause: Along a reverse fault, the rock layers above the fault surface move up relative to the rock layers beneath.

   Effect: ______________________________

5. Cause: Two oceanic plates converge, and the denser plate is forced beneath the other plate.

   Effect: ______________________________

6. At a transform boundary, two plates slide past one another.

   Effect: ______________________________

Skill: Sequencing

Directions: *Explain seafloor spreading by listing the steps in the process in order.*

7.

III. Applying Concepts

Writing Skills

Directions: *Answer questions 1 and 2 on the lines provided.*

1. **Relate** Why was Wegner's hypothesis of continental drift not widely accepted during his time?

2. **Defend** Use four pieces of evidence to construct an argument in favor of continental drift theory.

3. **Construct** Make a diagram to demonstrate one of the hypotheses about the relationship between heat and plate tectonics.

LAB Earthquake Depths

LAB A

Lab Preview

Directions: *Answer these questions before you begin the Lab.*

1. What information is contained in the table?

2. Scan the data table to answer this question: Which earthquake originated at the deepest level?

You learned in this chapter that Earth's crust is broken into sections called plates. Stresses caused by movement of plates generate energy within rocks that must be released. When this release is sudden and rocks break, an earthquake occurs.

Real-World Question

Can a study of the foci of earthquakes tell you about plate movement in a particular region?

Materials

graph paper
pencil

Goals

- **Observe** any connection between earthquake-focus depth and epicenter location using the data provided on the next page.
- **Describe** any observed relationship between earthquake-focus depth and the movement of plates at Earth's surface.

Analyze Your Data

❑ **1.** Use graph paper and the data table in your textbook to make a graph in your Science Journal plotting the depths of earthquake foci and the distances from the coast of a continent for each earthquake epicenter.

❑ **2.** Follow the graph in your textbook. Place *Distance from the coast* and units on the *x*-axis.

❑ Begin labeling at the far left with 100 km west. To the right of it should be 0 km, then 100 km east, 200 km east, 300 km east, and so on through 700 km east. What point on your graph represents the coast?

❑ **3.** Label the *y*-axis *Depth below Earth's surface.*

❑ Label the top of the graph *0 km* to represent Earth's surface.

❑ Label the bottom of the *y*-axis *–800 km.*

❑ **4.** **Plot** the focus depths against the distance and direction from the coast for each earthquake in the table.

LAB (continued) **LAB A**

Data and Observations

Refer to the Focus and Epicenter Data Table in your textbook.

Conclude and Apply

1. **Describe** any observed relationship between the location of earthquake epicenters and the depth of foci.

2. **Explain** why none of the plotted earthquakes occurred below 700 km.

3. Based on your graph, form a hypothesis to explain what is happening to the plates at Earth's surface in the vicinity of the plotted earthquake foci. In what direction are the plates moving relative to each other?

4. **Infer** what process is causing the earthquakes you plotted on your graph.

5. **Infer** whether these earthquakes are occurring along the eastern side of a continent or along the western side of a continent.

6. **Draw and label** a cross section of the Earth beneath this coast. Label the eastern plate, the western plate, and use arrows to show the directions the plates are moving.

7. **Form a hypothesis** to predict which continent these data might apply to. Apply what you have learned in this lab and the information in **Figure 2.** Explain your answer.

Communicating Your Data

Compare your graph with those of other members of your class. **For more help, refer to the Science Skill Handbook.**

Name Date Class

Earthquake Depths

LAB B

Lab Preview

Directions: *Answer these questions before you begin the Lab.*

1. What information is contained in the table?

____

2. Scan the data table to answer this question: Which earthquake originated at the deepest level?

____

You learned in this chapter that Earth's crust is broken into sections called plates. Stresses caused by movement of plates generate energy within rocks that must be released. When this release is sudden and rocks break, an earthquake occurs.

Real-World Question

Can a study of the foci of earthquakes tell you about plate movement in a particular region?

Materials

graph paper
pencil

Goals

- **Observe** any connection between earthquake-focus depth and epicenter location using the data provided on the next page.
- **Describe** any observed relationship between earthquake-focus depth and the movement of plates at Earth's surface.

Analyze Your Data

❏ 1. Use graph paper and the data table in your textbook to make a graph in your Science Journal plotting the depths of earthquake foci and the distances from the coast of a continent for each earthquake epicenter.

❏ 2. Follow the graph in your textbook. Place *Distance from the coast* and units on the *x*-axis. Begin labeling at the far left with 100 km west. To the right of it should be 0 km, then 100 km east, 200 km east, 300 km east, and so on through 700 km east. What point on your graph represents the coast?

❏ 3. Label the *y*-axis *Depth below Earth's surface.* Label the top of the graph *0 km* to represent Earth's surface. Label the bottom of the *y*-axis *–800 km.*

❏ 4. **Plot** the focus depths against the distance and direction from the coast for each earthquake in the table.

LAB (continued) **LAB B**

Data and Observations

Refer to the Focus and Epicenter Data Table in your textbook.

Conclude and Apply

1. **Describe** any observed relationship between the location of earthquake epicenters and the depth of foci.

2. **Explain** why none of the plotted earthquakes occurred below 700 km.

3. Based on your graph, form a hypothesis to explain what is happening to the plates at Earth's surface in the vicinity of the plotted earthquake foci. In what direction are the plates moving relative to each other?

4. **Infer** what process is causing the earthquakes you plotted on your graph.

5. **Infer** whether these earthquakes are occurring along the eastern side of a continent or along the western side of a continent.

6. **Draw and label** a cross section of the Earth beneath this coast. Label the eastern plate, the western plate, and use arrows to show the directions the plates are moving.

7. **Form a hypothesis** to predict which continent these data might apply to. Apply what you have learned in this lab and the information in **Figure 2.** Explain your answer.

(continued)

Challenge

1. **Hypothesize** Why are none of these sites in the middle of a plate?

2. **Analyze** Which earthquakes do you think had the highest Richter scale rating?

3. **Hypothesize** If you plotted volcanic activity for the same area, what do you think you would find?

Extension

Evaluate Imagine you are part of a research study. You will be testing new earthquake-detecting devices. You only have enough money for a limited number of sensors. Reference the map of earthquakes from your book, and use what you have learned to create a list of preferred locations for the sensors.

Communicating Your Data

Compare your graph with those of other members of your class. **For more help, refer to the Science Skill Handbook.**

Chapter Test A — Earthquakes

I. Testing Concepts

Directions: *In the blank at the left, write the letter of the term that best completes each statement.*

______ **1.** The ______ measures the strength of an earthquake.
a. focus
b. liquefaction
c. Richter magnitude scale
d. modified Mercalli intensity scale

______ **2.** The ______ describes the intensity of an earthquake by determining the amount of damage in a specific area.
a. focus
b. liquefaction
c. Richter magnitude scale
d. modified Mercalli intensity scale

______ **3.** Seismic waves change ______ as they pass through layers of Earth.
a. directions **b.** speeds **c.** temperature **d.** locations

______ **4.** The outer core of Earth is ______.
a. liquid **b.** solid **c.** gas **d.** crust

______ **5.** The motion of primary waves can be compared to a ______.
a. jump rope **b.** coiled spring **c.** floating toy **d.** bouncing ball

______ **6.** The motion of secondary waves can be compared to a ______.
a. jump rope **b.** coiled spring **c.** floating toy **d.** bouncing ball

______ **7.** The ______ wave is the most destructive.
a. primary **b.** secondary **c.** surface **d.** seismograph

Directions: *Match the descriptions in Column I with the terms in Column II. Write the letter of the correct term in the blank at the left.*

Column I	Column II
______ **8.** the vibrations produced by the breaking of rock	**a.** magnitude
______ **9.** the point where energy release first occurs	**b.** liquefaction
______ **10.** the point on Earth's surface directly above the earthquake focus	**c.** focus
______ **11.** a measure of the energy that is released during an earthquake	**d.** fault
______ **12.** the surfaces on which rocks move when they break	**e.** earthquake
______ **13.** an occurrence in which wet soil acts more like a liquid	**f.** epicenter

Chapter Test A (continued)

II. Understanding Concepts

Skill: Interpreting Illustrations

Directions: *Use the following terms to complete the concept map:* **strike-slip faults, reverse faults,** *and* **normal faults.**

1.

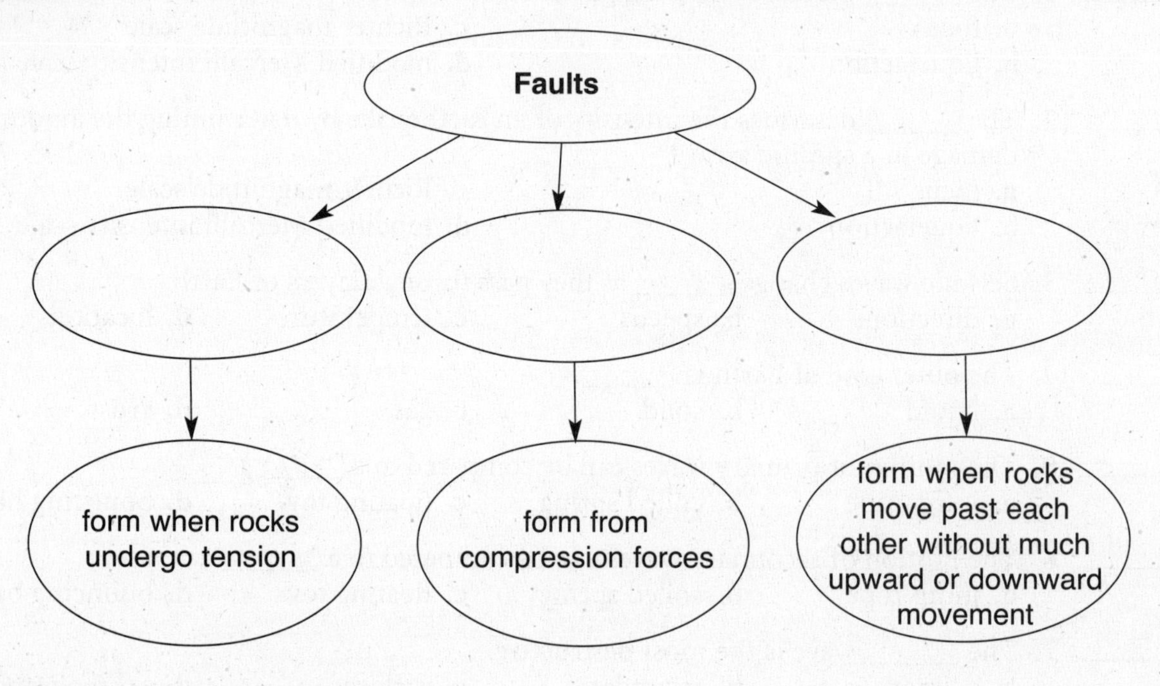

Skill: Completing and Using Charts

Directions: *Use the chart to answer the following questions.*

Distance	Time (minutes and seconds) Primary Wave	Secondary Wave
1,000 km	0 min 40 s	1 min 20 s
2,000 km	1 min 15 s	2 min 10 s
4,000 km	2 min 0 s	3 min 25 s
6,000 km	2 min 25 s	4 min 10 s
8,000 km	2 min 40 s	4 min 45 s
10,000 km	2 min 45 s	5 min 10 s

2. What is the travel time for primary waves at 1,000 km? ______________________

3. What is the travel time for secondary waves at 1,000 km? ______________________

4. What is the difference between the two waves at 1,000 km? ______________________

Chapter Test A (continued)

5. What is the travel time for primary waves at 8,000 km? ____________________

6. What is the travel time for secondary waves at 8,000 km? ____________________

7. What is the difference between the two waves at 8,000 km? ____________________

8. Which waves travel fastest? ____________________

9. Which waves travel slowest? ____________________

III. Applying Concepts

Writing Skills

Directions: *Respond to the following using complete sentences.*

1. **Describe** How do earthquakes occur?

____

____

____

____

____

____

2. **List** Name the layers of Earth, starting with the outside layer.

____

3. **Locate** Are you more likely to experience a damaging earthquake in Texas, Florida, or California? Why?

____

____

4. **Restate** What are four ways to make your home more earthquake-safe?

____

____

____

____

____

Chapter Test A (continued)

5. **Describe** What are the three types of forces that act on rocks?

6. **Apply** A man is at the beach and notices the water along a shoreline move rapidly toward the sea, exposing a large portion of land that normally is under water. What is happening? What action should he take?

Name Date Class

Earthquakes

I. Testing Concepts

Directions: *Circle the word or phrase in parentheses that best completes each statement.*

1. The buildup of stress in Earth's crust can become so great that rocks reach their (elastic limit, tectonic force), and an earthquake occurs.
2. A reverse fault is often located where plates (come together, move apart).
3. (Primary waves, Secondary waves) move through Earth by causing particles in rocks to vibrate at right angles to the direction of the waves.
4. To locate an earthquake's (epicenter, elastic limit), scientist use information from at least three seismograph stations.
5. By noting the change in the speed and path of (seismic waves, the Moho discontinuity), scientists have been able to determine the structure of Earth's interior.
6. Seismologists use the (seismograph, Richter scale) to describe the magnitude of earthquakes.
7. One way to make your home more seismic-safe is to put heavy items on (upper, lower) shelves.
8. The San Andreas Fault in California is an example of a (normal, strike-slip) fault.
9. Most of the destruction during an earthquake is caused by (surface, primary) waves.
10. The radius of the circle seismologists draw on a map is equal to the distance from a station to an earthquake's (epicenter, fault line).
11. An earthquake with a (vibration, magnitude) of 6.5 releases about 30 times as much energy as an earthquake that registers 5.5 on the Richter scale.
12. (Primary waves, Secondary waves) don't pass through liquid so they are stopped when they hit the liquid outer core.
13. Shaking from an earthquake can cause wet soil to be more (solid, liquid).
14. The slowest seismic waves are (secondary waves, surface waves).
15. Primary waves arrive at a seismograph station (first, second).
16. When rocks break because of stress, the energy released is in the form of a(n) (earthquake, tsunami).
17. The boundary between the upper mantle and the crust is called the (Moho, Gutenberg) discontinuity.

Name Date Class

Chapter Test B (continued)

18. The area where no seismic waves are detected after they are released by an earthquake is called the (shadow zone, asthenosphere).

19. The outermost layer of Earth is the (asthenosphere, lithosphere).

20. The farther apart primary, secondary, and surface waves arrive, the (closer, farther away) the epicenter is.

21. (Primary waves, Secondary waves) move through Earth, causing particles in rocks to move back and forth in the same direction as the waves.

22. Normal faults are created by (compression, tension).

23. Rocks are subject to the force of tension where Earth's plates (come together, move apart).

24. (Compression, Tension) forces are present where Earth's plates come together.

25. At a (strike-slip, reverse) fault, the rocks above the fault surface are forced up and over the rocks below the fault surface.

II. Understanding Concepts

Skill: Using Tables

Directions: *Use the information at the right to complete the table on the thickness of Earth's layers. Then answer the questions on the lines provided. You can use the space below the table for your calculations.*

Structure		Thickness (km)
Crust	Crust	1.
Mantle	Lithosphere	65 km
	Asthenosphere	600 km
	Solid Mantle	2.
Core	Liquid outer core	3.
	Solid inner core	1,480 km

core = 3,470 km thick
mantle = 2,865 km thick
Earth's radius = 6,370 km

4. Which layer has a thickness of 1,480 km? ______________________

5. Which is thicker, the liquid outer core or the solid inner core? ______________________

6. Which is thicker, the crust or the solid mantle? By how much?

____

Name _______________ Date _______________ Class _______________

Chapter Test B (continued)

Skill: Concept Mapping

Directions: *The following sentences appear in a concept map about tsunamis. Number the following sentences* **1** *to* **3** *in the order in which they would occur.*

_______ **7.** The water along the shoreline moves rapidly toward the sea, exposing a large portion that is normally underwater.

_______ **8.** A tsunami crashes on shore, forming a towering crest up to 30 m high.

_______ **9.** An earthquake causes a very long ocean wave over its focus.

Skill: Making and Using Graphs

Directions: *The table below shows distances and travel times for primary and secondary seismic waves. Use the data in the table to graph the travel times and distances on the graph. Then use the graph to answer the questions.*

	Time (minutes and seconds)	
Distance	**Primary Wave**	**Secondary Wave**
1,000 km	0 min 40 s	1 min 20 s
2,000 km	1 min 15 s	2 min 10 s
4,000 km	2 min 0 s	3 min 25 s
6,000 km	2 min 25 s	4 min 10 s
8,000 km	2 min 40 s	4 min 45 s
10,000 km	2 min 45 s	5 min 10 s

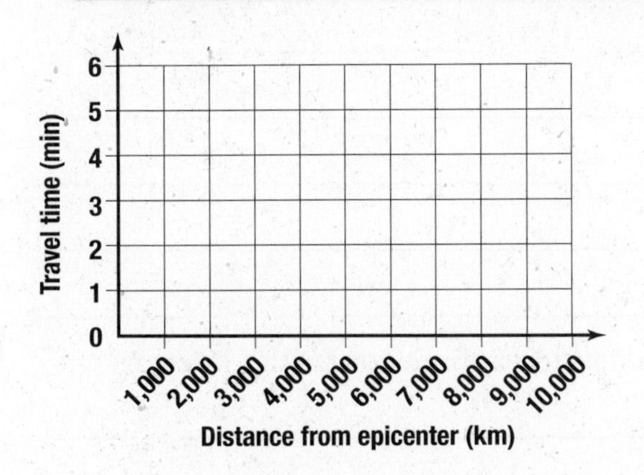

10. What is the difference between the travel times for primary and secondary waves

a. at 1,500 km? _______________ **b.** At 7,500 km? _______________

11. What happens to the difference in travel times as the distances increase?

____

____

Name ____________________ Date ____________ Class ____________

Chapter Test B (continued)

III. Applying Concepts

Directions: *Match the following terms with the items that are most closely related to each description.*

_____ **1.** liquefaction

_____ **2.** seismic-safe structures

_____ **3.** modified Mercalli scale

_____ **4.** Richter scale

_____ **5.** liquid outer core

a. buildings with flexible, circular moorings

b. an intensity-VII earthquake

c. stops secondary waves

d. a magnitude-5 earthquake

e. buildings collapse as soil beneath becomes liquid

IV. Writing Skills

Directions: *Answer the following questions on the lines provided.*

1. How do seismologists locate the epicenter of an earthquake?

2. Why would securing gas appliances help make your home more earthquake-safe?

3. How were scientists able to use seismic information to develop a model of Earth's interior?

Name ______________________ Date ______________________ Class ______________________

Chapter Test C — Earthquakes

I. Testing Concepts

Directions: *Determine whether the statements below are* **true** *or* **false**. *If the statement is false, change the underlined term to make it correct.*

______ **1.** The <u>length</u> of the lines traced on a seismograph can be used to determine an earthquake's magnitude.

____

______ **2.** The <u>magnitude</u> of an earthquake is determined by examining the amount of damage caused by an earthquake.

____

______ **3.** When rocks break along a fault, <u>shear</u> is created.

____

______ **4.** The distance in <u>arrival times</u> is used to calculate the distance to the epicenter.

____

______ **5.** <u>Two</u> seismograph stations are needed to determine the location of an epicenter.

____

Directions: *Fill in the blanks to complete the sentences.*

6. The ______________________ is the point where seismic energy is released.

7. The earthquake ______________________ is the point on Earth's surface directly above where the seismic energy is released.

8. During ______________________, wet soil acts more like a liquid, causing buildings to sink into the soil.

9. When water along the shoreline moves rapidly towards the sea, it is a warning sign of a(n) ______________________.

10. A compressed spring illustrates the motion of a(n) ______________________.

Chapter Test C (continued)

11. A jump rope wiggling in a curved motion illustrates the motion of a(n)

_________________________.

12. _________________________ are the most destructive waves.

13. A portion of the upper mantle, called the _________________________, consists of weak rock that can flow slowly.

14. The crust and part of the mantle just beneath it make up Earth's _________________________.

15. The bending of primary waves and the stopping of secondary waves creates the

_________________________.

II. Understanding Concepts

Skill: Concept Map

1. **Directions:** *Create a concept map showing the three types of faults and how they are created.*

Name Date Class

Chapter Test C (continued)

Skill: Making and Using Graphs

Directions: *The table below shows distances and travel times for primary and secondary seismic waves. Use the data in the table to graph the travel times and distances on the graph. Then use the graph to answer the questions.*

	Time (minutes and seconds)	
Distance	**Primary Wave**	**Secondary Wave**
1,000 km	0 min 40 s	1 min 20 s
2,000 km	1 min 15 s	2 min 10 s
4,000 km	2 min 0 s	3 min 25 s
6,000 km	2 min 25 s	4 min 10 s
8,000 km	2 min 40 s	4 min 45 s
10,000 km	2 min 45 s	5 min 10 s

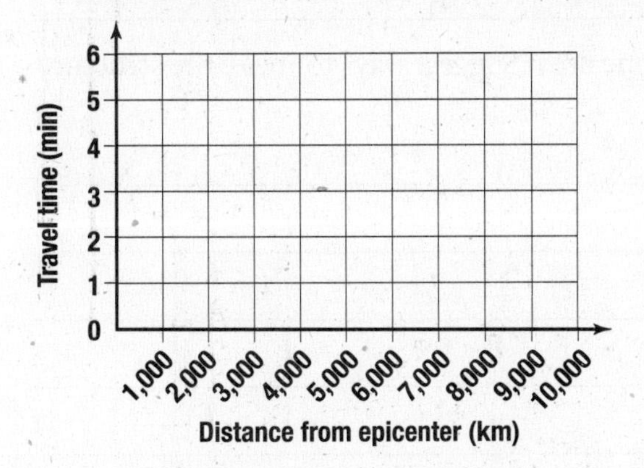

2. What is the difference between travel times at 2,000 km? ______ 10,000 km? ______

3. How would you expect the distance to change at 15,000 km?

____

4. What might the chart look like if surface waves were added?

____

5. Explain how these waves were measured and recorded.

____

____

____

____

Chapter Test C (continued)

III. Applying Concepts

Writing Skills

Directions: *Answer the following questions using complete sentences.*

1. **Debate** One friend says that earthquakes occur mostly in California. Another friend disagrees. Which friend is right? Why?

2. **Contrast** Explain the differences between the two ways to measure the effects of an earthquake.

3. **Suggest** A new school is being built in an earthquake-prone area. Suggest ways to make the structure safer and more resistant to earthquakes.

Name Date Class

Design Your Own

How do calderas form?

LAB A

Lab Preview

Directions: *Answer these questions before you begin the Lab.*

1. Why does this lab call for eye protection to be worn?

2. Will you need to conduct multiple trials of your experiment? Why or why not?

A caldera is a depression that forms when the top of a volcano collapses after an eruption.

Real-World Question

What might cause the top of a volcano to collapse?

Form a Hypothesis

Based on your reading about volcanoes, state a hypothesis about what would happen if the magma inside the magma chamber of a volcano were suddenly removed.

Possible Materials

small box
small balloon
paper
newspaper
flour
plastic tubing
clamp for tubing
tape
scissors

Goals

- **Design** a volcano setup that will demonstrate how a caldera could form.
- **Observe** what happens during trials with your volcano setup.
- **Describe** what you observe.

Safety Precautions 

Test Your Hypothesis

Make a Plan

- ❑ 1. As a group, agree upon the hypothesis and identify which results will support the hypothesis.
- ❑ 2. **Design** a volcano that allows you to test your hypothesis. What materials will you use to build your volcano?
- ❑ 3. What will you remove from inside your volcano to represent the loss of magma? How will you remove it? **Hint:** *It should be something that will allow the structure to keep its shape but can be removed quickly.*
- ❑ 4. Where will you place your volcano? What will you do to minimize messes?
- ❑ 5. **Identify** all constants, variables, and controls of the experiment. **Hint:** *The constant does not change. Variables are factors that change. The control is your standard of comparison.*

Follow Your Plan

- ❑ 1. Make sure your teacher approves your plan before you start.
- ❑ 2. **Construct** your volcano with any features that will be required to test your hypothesis.

LAB (continued) **LAB A**

- ❑ **3. Conduct** one or more appropriate trials to test your hypothesis.
  - ❑ Record any observations that you make and any other data that are appropriate to test your hypothesis.

Analyze Your Data

1. **Describe** in words or with a drawing what your volcano looked like before you began.

2. **Observe** what happened to your volcano during the experiment that you conducted. Did its appearance change?

3. **Describe** in words or with a drawing what your volcano looked like after the trial.

4. **Observe** What other observations did you make?

5. **Describe** any other data that you recorded.

Conclude and Apply

1. **Draw Conclusions** Did your observations support your hypothesis? Explain.

2. **Explain** how your demonstration was similar to what might happen to a real volcano. How was it different?

Communicating Your Data

Make a 4-sequence time-lapse diagram with labels and descriptions of how a caldera forms. Use your visual aid to describe caldera formation to students in another class.

Name Date Class

Design Your Own

How do calderas form?

LAB B

Lab Preview

Directions: *Answer these questions before you begin the Lab.*

1. Why does this lab call for eye protection to be worn?

2. Will you need to conduct multiple trials of your experiment? Why or why not?

A caldera is a depression that forms when the top of a volcano collapses after an eruption.

Real-World Question

What might cause the top of a volcano to collapse?

Form a Hypothesis

Based on your reading about volcanoes, state a hypothesis about what would happen if the magma inside the magma chamber of a volcano were suddenly removed.

Possible Materials

small box
small balloon
paper
newspaper
flour
plastic tubing
clamp for tubing
tape
scissors

Goals

- **Design** a volcano setup that will demonstrate how a caldera could form.
- **Observe** what happens during trials with your volcano setup.
- **Describe** what you observe.

Safety Precautions

Test Your Hypothesis

Make a Plan

❑ 1. As a group, agree upon the hypothesis and identify which results will support the hypothesis.

❑ 2. **Design** a volcano that allows you to test your hypothesis. What materials will you use to build your volcano?

❑ 3. What will you remove from inside your volcano to represent the loss of magma? How will you remove it?

❑ 4. Where will you place your volcano? What will you do to minimize messes?

❑ 5. **Identify** all constants, variables, and controls of the experiment.

Follow Your Plan

❑ 1. Make sure your teacher approves your plan before you start.

❑ 2. **Construct** your volcano with any features that will be required to test your hypothesis.

❑ 3. **Conduct** one or more appropriate trials to test your hypothesis. Record any observations that you make and any other data that are appropriate to test your hypothesis.

LAB (continued) **LAB B**

Analyze Your Data

1. **Describe** in words or with a drawing what your volcano looked like before you began.

2. **Observe** what happened to your volcano during the experiment that you conducted. Did its appearance change?

3. **Describe** in words or with a drawing what your volcano looked like after the trial.

4. **Observe** What other observations did you make?

5. **Describe** any other data that you recorded.

Conclude and Apply

1. **Draw Conclusions** Did your observations support your hypothesis? Explain.

2. **Explain** how your demonstration was similar to what might happen to a real volcano. How was it different?

Challenge

1. **Analyze** Why do you think scientists monitor activity at calderas?

Name _______________ Date _______________ Class _______________

(continued)

LAB B

2. **Hypothesize** Could a caldera form from processes that are not volcanic? Why or why not?

____

____

3. **Consider** Can calderas occur in all three types of volcanoes? Why or why not?

____

____

____

Extension

Predict Does the size of an eruption—large or small—influence the formation of a caldera? How could you revise your lab to test the influence of the size of the eruption? What is your new hypothesis? What are your new materials? How do your procedures change?

Communicating Your Data

Make a 4-sequence time-lapse diagram with labels and descriptions of how a caldera forms. Use your visual aid to describe caldera formation to students in another class.

Name ________ Date ________ Class ________

Volcanoes

I. Testing Concepts

Directions: *Match the descriptions in Column I with the terms in Column II. Write the letter of the correct term in the blank at the left.*

Column I

______ 1. an unusually hot area at the boundary between Earth's mantle and core where volcanoes form

______ 2. bits of rock or solidified lava dropped from the air

______ 3. a flat opening from which lava flows

______ 4. a tall opening in Earth that erupts with gases, ash, and lava

______ 5. steep-walled depressions around a vent

Column II

a. volcano

b. vent

c. crater

d. hot spot

e. tephra

Directions: *In the blank at the left, write the letter of the term that best completes each statement.*

______ 6. ______ lava flows carry sharp angular chunks of rock called scoria.
a. Aa b. Pillow c. Pahoehoe d. Magma

______ 7. Lava oozes out of cracks in the ocean floor, causing ______ lava.
a. aa b. pillow c. pahoehoe d. magma

______ 8. ______ lava flows develop a smooth skin and form ropelike patterns when they cool.
a. Aa b. Pillow c. Pahoehoe d. Magma

______ 9. Basaltic lava can flow through large cracks called ______.
a. craters b. fissures c. batholiths d. calderas

______ 10. ______, not volcanoes, account for the greatest volume of erupted volcanic material.
a. Batholiths b. Calderas c. Volcanic necks d. Flood basalts

______ 11. Basaltic magma can flow through ______, which are long, deep cracks in Earth's surface.
a. rift zones b. plate boundaries c. dikes d. sills

Name Date Class

Chapter Test A (continued)

II. Understanding Concepts

Skill: Categorizing

Directions: *Fill in the blanks to identify and describe each type of volcano and how it is formed. Use the following words:* **shield, composite, cinder cone, alternating layers of lava and tephra, loose layers of tephra,** *and* **flat layers of silica-poor lava.**

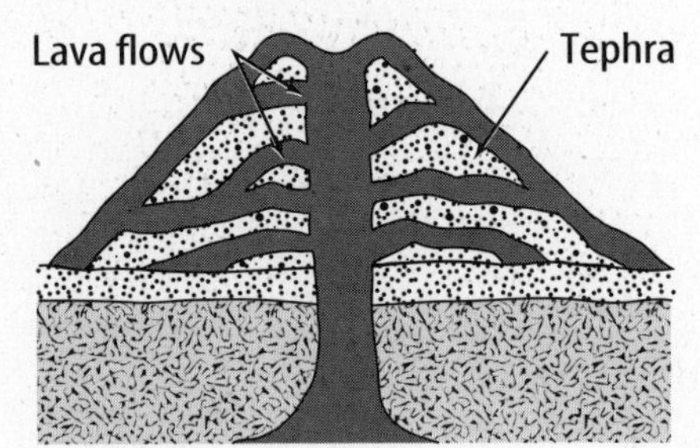

Figure 1

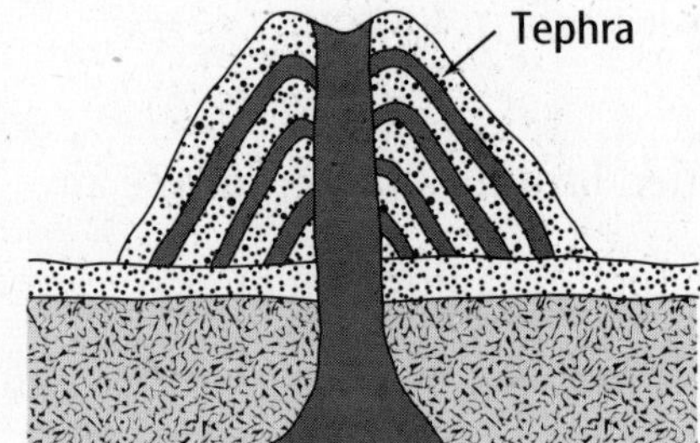

Figure 2

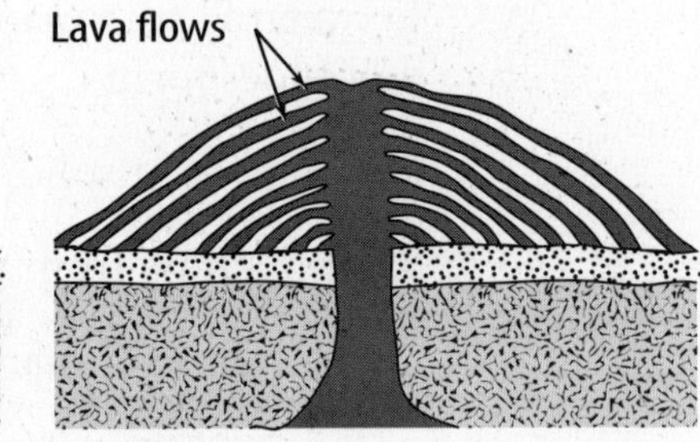

Figure 3

1. Figure 1 is a(n) ______________________________.

It is formed by ______________________________.

2. Figure 2 is a(n) ______________________________.

It is formed by ______________________________.

3. Figure 3 is a(n) ______________________________.

It is formed by ______________________________.

Skill: Outlining

Directions: *Complete the outline showing what conditions control eruptions. Use the following words:* **granitic magma, carbon dioxide, andesitic composition, basaltic magma,** *and* **water vapor.**

4. I. What controls eruptions?

A. Trapped Gases

1. ______________________

2. ______________________

B. Composition of Magma

1. Silica poor

a. ______________________

2. Silica rich

a. ______________________

3. Medium silica

a. ______________________

Name ______________________ Date ______________ Class ______________

Chapter Test A (continued)

Skill: Interpreting Scientific Illustrations

Directions: *Write the answer in the space provided.*

5. You could recognize a caldera in an illustration by its ____________________.

6. You could recognize a volcanic neck in an illustration by its ____________________.

III. Applying Concepts

Writing Skills

Directions: *Answer the following questions using complete sentences.*

1. Describe What are some safety concerns for people living near a volcano?

____

____

____

____

2. Describe Discuss three kinds of intrusive igneous rock features.

____

____

____

____

____

3. Contrast How are volcanoes formed at divergent plate boundaries different from those formed at convergent plate boundaries?

____

____

____

____

____

____

____

____

____

Chapter Test A (continued)

4. **Analyze** What causes an eruption to be quiet or explosive?

Name _______________ Date _______________ Class _______________

Volcanoes

I. Testing Concepts

Directions: *In the blank at the left, write the letter of the term or phrase that best completes the statement.*

______ **1.** A mountain that forms when layers of lava and ash erupt and build up is a ______.
a. caldera **b.** volcano **c.** vent **d.** explosive

______ **2.** The Soufriére Hills volcano is an example of a ______ volcano.
a. composite **b.** cinder cone **c.** shield **d.** Hawaiian

______ **3.** Ship Rock in New Mexico is an example of a ______.
a. caldera **b.** volcanic neck **c.** sill **d.** all of these

______ **4.** Hot spots begin at ______.
a. the boundary between the mantle and the outer core
b. where plates are moving apart
c. where plates are moving together
d. cinder cones

______ **5.** Kilauea in Hawaii is the world's most ______ volcano.
a. dormant **b.** active **c.** quiet **d.** explosive

______ **6.** Volcanoes occur at all of the following **EXCEPT** ______.
a. where plates are moving apart
b. where plates are moving together
c. hot spots
d. cool areas in the mantle

______ **7.** One factor that determines whether a volcanic eruption will be quiet or explosive is the ______.
a. number of cinder cones present
b. height of the volcano's vent
c. amount of water vapor and other gases trapped in the magma
d. temperature of the magma

______ **8.** ______ content makes it more likely that a volcano will erupt violently.
a. High silica
b. Low silica
c. Low pyrocrastic
d. High pyrocrastic

______ **9.** Dikes are formed when ______.
a. the top of a volcano collapses down
b. magma enters a horizontal crack and hardens
c. magma enters a vertical crack and hardens
d. magma cools underground before reaching the surface

______ **10.** A batholith is created when ______.
a. magma enters a vertical crack and hardens
b. the top of a volcano collapses down
c. magma cools underground before reaching the surface
d. magma enters a horizontal crack and hardens

Chapter Test B (continued)

Directions: *Determine whether each of the following statements is true or false. Write* **true** *or* **false** *in the blank. If the statement is false rewrite it so that it is true.*

______ **11.** All volcanic material is the same size.

____

______ **12.** Magma is forced upward because it is denser than the surrounding rock.

____

____

______ **13.** Volcanoes can form on the ocean floor.

____

______ **14.** A volcanic neck forms when a volcano's core erodes.

____

____

______ **15.** Gas trapped in magma under high pressure can cause explosive eruptions.

____

____

______ **16.** Most igneous activity takes place above ground in volcanoes.

____

____

______ **17.** Today people are never killed by volcanic eruptions.

____

____

______ **18.** A cinder cone volcano is caused by a quiet eruption.

____

____

______ **19.** There is no relationship between the movement of Earth's plates and volcanoes.

____

____

Chapter Test B (continued)

II. Understanding Concepts

Skill: Sequencing

Directions: *Beginning with 1 for the smallest, number the following in sequence to indicate the size of tephra.*

1. ______ **a.** cinders

______ **b.** ash

______ **c.** bombs and blocks

Directions: *Number the following steps in the correct sequence to show the formation of a caldera.*

2. ______ **a.** A large opening is produced.

______ **b.** The top of a volcano collapses down.

______ **c.** Magma is forced upward toward Earth's surface.

Skill: Sequencing

Directions: *Identify each type of volcano and describe how it's formed.*

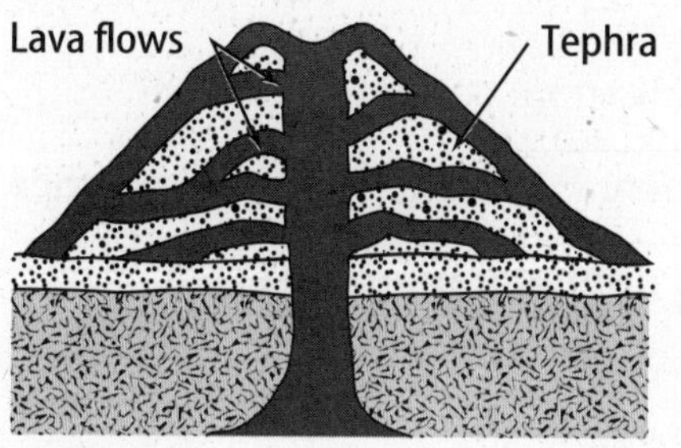

Figure 1

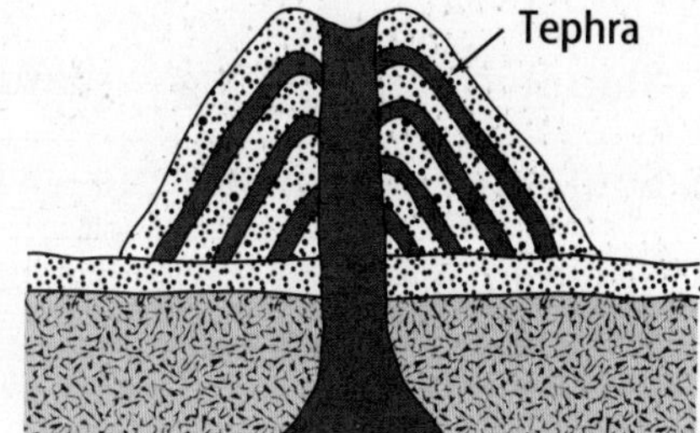

Figure 2

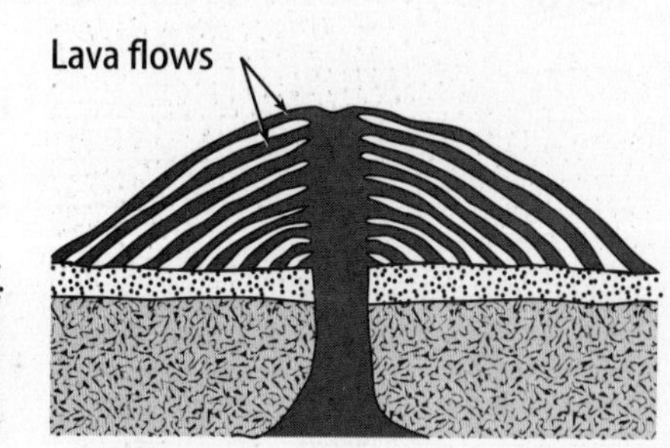

Figure 3

3. Figure 1 is a ______________________________

It's formed by ______________________________

4. Figure 2 is a ______________________________

It's formed by ______________________________

5. Figure 3 is a ______________________________

It's formed by ______________________________

Chapter Test B (continued)

Skill: Concept Mapping

Directions: *Answer the following questions on the lines provided.*

6. There are two events in the formation of a dike. What is the first event?

____

7. What is the second event?

____

Skill: Comparing and Contrasting

Directions: *Answer the following question on the lines provided.*

8. Compare and contrast silica-rich and silica-poor magma.

____

____

III. Applying Concepts

Directions: *Identify each type of volcano or volcanic feature by writing* **composite, shield, cinder cone, batholith, volcanic neck,** *or* **caldera** *on the lines provided.*

_______________ 1. Ship Rock, New Mexico—hard magma core

_______________ 2. Soufriére Hills, Monserrat—where Earth's plates come together

_______________ 3. Yosemite National Park granite domes, California—remains of something larger

_______________ 4. Kilauea, Hawaii—quiet lava flows

_______________ 5. Crater Lake, Oregon—bigger than a crater

_______________ 6. Paricutin, Mexico—pile of tephra

IV. Writing Skills

Directions: *Answer the following questions using complete sentences.*

1. Why do volcanoes form at plate boundaries and hot spots?

____

____

____

2. How are a soft drink in a can and magma alike?

____

____

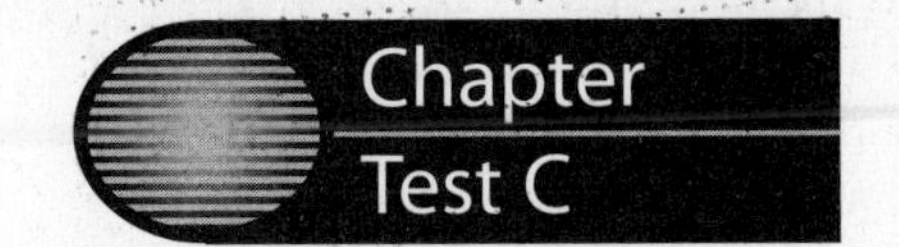

Volcanoes

I. Testing Concepts

Directions: *Determine whether the statements below are* **true** *or* **false**. *If a statement is false, change the underlined word(s) to make it correct.*

______ 1. When sulfurous gases from volcanoes mix with water vapor in the atmosphere, acid rain forms.

____

______ 2. The temperatures inside a pyroclastic flow can be high enough to ignite wood.

____

______ 3. Volcanoes that form on divergent plate boundaries tend to erupt more violently than other volcanoes do.

____

______ 4. The Pacific Plate is stationary over a hot spot.

____

______ 5. Aa magma carries sharp angular chunks of rock that is called andesitic.

____

Directions: *Fill in the blanks to complete the sentences.*

6. A(n) ______________________ is volcanic ash and debris that rushes down the side of a volcano.
7. The Mid-Atlantic Ridge is a(n) ______________________ plate boundary.
8. Volcanoes often form in places where plates are moving and at ______________________.
9. The steep-walled depression around a volcano's vent is the ______________________.
10. Lava flows out through an opening called a(n) ______________________.
11. When sulfurous gases from volcanoes mix with water vapor in the atmosphere,

    ______________________ forms.
12. Falling volcanic ash can collapse buildings, block roads, and cause ______________________ in people and animals.

Name Date Class

Chapter Test C (continued)

II. Understanding Concepts

Skill: Creating a Chart

Directions: *Create a chart describing the three types of volcanoes and how they are formed.*

1.

Skill: Outlining

Directions: *Create an outline to show what conditions control eruptions.*

2.

Skill: Interpreting Scientific Illustrations

Directions: *Write the answer in the space provided.*

3. You can recognize a caldera in an illustration by its ____________________.

   A caldera is formed by ____.

4. You can recognize a volcanic neck in an illustration by its ____________________.

   A volcanic neck is formed by ____.

Chapter Test C (continued)

III. Applying Concepts

Skill: Categorize

Directions: *Categorize the following by placing an* **X** *next to intrusive igneous rock features.*

1. ______ batholith

2. ______ volcanic neck

3. ______ sill

4. ______ dike

5. ______ caldera

6. Describe how the features you marked are formed.

____

____

____

____

Skill: Concept Map

7. Directions: *Create a concept map naming and describing the types of lava.*

Writing Skills

Directions: *Answer the following questions using complete sentences.*

8. Consider What are the disadvantages of living near a volcano?

____

____

____

____

____

Chapter Test C (continued)

9. **Analyze** If you were looking for a potential volcano location, what conditions would you look for?

Name Date Class

Model and Invent

Trace Fossils

LAB A

Lab Preview

Directions: *Answer these questions before you begin the Lab.*

1. What are trace fossils?

____

____

2. How will you model trace fossils?

____

____

Trace fossils can tell you a lot about the activities of organisms that left them. They can tell you how an organism fed or what kind of home it had.

Real-World Question

How can you model trace fossils that can provide information about the behavior of organisms?

Thinking Critically

What materials can you use to model trace fossils? What types of behavior could you show with your trace fossil model?

Goals

- **Construct** a model of trace fossils.
- **Describe** the information that you can learn from looking at your model.

Possible Materials

construction paper
plastic (a fairly rigid type)
plaster of paris
sturdy cardboard
pipe cleaners
wire
scissors
toothpicks
clay
glue

Safety Precautions

Make a Model

❑ 1. **Decide** how you are going to make your model. What materials will you need?

❑ 2. **Decide** what types of activities you will demonstrate with your model. Were the organisms feeding? Resting? Traveling? Were they predators? Prey?

❑ How will your model indicate the activities you chose?

❑ 3. What is the setting of your model? Are you modeling the organism's home? Feeding areas? Is your model on land or water?

❑ How can the setting affect the way you build your model?

❑ 4. Will you only show trace fossils from a single species or multiple species?

❑ If you include more than one species, how will you provide evidence of any interaction between the species?

Check the Model Plans

❑ 1. Compare your plans with those of others in your class. Did other groups mention details that you had forgotten to think about? Are there any changes you would like to make to your plan before you continue?

❑ 2. Make sure your teacher approves your plan before you continue.

(continued)

Test Your Model

❑ 1. Following your plan, construct your model of trace fossils.

❑ 2. Have you included evidence of all the behaviors you intended to model?

Analyze Your Data

1. **Evaluate** Now that your model is complete, do you think that it adequately shows the behaviors you planned to demonstrate? Is there anything that you think you might want to do differently if you were going to make the model again?

2. **Describe** how using different kinds of materials might have affected your model. Can you think of other materials that would have allowed you to show more detail than you did?

Conclude and Apply

1. **Compare and contrast** your model of trace fossils with trace fossils left by real organisms. Is one more easily interpreted than the other? Explain.

2. **List** behaviors that might not leave any trace fossils. Explain.

Communicating Your Data

Ask other students in your class or another class to look at your model and describe what information they can learn from the trace fossils. Did their interpretations agree with what you intended to show?

Name Date Class

Model and Invent

Trace Fossils

LAB B

Lab Preview

Directions: *Answer these questions before you begin the Lab.*

1. What are trace fossils?

____

____

2. How will you model trace fossils?

____

____

Trace fossils can tell you a lot about the activities of organisms that left them. They can tell you how an organism fed or what kind of home it had.

Real-World Question

How can you model trace fossils that can provide information about the behavior of organisms?

Thinking Critically

What materials can you use to model trace fossils? What types of behavior could you show with your trace fossil model?

Goals

- **Construct** a model of trace fossils.
- **Describe** the information that you can learn from looking at your model.

Possible Materials

construction paper
plastic (a fairly rigid type)
plaster of paris
sturdy cardboard
pipe cleaners
wire
scissors
toothpicks
clay
glue

Safety Precautions

Make a Model

❏ 1. **Decide** how you are going to make your model. What materials will you need?

❏ 2. **Decide** what types of activities you will demonstrate with your model. Were the organisms feeding? Resting? Traveling? Were they predators? Prey? How will your model indicate the activities you chose?

❏ 3. What is the setting of your model? Are you modeling the organism's home? Feeding areas? Is your model on land or water? How can the setting affect the way you build your model?

❏ 4. Will you only show trace fossils from a single species or multiple species? If you include more than one species, how will you provide evidence of any interaction between the species?

Check the Model Plans

❏ 1. Compare your plans with those of others in your class. Did other groups mention details that you had forgotten to think about? Are there any changes you would like to make to your plan before you continue?

❏ 2. Make sure your teacher approves your plan before you continue.

(continued) **LAB B**

Test Your Model

❑ **1.** Following your plan, construct your model of trace fossils.
❑ **2.** Have you included evidence of all the behaviors you intended to model?

Analyze Your Data

1. **Evaluate** Now that your model is complete, do you think that it adequately shows the behaviors you planned to demonstrate? Is there anything that you think you might want to do differently if you were going to make the model again?

2. **Describe** how using different kinds of materials might have affected your model. Can you think of other materials that would have allowed you to show more detail than you did?

Conclude and Apply

1. **Compare and contrast** your model of trace fossils with trace fossils left by real organisms. Is one more easily interpreted than the other? Explain.

2. **List** behaviors that might not leave any trace fossils. Explain.

Challenge

1. **Analyze** What information could be found by looking at the trace fossil in its surroundings?

2. **Classify** Would an animal's den and a tunnel dug by an insect be considered trace fossils? Why or why not?

3. Contrast How do trace fossils differ from other fossil types?

Extension

Develop Think about what you learned from your model and your observations of classmates' models. Create a checklist of questions that a scientist might ask when investigating a trace fossil. Organize the questions into categories.

Communicating Your Data

Ask other students in your class or another class to look at your model and describe what information they can learn from the trace fossils. Did their interpretations agree with what you intended to show?

Name Date Class

Clues to Earth's Past

I. Testing Concepts

Directions: *In the blank at the left, write the letter of the term that best completes each statement.*

______ 1. During ______, isotopes that are unstable break down into other isotopes and particles.
a. superposition
b. indexing
c. radioactive decay
d. radiometric dating

______ 2. Hutton's principle of ______ states that Earth processes occurring today are similar to those that occurred in the past.
a. uniformitarianism
b. unconformity
c. radioactivity
d. radiometric dating

______ 3. Superposition states that in undisturbed rock, the oldest layers are ______.
a. on the top b. on the bottom c. undisturbed d. compacted

______ 4. ______ develop when agents of erosion remove rock layers by washing or scraping them away.
a. Superpositions b. Angularities c. Fossil casts d. Unconformities

______ 5. Preserved ______ can provide information about animal size, speed, and behavior.
a. burrows b. tracks c. skin d. teeth

______ 6. ______ have been found in tar, ice, and amber.
a. Original remains
b. Trace fossils
c. Permineralized fossils
d. Carbon films

______ 7. ______ are the remains of species that existed on Earth for relatively short periods of time, were abundant, and were widespread geographically.
a. Casts b. Unconformities c. Index fossils d. Half-lives

Directions: *Match the descriptions on the left with the terms on the right. Write the letter of the correct term in the blank at the left.*

______ 8. the remains, imprints, or traces of prehistoric organisms

______ 9. the age of an object in comparison to the ages of other things

______ 10. the age in years of a rock or other object

______ 11. the time it takes for half of the atoms in an isotope to decay

a. relative age
b. fossils
c. absolute age
d. half-life

Chapter Test A (continued)

II. Understanding Concepts

Skill: Interpreting Data

Directions: *Study the figure of the rock record. Then answer the questions on the lines provided.*

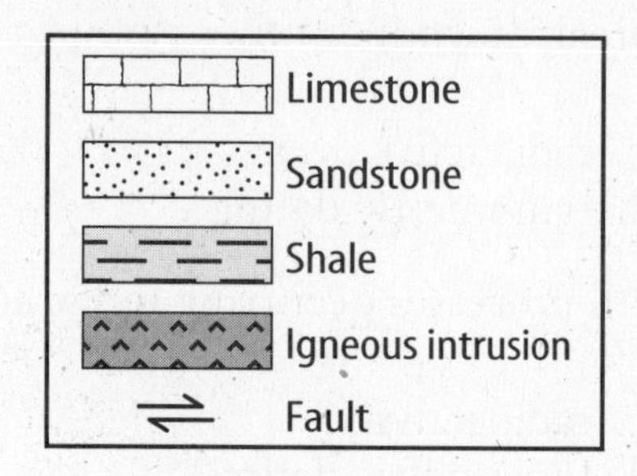

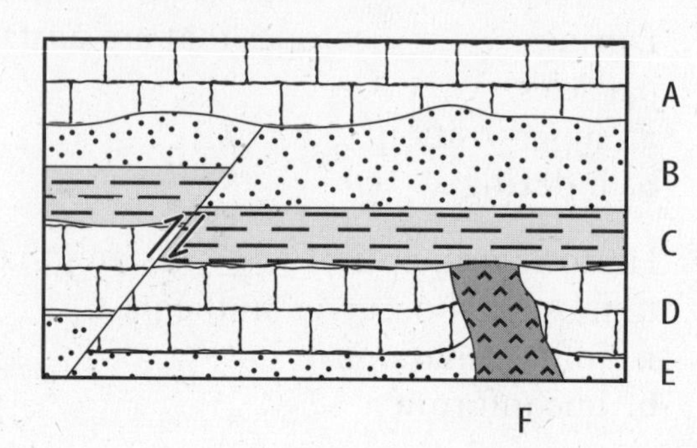

1. What type of rock is in the level labeled A? ____________________
2. If undisturbed, which level is the newest? ____________________
3. What is indicated by the long diagonal line? ____________________
4. Did the event indicated by the diagonal line occur before or after the sediment in level A was deposited? ____________________
5. What is indicated by the wide, gray shaft in layers D and E? ____________________

Skill: Categorizing

Directions: *Write the word in the blank next to each example to show how each fossil was formed. Use the following words:* **carbon film, trace fossils, coal, cast, permineralized remains, original remains,** *and* **mold.**

____________________ 6. A woolly mammoth's tusk is found with its gap filled with minerals from groundwater.

____________________ 7. A thin layer of carbon residue forms the silhouette of a fern leaf.

____________________ 8. In a swampy region, large volumes of plant matter are completely carbonized.

____________________ 9. The hard part of a snail shell decays, leaving behind a cavity in the rock.

____________________ 10. A starfish decays, leaving a cavity in a rock. The cavity is filled with mineral-rich water.

____________________ 11. A saber-toothed tiger is found frozen in ice.

____________________ 12. Tracks of a *Triceratops* herd are found on a ranch.

Chapter Test A (continued)

Skill: Interpreting Scientific Illustrations

Directions: *Respond to the following using these terms:* **nonconformity, angular unconformity,** *and* **disconformity.**

13. If you saw a diagram of horizontal layers covering tiled, eroded layers, you would be looking at a(n) _______________.

14. If you saw a diagram of parallel rock layers with layers missing, you would be looking at a(n) _______________.

15. If you saw a diagram of uplifted and eroded metamorphic rocks topped by sedimentary rocks, you would be looking at a(n) _______________.

III. Applying Concepts

Skill: Using Tables

1. Complete the table below to show the amounts of parent and daughter materials left of a radioactive element after three half-lives, if the original parent had a mass of 80 g.

Number of Half-Lives	Parent Material	Daughter Material
1	40 g	40 g
2	20 g	60 g
3		

2. Explain what happens to the parent material.

____

____

3. Explain what happens to the daughter material.

____

____

4. How are these two related?

____

____

Chapter Test A (continued)

5. How can knowing the half-life of an isotope help to determine a rock's age?

Writing Skills

Directions: *Answer the following questions using complete sentences.*

6. Confirm What are two conditions necessary for fossils to form?

7. Explain How might rock layers be correlated with other rock layers in different areas?

Name ______ Date ______ Class ______

Clues to Earth's Past

I. Testing Concepts

Directions: *Match the terms in Column I with their descriptions in Column II. Write the letter of the correct descriptions in the blank at the left.*

Column I

______ **1.** cast

______ **2.** carbonaceous film

______ **3.** index fossils

______ **4.** fossil

______ **5.** half-life

______ **6.** principle of superposition

______ **7.** absolute dating

______ **8.** mold

______ **9.** radioactive decay

______ **10.** relative dating

______ **11.** unconformities

______ **12.** radiometric dating

______ **13.** uniformitarianism

______ **14.** permineralized remains

Column II

a. produced when sediments fill in a cavity made when an object decayed

b. cavity in rock made when an organism decayed

c. principle that Earth's processes occurring today are similar to those that occurred in the past

d. process that uses the properties of atoms in rocks and other objects to determine their ages

e. states that in a sequence of undisturbed rocks, the oldest rocks are on the bottom and the rocks become progressively younger toward the top

f. gaps in rock records made when agents of erosion remove existing rock layers

g. method by which a geologist can calculate the absolute age of the rock by knowing the half-life of an isotope

h. time it takes for half of an isotope's atoms to decay

i. fossil of thin layer of carbon atoms and molecules

j. formed when original materials in skeletal remains are replaced by minerals

k. method by which order of events or age of rocks is determined by examining the position of rocks in a layer

l. remains, imprints, or traces of once-living organisms

m. process that occurs when the number of protons in an atom is changed and a new element is formed

n. fossils of species that existed for short periods and were widespread

Name _______________ Date _______________ Class _______________

Chapter Test B (continued)

Directions: *Determine whether each of the following statements is true or false. Write* **true** *or* **false** *in the blank. Rewrite each false statement to make it true.*

_______________ **15.** A fossil may tell a geologist when, where, and how an organism lived.

____

_______________ **16.** A permineralized bone is composed of calcium.

____

_______________ **17.** The soft parts of organisms are most likely to become fossils.

____

_______________ **18.** Preserved animal tracks are trace fossils.

____

_______________ **19.** Only a radioactive isotope will have a half-life.

____

_______________ **20.** Any fossil can be dated by the amount of carbon-14 it contains.

____

II. Understanding Concepts

Skill: Concept Mapping

Directions: *Complete the concept map below by writing the conditions for fossil formation and the types of fossils in the circles.*

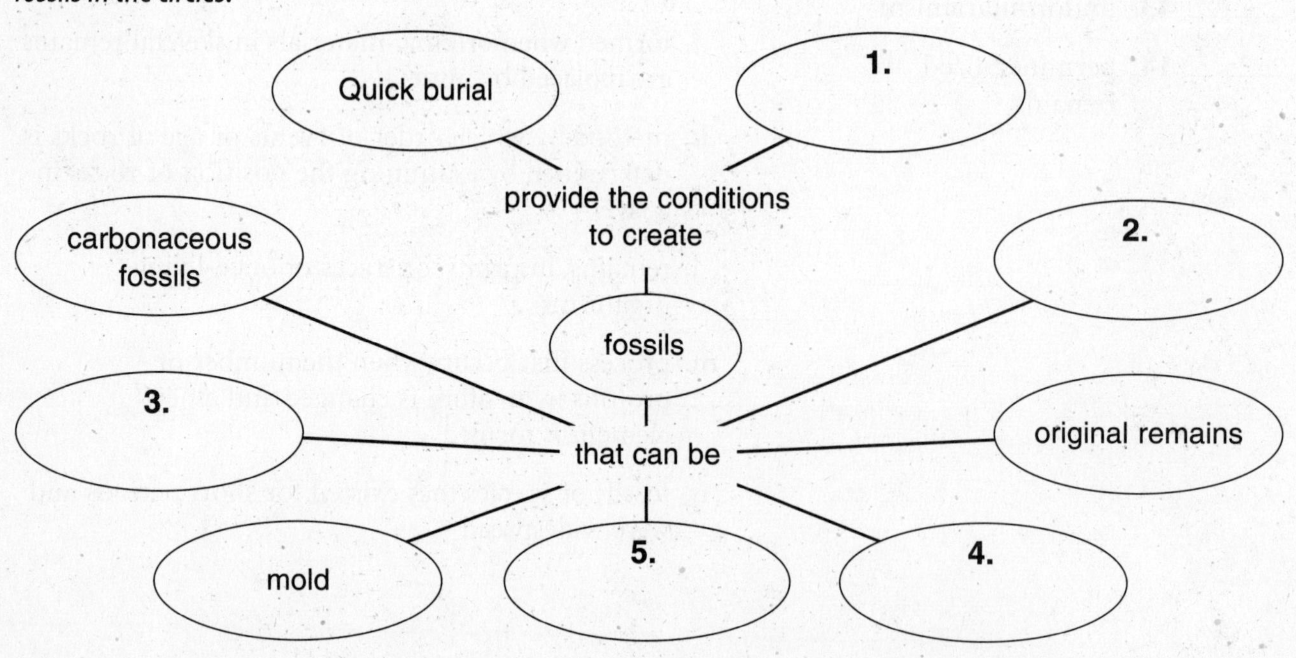

6. What is the difference between relative and absolute dating?

____

____

Skill: Interpreting Data

Directions: *Study the figure of the rock record. Then answer the questions on the lines provided.*

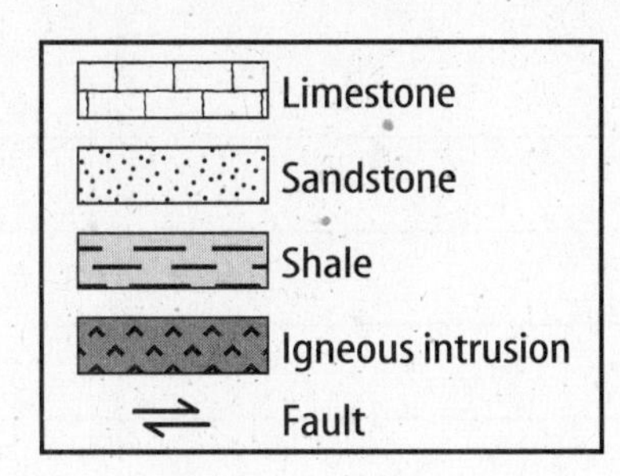

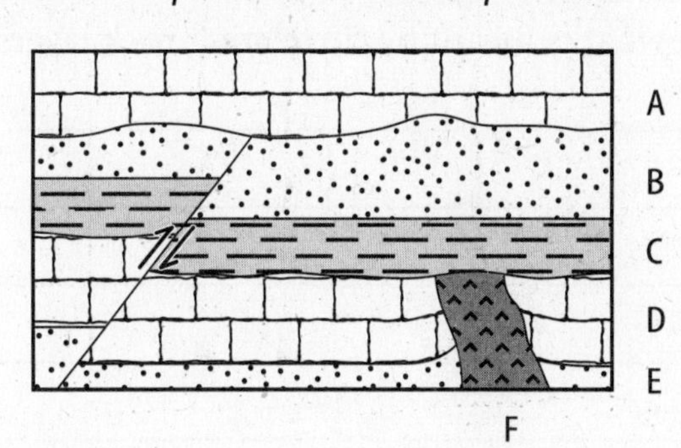

7. List events A–F in the order they occurred, beginning with the oldest event.

____

8. When did the fault occur?

____

Skill: Using Tables

9. Complete the table below to show the amounts of parent and daughter materials left of a radioactive element after three half-lives if the original parent had a mass of 80 g.

Number of half-lives	Parent material	Daughter product
1		
2		
3		

III. Applying Concepts

Writing Skills

Directions: *Answer the following questions using complete sentences.*

1. If horizontal layers of sedimentary rock have a vertical fault running through them, how might a geologist use relative dating to determine when the fault occurred?

____

____

____

____

Chapter Test B (continued)

2. **Explain** how a trace fossil can provide information on how an organism lived.

3. **Explain** what is meant by correlating rock layers.

4. Do all rocks contain fossils? Describe the conditions necessary for fossils to form.

5. **Explain** what the term *half-life* means and how knowing the half-life of an isotope can help a geologist establish the age of a rock or fossil.

Name ______________________ Date ______________ Class ______________

Clues to Earth's Past

I. Testing Concepts

Directions: *Fill in the blanks to complete the sentences.*

1. Fossils are the remains, ______________________, or traces of prehistoric organisms.
2. The relative age of something is its age ______________________ to other things.
3. The ______________________ is the age, in years, of a rock or other object.
4. ______________________ uses the half-life of an object to determine its age.
5. The ______________________ of an isotope is the time it takes for half of the atoms in the isotope to decay.
6. In the process of ______________________, some isotopes are unstable and break into other isotopes and particles, giving off energy.

Directions: *Determine whether the statements below are* **true** *or* **false**. *Rewrite the underlined word(s) in the false statements to make them correct.*

______ 7. Fossils are evidence of not only when and where <u>animals</u> once lived, but also how they lived.

____

______ 8. Coal provides a <u>good</u> fossil resource.

____

______ 9. For a fossil to be an index fossil, it must be spread over a wide area, and the organism must have lived over a <u>long</u> period of time.

____

______ 10. The principle of superposition states that in undisturbed layers of rock, the <u>oldest</u> rocks are at the top.

____

______ 11. Gaps in rock sequence are called <u>radioactive decay</u>.

____

______ 12. <u>Hydrogen</u> is useful for dating bones, wood, and charcoal up to 75,000 years old.

____

______ 13. <u>Uniformitarianism</u> states that Earth processes occurring today are similar to those that occurred in the past.

____

Chapter Test C (continued)

_______ **14.** Some isotopes are unstable and decay into other isotopes and particles.

____

II. Understanding Concepts

Skill: Interpreting Data

Directions: *Study the figure of the rock record. Then answer the questions on the lines provided.*

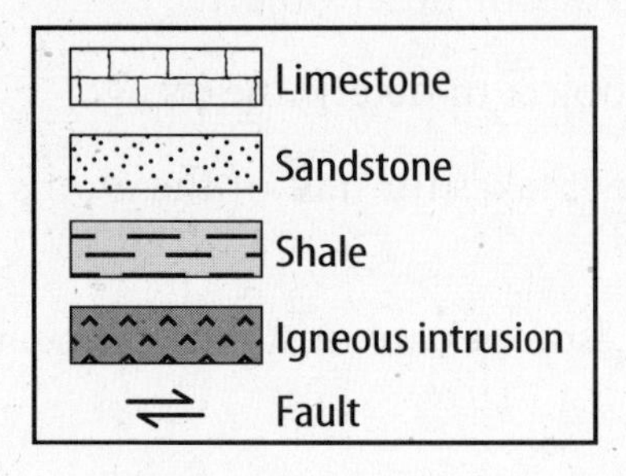

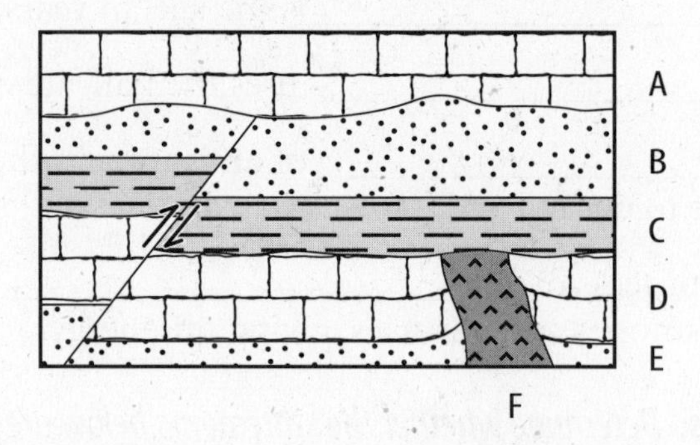

1. List events A–F in the order in which they occurred, beginning with the oldest event.

____

2. Describe the two interruptions to the rock layer.

____

____

____

3. Would it be possible for a geologist to find the same index fossil in layers C and B? Why?

____

Skill: Categorizing

Directions: *Label each type of fossil in the blank next to its description.*

_______________ **4.** A saber-toothed tiger's tooth is found with its gap filled with minerals from groundwater.

_______________ **5.** A thin layer of carbon residue forms the silhouette of a fern leaf.

_______________ **6.** In a swampy region, large volumes of plant matter are completely carbonized.

_______________ **7.** The hard part of a snail shell decays, leaving behind a cavity in the rock.

_______________ **8.** A starfish decays, leaving a cavity in a rock. The cavity is then filled with mineral-rich water.

_______________ 9. A saber-toothed tiger is found frozen in ice.

_______________ 10. Tracks of a *Triceratops* herd are found on a ranch.

Skill: Interpreting Scientific Illustrations

Directions: *Complete the sentence by filling in the correct term.*

11. If you saw a diagram of horizontal layers covering tiled, eroded layers, you would be looking at a(n) _______________.

12. If you saw a diagram of parallel rock layers with layers missing, you would be looking at a(n) _______________.

13. If you saw a diagram of uplifted and eroded metamorphic rocks topped by sedimentary rocks, you would be looking at a(n) _______________.

III. Applying Concepts

1. Fill in the table below so that it shows the amounts of parent and daughter materials left of a radioactive element after three half-lives, if the original parent had a mass of 80 g.

Number of Half-Lives	Parent Material	Daughter Material
1		
2		
3		

2. **Describe** what is happening to the material in the table.

____

____

3. What would happen to the parent material after many half-lives?

____

4. **Contrast** the two types of decay.

____

____

5. How can knowing the half-life of an isotope help to determine a rock's age?

____

____

____

Chapter Test C (continued)

Writing Skills

Directions: *Answer the following questions using complete sentences.*

6. **Decide** A soft-shelled animal dies on the forest floor. An armored animal becomes stuck in a tar pit and dies. Which animal is most likely to form a fossil? Why?

7. **Infer** A geologist notices the same rock pattern of shale and sandstone in southern Texas and in northern Texas. What is one explanation for this? How could the geologist confirm the explanation?

Name Date Class

Use the Internet

Discovering the Past

LAB A

Imagine what your state was like millions of years ago. What animals might have been roaming around the spot where you now sit? Can you picture a **Tyrannosaurus rex** ***roaming the area that is now your school? The animals and plants that once inhabited your region might have left some clues to their identity—fossils. Scientists use fossils to piece together what Earth looked like in the geologic past. Fossils can help determine whether an area used to be dry land or underwater. Fossils can help uncover clues about how plants and animals have evolved over the course of time. Using the resources of the Internet and by sharing data with your peers, you can start to discover how North America has changed through time.***

Real-World Question

How has your area changed over geologic time?

Form a Hypothesis

How might the area where you are now living have looked thousands or millions of years ago? Do you think that the types of animals and plants have changed much over time? Form a hypothesis concerning the change in organisms and geography from long ago to the present day in your area.

Goals

- **Gather** information about fossils found in your area.
- **Communicate** details about fossils found in your area.
- **Synthesize** information from sources about the fossil record and the changes in your area over time.

Data Source

Science Online Visit **msscience.com** for more information about fossils and changes over geologic time and for data collected by other students.

Make a Plan

- ❑ **1. Determine** the age of the rocks that make up your area. Were they formed during Precambrian time, the Paleozoic Era, the Mesozoic Era, or the Cenozoic Era?
- ❑ **2.** Gather information about the plants and animals found in your area during one of the above geologic time intervals.
  - ❑ Find specific information on when, where and how the fossil organisms lived. If no fossils are known from your area, find out information about the fossils found nearest your area.

Follow Your Plan

- ❑ **1.** Make sure your teacher approves your plan before you start.
- ❑ **2.** Go to **msscience.com** to post your data in the table. Add any additional information you think is important to understanding the fossils found in your area.

Name Date Class

(continued)

LAB A

Data and Observations

Table 1

Fossil Name	Plant or Animal Fossil	Age of Fossil	Detail about Fossil	Location

Analyze Your Data

1. What present-day relatives of prehistoric animals or plants exist in your area?

2. How have the organisms in your area changed over time? Is your hypothesis supported? Why or why not?

3. What other information did you discover about your area's climate or environment from the geologic time period you investigated?

Conclude and Apply

1. **Describe** the plant and animal fossils that have been discovered in your area. What clues did you discover about the environment in which these organisms lived? How do these compare to the environment of your area today?

2. **Infer** from the fossil organisms found in your area what the geography and climate were like during the geologic time period you chose.

Communicating Your Data

Find this lab using the link below.

Science Online mssscience.com

Name Date Class

Use the Internet

Discovering the Past

LAB B

Imagine what your state was like millions of years ago. What animals might have been roaming around the spot where you now sit? Can you picture a* Tyrannosaurus rex *roaming the area that is now your school? The animals and plants that once inhabited your region might have left some clues to their identity—fossils. Scientists use fossils to piece together what Earth looked like in the geologic past. Fossils can help determine whether an area used to be dry land or underwater. Fossils can help uncover clues about how plants and animals have evolved over the course of time. Using the resources of the Internet and by sharing data with your peers, you can start to discover how North America has changed through time.

Real-World Question

How has your area changed over geologic time?

Form a Hypothesis

How might the area where you are now living have looked thousands or millions of years ago? Do you think that the types of animals and plants have changed much over time? Form a hypothesis concerning the change in organisms and geography from long ago to the present day in your area.

Goals

- **Gather** information about fossils found in your area.
- **Communicate** details about fossils found in your area.
- **Synthesize** information from sources about the fossil record and the changes in your area over time.

Data Source

Science Online Visit **msscience.com** for more information about fossils and changes over geologic time and for data collected by other students.

Make a Plan

❑ 1. **Determine** the age of the rocks that make up your area. Were they formed during Precambrian time, the Paleozoic Era, the Mesozoic Era, or the Cenozoic Era?

❑ 2. Gather information about the plants and animals found in your area during one of the above geologic time intervals. Find specific information on when, where and how the fossil organisms lived. If no fossils are known from your area, find out information about the fossils found nearest your area.

Follow Your Plan

❑ 1. Make sure your teacher approves your plan before you start.

❑ 2. Go to **msscience.com** to post your data in the table. Add any additional information you think is important to understanding the fossils found in your area.

(continued)

Data and Observations

Table 1

Fossil Name	Plant or Animal Fossil	Age of Fossil	Detail about Fossil	Location

Analyze Your Data

1. What present-day relatives of prehistoric animals or plants exist in your area?

2. How have the organisms in your area changed over time? Is your hypothesis supported? Why or why not?

3. What other information did you discover about your area's climate or environment from the geologic time period you investigated?

Conclude and Apply

1. **Describe** the plant and animal fossils that have been discovered in your area. What clues did you discover about the environment in which these organisms lived? How do these compare to the environment of your area today?

2. **Infer** from the fossil organisms found in your area what the geography and climate were like during the geologic time period you chose.

(continued) **LAB B**

Challenge

1. **Analyze** Was there a relationship between the climate or land changes and the plant and animal changes you found?

____

____

2. **Analyze** Were there many fossils found in your area during this period? Explain why or why not.

____

____

3. **Infer** What information were you unable to determine from your fossils?

____

____

Extension

Compile Gather the information each group researched. Use this information to create a geographical time line for your area. Fill in any missing gaps. Research any inconsistencies. How has your area changed over the years? How has it remained the same?

Communicating Your Data

Find this lab using the link below.

Science Online **msscience.com**

Name ________________ Date ________________ Class ________________

Geologic Time

I. Testing Concepts

Directions: *Match the descriptions of geologic time in Column I with the terms in Column II. Write the letter of the correct term in the blank at the left.*

Column I	Column II
______ **1.** the longest subdivision of geologic time	**a.** period
______ **2.** marked by major, striking, and worldwide changes in the types of fossils present	**b.** era
______ **3.** characterized by the types of life existing worldwide at the time	**c.** epoch
______ **4.** characterized by the types of life existing but may vary from continent to continent	**d.** eon

Directions: *In the blank at the left, write the letter of the term that best completes each statement.*

______ **5.** According to ______, environmental changes can affect an organism's survival.
a. organic evolution
b. species evolution
c. natural evolution
d. dominant evolution

______ **6.** A ______ is a group of organisms that normally reproduces only with other members of its group.
a. class
b. cyanobacteria
c. species
d. phylum

______ **7.** The theory of ______ states that organisms with characteristics that are suited to a certain environment have a better chance of surviving and reproducing.
a. species
b. evolution
c. extinction
d. natural selection

______ **8.** ______ are small, hard-shelled organisms that crawled on the seafloor.
a. Hyoliths
b. Trilobites
c. *Archaeopteryx*
d. Cyanobacteria

______ **9.** The supercontinent ______ existed when all of the continents came together to form one large landmass.
a. Laurasia
b. Gondwanaland
c. Pangaea
d. Precambrian

______ **10.** Blue-green algae called ______ are thought to be one of the earliest forms of life on Earth.
a. cyanobacteria
b. trilobites
c. *Archaeopteryx*
d. Hyoliths

Name Date Class

Chapter Test A (continued)

II. Understanding Concepts

Skill: Sequencing

Directions: *Sequence the following from the longest period of time to the shortest.*

______ **1.** era

______ **2.** epoch

______ **3.** period

______ **4.** eon

Skill: Outlining

Directions: *Complete the outline showing how geologic time can be divided into units. Use the following terms:* **Mesozoic Era, Precambrian Time, Cenozoic Era, Phanerozoic Eon,** *and* **Paleozoic Era.**

5. Title: ____________________

I. ____________________

A. ____________________

1. Trilobites live in oceans.
2. First land plants appear.

B. ____________________

1. Dinosaurs roam Earth.
2. Gymnosperms are abundant.

C. ____________________

1. Mammals are common.
2. Angiosperms are abundant.

Skill: Cause and Effect

Directions: *Identify the effect for each pair.*

6. ______ Cyanobacteria contained chlorophyll and used photosynthesis.

______ Cyanobacteria produced oxygen, which helped change Earth's atmosphere.

7. ______ Ancient fish had lungs as well as gills.

______ The oceans were low in oxygen.

8. ______ Some amphibians were able to survive farther away from water.

______ Some amphibians evolved eggs that did not dry out.

9. ______ Some trilobites had eyes in the front of their heads.

______ Some trilobites' eyes adapted to active swimming.

Name Date Class

III. Applying Concepts

Writing Skills

Directions: *Answer the following questions using complete sentences.*

1. **Consider** How might plate tectonics affect a species?

2. **Describe** What changes in Earth and its life-forms occurred at the end of the Paleozoic Era?

3. **Explain** Why does little fossil evidence exist for Precambrian time, even though it was the longest period of Earth's history?

4. **Contrast** How did the life-forms of the Mesozoic Era differ from those of the Cenozoic Era?

5. **Relate** Explain Darwin's theory of natural selection.

Chapter Test A (continued)

6. **Contrast** Why do scientists think dinosaurs are more closely related to mammals and birds than to reptiles?

Name Date Class

Chapter Test B

Geologic Time

I. Testing Concepts

Directions: *Write the letter of the term or phrase that correctly completes the statement or answers the question.*

______ **1.** Geologic time is divided into units based on ______.
a. geologic changes
b. fossils and rocks
c. types of life-forms living during certain periods
d. all of these

______ **2.** Humans appeared in the ______ Era.
a. Cenozoic
b. Paleozoic
c. Mesozoic
d. Devonian

______ **3.** The major divisions in geologic time are ______.
a. epochs
b. periods
c. centuries
d. eons

______ **4.** Changes in the exoskeleton of trilobites probably occurred because of ______.
a. geographic isolation
b. changing environments
c. the competition for survival
d. all of these

______ **5.** Species of ______ existed during the Mesozoic Era.
a. birds
b. mammals
c. both a and b
d. neither a nor b

______ **6.** Life-forms that first appeared in the Cenozoic Era include ______.
a. humans
b. reptiles
c. mammals
d. all of these

______ **7.** The development of ozone in the stratosphere and oxygen in the atmosphere first made possible the development of ______.
a. complex organisms
b. single-cell organisms
c. cyanobacteria
d. all of these

______ **8.** Today, many scientists think that ______.
a. birds evolved from dinosaurs
b. dinosaurs evolved from reptiles
c. birds evolved from amphibians
d. both a and b

______ **9.** Ediacaran organisms first appeared during the ______.
a. Precambrian Time
b. Cambrian Period
c. Permian Period
d. none of these

______ **10.** As ______ evolved, they changed Earth's atmosphere by producing oxygen.
a. cyanobacteria
b. trilobites
c. reptiles
d. dinosaurs

Chapter Test B (continued)

_____ **11.** A life-form that evolved during the Paleozoic Era was _____.
a. cyanobacteria
b. humans
c. reptiles
d. dinosaurs

_____ **12.** The end of the Paleozoic Era might have involved _____.
a. the development of humans
b. mass extinctions of land and sea animals
c. the appearance of marine animals with hard parts
d. both a and b

_____ **13.** A life-form that evolved during the Mesozoic Era was the _____.
a. human
b. dinosaur
c. reptile
d. cyanobacteria

_____ **14.** Large mammals of the Cenozoic Era may have become extinct because of activity by _____.
a. volcanoes
b. humans
c. plate tectonics
d. all of these

_____ **15.** Trilobites can be used to study the passage of geologic time because _____.
a. they burrowed into sediments
b. they lived in the oceans
c. they lived throughout the Paleozoic Era
d. their physical features changed through time

_____ **16.** A trilobite with no eyes was best adapted for life _____.
a. on land
b. as an active swimmer
c. near the water's surface
d. deeper than light could penetrate

_____ **17.** Plate tectonics may affect changes in species because movement of plates causes a change in _____.
a. Earth's surface
b. climates
c. the environment
d. all of these

_____ **18.** Plate tectonics during the Mesozoic Era caused _____.
a. Pangaea to separate
b. Pangaea to form
c. human life to form
d. dinosaurs to become extinct

II. Understanding Concepts

Skill: Recognizing Cause and Effect

Directions: *Answer the following questions on the lines provided.*

1. What effect does plate tectonics have on evolution of new species? _____________________

____

2. How did plate tectonics affect the evolution of dominant animal life during the Mesozoic Era?

____

____

Chapter Test B (continued)

3. What is one effect of increased human activity in the Cenozoic Era on habitats of some species?

4. What trait has made angiosperms the dominant land plant today?

Skill: Sequencing Events

Directions: *List the events below in correct sequence according to the geologic time scale. List the oldest event as 5 and the most recent as 9.*

development of birds **dinosaurs as dominant life-form**
appearance of humans **evolution of cyanobacteria**
disappearance of Ediacaran fauna

5.
6.
7.
8.
9.

Skill: Making a Table

Directions: *Fill in the table showing the Cenozoic Era on the geologic time scale. Include periods, epochs, and information about species.*

10.

Cenozoic Era

Period	Epochs	Species

Chapter Test B (continued)

III. Applying Concepts

Writing Skills

Directions: *Answer the following questions in complete sentences on the lines provided.*

1. How does plate tectonics affect development of new species?

2. Why is little known about 90 percent of Earth's history?

3. Why were reptiles able to develop from amphibians?

4. **Describe** some of the changes in the land and its life-forms that occurred at the end of the Paleozoic Era.

5. Why couldn't complex organisms develop before the establishment of an ozone layer?

6. Why do trilobites make excellent index fossils?

7. What is the most significant difference between Precambrian and Paleozoic life-forms?

8. **Explain** why modern birds are related to the Archaeopteryx even though not descended from it.

9. **Contrast** the animal life of the Mesozoic Era with that of the early Cenozoic Era.

Name _______ Date _______ Class _______

Chapter Test C

Geologic Time

I. Testing Concepts

Directions: *Identify each statement as* **true** *or* **false**. *If a statement is false, change the underlined word(s) to make it true.*

_______ **1.** The organic evolution divides Earth's history into time units partially based on fossil records.

____

_______ **2.** According to most theories on organic evolution, environmental changes can affect an organism's survival.

____

_______ **3.** Natural selection proposes that organisms with characteristics that are suited to a certain niche have a better chance of surviving and reproducing.

____

_______ **4.** Hyoliths are small, hard-shelled organisms that are index fossils for Precambrian time.

____

_______ **5.** At one point, the continents formed one large supercontinent called Laurasia.

____

_______ **6.** Cyanobacteria are blue-green algae found during Precambrian time.

____

_______ **7.** Some people suggest that the appearance of humans could have led to the expansion of many animal species.

____

_______ **8.** The earliest mammals were small creatures that resembled today's monkeys and gorillas.

____

_______ **9.** *Archaeopteryx* were early birds found during the Jurassic Period.

____

_______ **10.** Hyoliths were organisms that became extinct at the end of the Paleozoic Era.

____

_______ **11.** Reptiles probably evolved from fish that had leglike fins and lungs.

____

Chapter Test C (continued)

II. Understanding Concepts

Skill: Sequencing

Directions: *List the major divisions of geologic time from longest to shortest.*

1. ____________________ 3. ____________________

2. ____________________ 4. ____________________

Skill: Classify

Directions: *Circle the life-form that does not belong in each sequence.*

5. Precambrian: cyanobacteria, early worms, early jellyfish, vertebrates
6. Paleozoic: trilobites, dinosaurs, vertebrates, ancient fish
7. Mesozoic: humans, mammals, reptiles, amphibians
8. Cenozoic: mammals, reptiles, trilobites, amphibians

Skill: Outlining

Directions: *Create an outline showing the three major divisions of the Phanerozoic Eon. Include information about the plants and animals in each era.*

9.

Skill: Cause and Effect

Directions: *Identify the effect for each cause.*

10. Cyanobacteria contained chlorophyll and used photosynthesis.

____

11. The oceans were low in oxygen.

____

12. Some amphibians evolved eggs that did not dry out.

____

13. Some trilobites' eyes adapted to active swimming.

____

Chapter Test C (continued)

III. Applying Concepts

Writing Skills

Directions: *Respond to the following using complete sentences.*

1. **Hypothesize** Explain the breakup of Pangaea. How could this breakup affect land species on the northern mass?

2. **Infer** Why do you think that mammals flourished after the extinction of dinosaurs?

3. **Evaluate** A museum has a trilobite sample that is dated in the Cenozoic Era. Evaluate the museum's dating of the sample.

4. **Consider** How would Darwin's theory of natural selection explain how amphibian eggs changed to reptile eggs over time?

5. **Analyze** Why are angiosperms currently more prominent than gymnosperms?

6. **Explain** Why are cyanobacteria a significant feature of Precambrian time?

Design Your Own

The Heat Is On

LAB A

Lab Preview

Directions: *Answer these questions before you begin the Lab.*

1. What does the safety symbol shaped like an oven mitt mean?

____

2. What two substances will you be comparing?

____

Sometimes, a plunge in a pool or lake on a hot summer day feels cool and refreshing. Why does the beach sand get so hot when the water remains cool? A few hours later, the water feels warmer than the land does.

Real-World Question

How do soil and water compare in their abilities to absorb and emit heat?

Form a Hypothesis

Form a hypothesis about how soil and water compare in their abilities to absorb and release heat. Write another hypothesis about how air temperatures above soil and above water differ during the day and night.

Safety Precautions

WARNING: *Be careful when handling the hot overhead light. Do not let the light or its cord make contact with water.*

Possible Materials

ring stand
soil
metric ruler
water
masking tape
clear-plastic boxes (2)
overhead light with reflector
thermometers (4)
colored pencils (4)

Goals

- **Design** an experiment to compare heat absorption and release for soil and water.
- **Observe** how heat release affects the air above soil and above water.

Test Your Hypothesis

Make a Plan

❑ 1. As a group, agree upon and write your hypothesis.

❑ 2. **List** the steps that you need to take to test your hypothesis. Include in your plan a description of how you will use your equipment to compare heat absorption and release for water and soil. **Hint:** *Where will you place the thermometers? How will you attach the thermometers and the light?*

❑ 3. **Copy** the data table into your Science Journal for both parts of your experiment—when the light is on and energy can be absorbed and when the light is off and energy is released to the environment.

Follow Your Plan

❑ 1. Make sure your teacher approves your plan and your data table before you start.

❑ 2. Carry out the experiment as planned.

❑ 3. During the experiment, record your observations and complete the data table in your Science Journal.

(continued)

LAB A

- ❑ **4.** Include the temperatures of the soil and the water in your measurements.
  - ❑ Also compare heat release for water and soil.
  - ❑ Include the temperatures of the air immediately above both of the substances.
  - ❑ Allow 15 min for each test.

Analyze Your Data

Time	Lights On (temp in °C)				Lights Off (temp in °C)			
	in soil	above soil	in water	above water	in soil	above soil	in water	above water
0								
2								
4								
6								
8								

1. Use your colored pencils and the information in your data tables to make line graphs. Show the rate of temperature increase for soil and water. Use one color for soil and another color for water. Graph the rate of temperature decrease for soil and water after you turn the light off.
2. **Analyze** your graphs. When the light was on, which heated up faster—the soil or the water?

____

____

3. **Compare** how fast the air temperature over the water changed with how fast the temperature over the land changed after the light was turned off.

____

____

Conclude and Apply

1. Were your hypotheses supported or not? Explain.

____

____

____

____

2. **Infer** from your graphs which cooled faster—the water or the soil.

____

____

(continued)

3. **Compare** the temperatures of the air above the water and above the soil 15 minutes after the light was turned off. How do water and soil compare in their abilities to absorb and release heat?

Communicating Your Data

Make a poster showing the steps you followed for your experiment. Include graphs of your data. Display your poster in the classroom.

Name Date Class

Design Your Own

The Heat Is On

LAB B

Lab Preview

Directions: *Answer these questions before you begin the Lab.*

1. What does the safety symbol shaped like an oven mitt mean?

2. What two substances will you be comparing?

Sometimes, a plunge in a pool or lake on a hot summer day feels cool and refreshing. Why does the beach sand get so hot when the water remains cool? A few hours later, the water feels warmer than the land does.

Real-World Question

How do soil and water compare in their abilities to absorb and emit heat?

Form a Hypothesis

Form a hypothesis about how soil and water compare in their abilities to absorb and release heat. Write another hypothesis about how air temperatures above soil and above water differ during the day and night.

Safety Precautions

WARNING: *Be careful when handling the hot overhead light. Do not let the light or its cord make contact with water.*

Possible Materials

ring stand
soil
metric ruler
water
masking tape
clear-plastic boxes (2)
overhead light with reflector
thermometers (4)
colored pencils (4)

Goals

- **Design** an experiment to compare heat absorption and release for soil and water.
- **Observe** how heat release affects the air above soil and above water.

Test Your Hypothesis

Make a Plan

❑ 1. As a group, agree upon and write your hypothesis.

❑ 2. **List** the steps that you need to take to test your hypothesis. Include in your plan a description of how you will use your equipment to compare heat absorption and release for water and soil.

❑ 3. **Design** a data table in your Science Journal for both parts of your experiment—when the light is on and energy can be absorbed and when the light is off and energy is released to the environment.

Follow Your Plan

❑ 1. Make sure your teacher approves your plan and your data table before you start.

❑ 2. Carry out the experiment as planned.

❑ 3. During the experiment, record your observations and complete the data table in your Science Journal.

(continued)

LAB B

❑ **4.** Include the temperatures of the soil and the water in your measurements. Also compare heat release for water and soil. Include the temperatures of the air immediately above both of the substances. Allow 15 min for each test.

Analyze Your Data

1. Use your colored pencils and the information in your data tables to make line graphs. Show the rate of temperature increase for soil and water. Graph the rate of temperature decrease for soil and water after you turn the light off.
2. **Analyze** your graphs. When the light was on, which heated up faster—the soil or the water?

Put table here:

____

____

3. **Compare** how fast the air temperature over the water changed with how fast the temperature over the land changed after the light was turned off.

____

____

Conclude and Apply

1. Were your hypotheses supported or not? Explain.

____

____

____

____

2. **Infer** from your graphs which cooled faster—the water or the soil.

____

____

3. **Compare** the temperatures of the air above the water and above the soil 15 minutes after the light was turned off. How do water and soil compare in their abilities to absorb and release heat?

Challenge

1. **Infer** You are planning a trip. You notice that an island location is hot during the day and warm at night. However, a desert location is hot during the day and cool at night. How can you explain this?

2. **Hypothesize** Sand has very little moisture in it. Other soil types, like clay, have greater amounts of moisture. Do you think that soils with more water would heat and cool the same as sand? Explain your answer.

3. **Infer** Areas around large lakes can experience lake effect. When other areas are experiencing frosts in the early fall, the areas near the lake do not. How might your lab help to explain this?

Extension

Apply Some gardeners place a layer of clear plastic on top of their soil. This process is called soil solarization. It is generally done to prevent weeds and pathogens from growing. What do you think this layer of plastic would do to the soil temperature? Revise your lab to test the temperature of the soil with a layer of plastic.

Communicating Your Data

Make a poster showing the steps you followed for your experiment. Include graphs of your data. Display your poster in the classroom.

Name Date Class

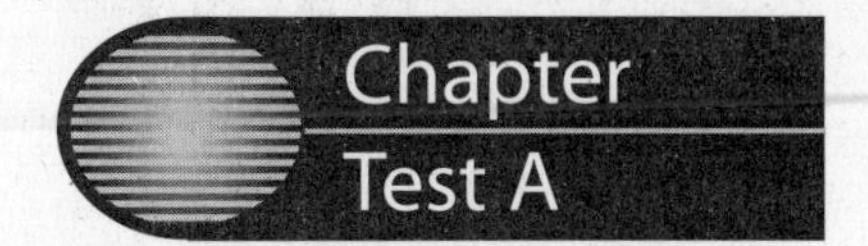

Atmosphere

I. Testing Concepts

Directions: *Circle the term that best completes the sentence.*

1. Earth's (crust, atmosphere) is a thin layer of air that forms a protective covering around the planet.

2. We live in the (stratosphere, troposphere).

3. Within the mesosphere and thermosphere is a layer of electrically charged particles called the (ionosphere, exosphere).

4. The (mesosphere, ozone layer) helps to shield Earth from the Sun's harmful rays.

5. Too much exposure to (ultraviolet radiation, ozone) can damage skin and cause cancer.

6. Evidence exists that some chemicals, such as (chlorofluorocarbons, carbon dioxide), are destroying the ozone layer.

7. *Hydrosphere* is a term that describes all of the (water, oxygen) on Earth's surface.

8. Narrow belts of strong winds, called (trade winds, jet streams), blow near the top of the troposphere.

9. A (sea breeze, land breeze) blows from large bodies of water toward land.

Directions: *Match each description on the left with the correct term on the right. Write the letter of the correct term in the blank at the left.*

_____ **10.** transfer of energy in the form of rays or waves

_____ **11.** transfer of energy that occurs when molecules bump into one another

_____ **12.** transfer of heat by the flow of material

_____ **13.** process of water vapor turning into a liquid

a. condensation

b. convection

c. conduction

d. radiation

Name Date Class

Chapter Test A (continued)

II. Understanding Concepts

Skill: Using a Graph

Directions: *Use the circle graph to answer the following questions.*

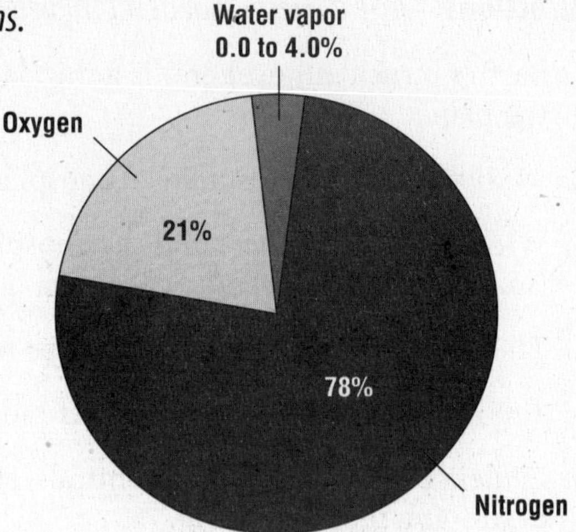

1. Which gas represents the largest percentage of the atmosphere?

____

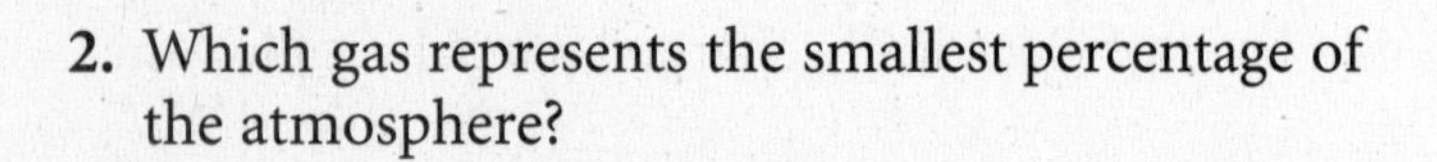

2. Which gas represents the smallest percentage of the atmosphere?

____

3. Which gas represents approximately one fourth of the atmosphere?

____

Skill: Comparing and Contrasting

Directions: *Use the chart to answer the questions.*

Thermometer	Original temperature reading	Temperature after heat applied for 15 minutes	Temperature after heat turned off for 15 minutes
Above sand	25°C	33°C	26°C
Above water	25°C	28°C	27°C

4. What is the difference between the original temperature of the sand and the sand after heating? _______________
5. What is the difference between the original temperature of the water and the water after heating? _______________
6. Which material did the air heat faster? _______________
7. What is the difference between the heated temperature of the sand and the cooled temperature of the sand? _______________
8. What is the difference between the heated temperature of the water and the cooled temperature of the water? _______________
9. Over which material did the air cool faster? _______________
10. How is the heat energy being transferred? _______________

Chapter Test A (continued)

Skill: Sequencing

Directions: *List the layers of the atmosphere from the closest to Earth's surface to the farthest away. Use the following terms:* **thermosphere**, **stratosphere**, **exosphere**, **mesosphere**, *and* **troposphere**.

11. ______________________

12. ______________________

13. ______________________

14. ______________________

15. ______________________

III. Applying Concepts

Skill: Using Scientific Illustrations

Directions: *Use the diagram to answer the following question.*

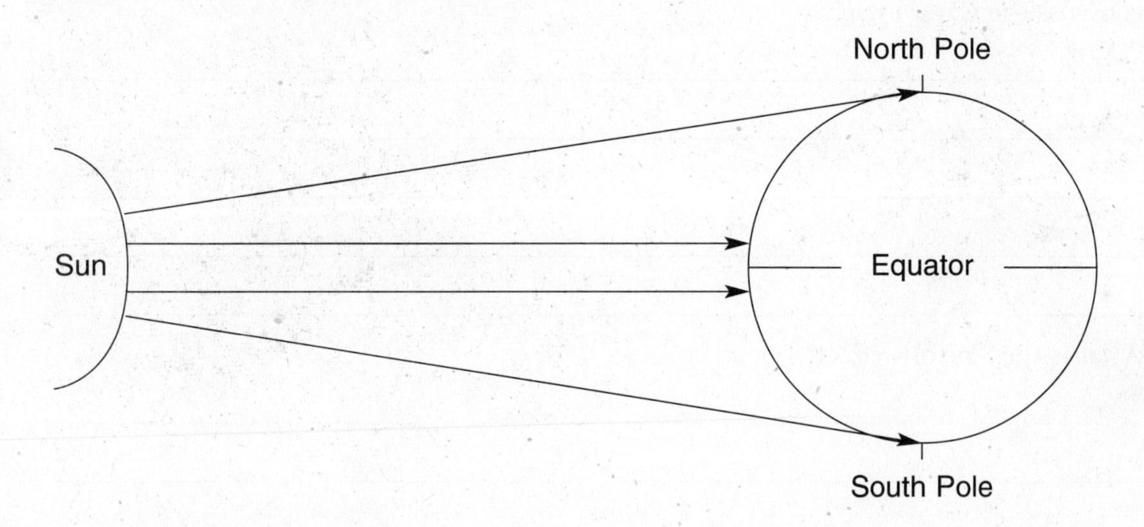

1. **Explain** Why do different latitudes on Earth receive different amounts of solar energy?

____

____

____

Chapter Test A (continued)

Writing Skills

Directions: *Respond to the following using complete sentences.*

2. **Explain** Why is air pressure greater near Earth's surface?

3. **Restate** What are the three things that can happen to the energy Earth receives from the Sun?

4. **Describe** Discuss the water cycle.

5. **Explain** What is the Coriolis effect?

Name Date Class

Atmosphere

I. Testing Concepts

Directions: *In the blank to the left, write the letter of the term or phrase that correctly completes each statement.*

______ **1.** The ______ is the layer of the atmosphere nearest to Earth's surface.
a. mesosphere **b.** troposphere **c.** stratosphere **d.** ionosphere

______ **2.** The ______ are windless zones near the equator.
a. doldrums **c.** polar easterlies
b. prevailing westerlies **d.** trade winds

______ **3.** In the water cycle, evaporated water ______.
a. precipitates as rain or snow **c.** becomes groundwater
b. runs into lakes, streams, and oceans **d.** condenses into clouds

______ **4.** ______ is the transfer of energy by electromagnetic waves.
a. Conduction **b.** Convection **c.** Radiation **d.** Condensation

______ **5.** Electrically-charged particles are found primarily in the ______.
a. troposphere **b.** exosphere **c.** ionosphere **d.** stratosphere

______ **6.** The ______ are responsible for the movement of much of the weather across the United States.
a. prevailing westerlies **c.** trade winds
b. polar easterlies **d.** doldrums

______ **7.** The ______ merges into outer space.
a. troposphere **b.** stratosphere **c.** mesosphere **d.** exosphere

______ **8.** Too much exposure to ______ can cause skin cancer.
a. water vapor **c.** ultraviolet radiation
b. air pressure **d.** ozone

______ **9.** Air in the ______ is warmed by heat from Earth's surface.
a. troposphere **b.** exosphere **c.** stratosphere **d.** thermosphere

______ **10.** ______ is the transfer of heat by the flow of a heated material.
a. Radiation **b.** Conduction **c.** Convection **d.** Absorption

______ **11.** The ______ is caused by Earth's rotation.
a. jet stream **b.** Coriolis effect **c.** doldrums **d.** trade winds

______ **12.** Air above the ______ is heated more than at any other place on Earth.
a. north pole **b.** south pole **c.** equator **d.** United States

______ **13.** Chlorofluorocarbons destroy the ozone layer by ______.
a. adding more ozone molecules **c.** destroying ozone molecules
b. blocking ultraviolet radiation **d.** increasing nitrogen levels

Chapter Test B (continued)

_____ **14.** Steady winds between the equator and 30° latitude north or south are known as _____.
a. doldrums **b.** jet streams **c.** easterlies **d.** trade winds

_____ **15.** Air currents that blow near the north and south poles are the _____.
a. polar easterlies **b.** trade winds **c.** polar westerlies **d.** jet streams

_____ **16.** Reflection and absorption by the atmosphere prevent some _____ from reaching Earth's surface.
a. ozone **b.** radiation **c.** nitrogen **d.** oxygen

_____ **17.** Sea and land breezes happen because _____.
a. the land heats and cools more slowly than the water
b. the land heats and cools more quickly than the water
c. air moves more easily over water than over land
d. air moves more easily over land than over water

_____ **18.** The distinct wind patterns on Earth's surface are created by _____ and by the Coriolis effect.
a. differences in heating **c.** magnetic fields
b. the ozone layer **d.** the jet streams

_____ **19.** Temperatures in the thermosphere are _____.
a. hot and cold **c.** very cold
b. constantly changing **d.** very warm

_____ **20.** _____ is the only substance that exists as a solid, liquid, and gas in Earth's atmosphere.
a. Nitrogen **b.** Ozone **c.** Water **d.** Radiation

Directions: *In the blank at the left, write the letter of the term that matches each description.*

_____ **21.** transfer of energy through space
_____ **22.** transfer of energy through contact
_____ **23.** transfer of heat causing differences in air density
_____ **24.** transfer of energy from land and water to air by direct contact
_____ **25.** transfer of energy from the Sun to Earth's surface

a. conduction
b. convection
c. radiation

Directions: *Match the terms in the left column with the phrases in the right column. Write the letter of the correct phrase in the blank at the left.*

_____ **26.** nitrogen
_____ **27.** smog
_____ **28.** water vapor
_____ **29.** oxygen
_____ **30.** ozone

a. 21 percent of the atmosphere
b. zero to four percent of air
c. most common gas in air
d. normally found in the upper stratosphere
e. caused when pollutants mix with oxygen and other chemicals in the presence of sunlight

Chapter Test B (continued)

II. Understanding Concepts

Skill: Comparing and Contrasting

Directions: *Use the chart to answer the questions.*

Thermometer	Original temperature reading	Temperature after heat applied for 15 minutes	Temperature after heat turned off for 15 minutes
Above sand	25°C	33°C	26°C
Above water	25°C	28°C	27°C

1. Over which material did the air heat faster?

____

2. Over which material did the air cool faster?

____

3. How can the temperatures of sand and water affect the climate of the area?

____

____

4. How does this information explain the difference between land and sea breezes?

____

____

____

Skill: Using a Graph

Directions: *Use the circle graph to answer the following questions.*

5. Which gas makes up about one-fifth of Earth's atmosphere?

____

6. About what percent of Earth's atmosphere does water vapor make up?

____

7. How could you express the amount of nitrogen in Earth's atmosphere as a fraction?

____

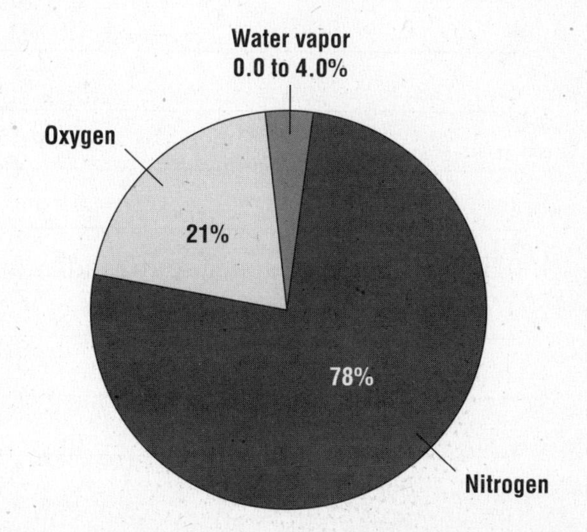

Chapter Test B (continued)

Skill: Concept Mapping

Directions: *The following sentences appear in an events-chain concept map that shows how CFCs destroy the ozone layer. Number the sentences in the order in which they would appear on the map.*

______ **8.** A regular two-atom O_2 molecule is formed.

______ **9.** A chlorine atom from a chlorofluorocarbon molecule comes near a molecule of ozone.

______ **10.** The ozone molecule breaks apart.

III. Applying Concepts

Writing Skills

Directions: *Answer the following questions in complete sentences on the lines provided.*

1. You can't see, touch, or smell the ozone layer. Why is it important to you?

2. Many cities are trying to reduce their smog levels. Why?

3. Where is the air pressure the greatest, at sea level or on a mountaintop? Explain.

4. If you were standing at the equator, which way would the cold air coming from the South Pole appear to be moving?

5. Three things can happen to the radiation that Earth receives from the Sun. What are they?

Name ______________________ Date ______________ Class ______________

Atmosphere

I. Testing Concepts

Directions: *Determine whether the statements below are* **true** *or* **false**. *If false, change the underlined term to make the sentence true.*

______ **1.** The windless, rainy area near the equator is called the <u>jet stream</u>.

____

______ **2.** The trade winds create steady winds that blow in <u>polar</u> regions.

____

______ **3.** Narrow belts of strong winds, called jet streams, blow near the top of the <u>troposphere</u>.

____

______ **4.** <u>Sea breezes</u> are created during the day because solar radiation warms the land more than the water.

____

______ **5.** <u>Sea breezes</u> flow toward the water from the land.

____

Directions: *Fill in the blank to complete each sentence.*

6. The atmosphere keeps Earth's ______________ at a range that can support life.

7. Within the mesosphere and thermosphere is a layer of ______________ ______________ called the ionosphere.

8. The ozone layer absorbs most of the ______________ that enters the atmosphere, protecting your skin from damage.

9. When a chlorine atom from a(n) ______________ molecule comes near a molecule of ozone, the ozone molecule breaks apart.

10. The constant cycling of water between the atmosphere and the ______________ plays an important role in determining weather patterns.

11. Clouds form when ______________ occurs high in the atmosphere.

12. The destruction of ozone molecules seems to cause a seasonal reduction in ozone over ______________, called the ozone hole.

Name Date Class

Chapter Test C (continued)

II. Understanding Concepts

Skill: Using a Graph

Directions: *Use the graph to answer the following questions.*

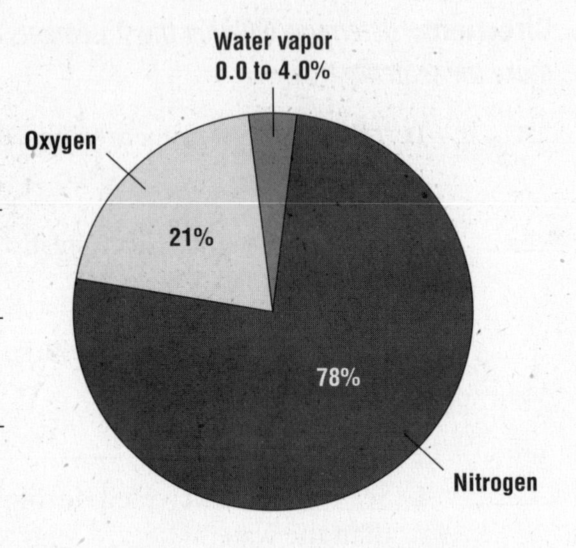

1. Which gas represents approximately three-fourths of the atmosphere?

____

2. What is missing from this diagram?

____

3. What would be an appropriate title for this graph?

____

Skill: Comparing and Contrasting

Directions: *Use the chart to answer the questions.*

Thermometer	Original temperature reading	Temperature after heat applied for 15 minutes	Temperature after heat turned off for 15 minutes
Above sand	25°C	33°C	26°C
Above water	25°C	28°C	27°C

4. Contrast the heating of the air over sand and water in the table.

____

5. Contrast the cooling of the air over sand and water in the table.

____

6. How does this information explain the difference between land and sea breezes?

____

____

____

____

7. How is heat transferred in this example?

____

Chapter Test C (continued)

Skill: Sequencing

Directions: *List the layers of the atmosphere from the closest to Earth's surface to the farthest away.*

8. ______________________________

9. ______________________________

10. ______________________________

11. ______________________________

12. ______________________________

III. Applying Concepts

Skill: Concept Map

1. Create a concept map that shows what happens to energy Earth receives from the Sun.

Skill: Scientific Illustrations

2. Create and label an illustration to show how different latitudes on Earth receive different amounts of solar energy.

Writing Skills

Directions: *Respond to the following using complete sentences.*

3. **Reason** Planes are equipped with oxygen masks in case the plane's cabin loses pressure. Why are these necessary?

4. **Analyze** What is the relationship between the water cycle and the climate?

5. **Analyze** What causes the Coriolis effect?

Name Date Class

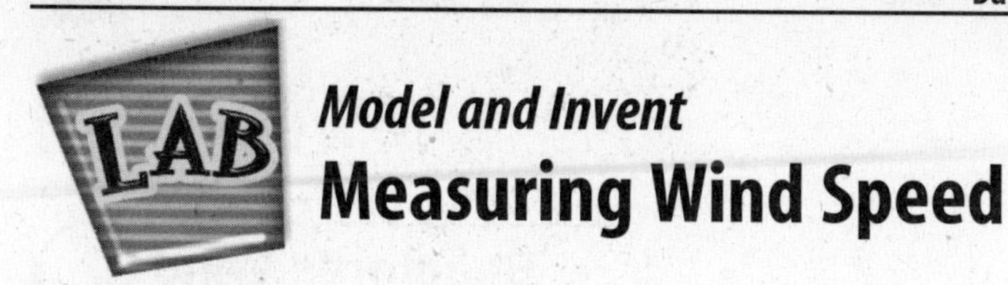

Model and Invent

Measuring Wind Speed

LAB A

Lab Preview

Directions: *Answer these questions before you begin the Lab.*

1. Who was Admiral Beaufort?

____

2. How could different sizes and shapes of paper be used to measure wind speed?

____

When you watch a gust of wind blow leaves down the street, do you wonder how fast the wind is moving? For centuries, people could only guess at wind speeds, but in 1805, Admiral Beaufort of the British navy invented a method for estimating wind speeds based on their effect on sails. Later, Beaufort's system was modified for use on land. Meteorologists use a simple instrument called an anemometer to measure wind speeds, and they still use Beaufort's system to estimate the speed of the wind. What type of instrument or system can you invent to measure wind speed?

Real-World Question

How could you use simple materials to invent an instrument or system for measuring wind speeds? What observations do you use to estimate the speed of the wind?

Goals

- **Invent** an instrument or devise a system for measuring wind speeds using common materials.
- **Devise** a method for using your invention or system to compare different wind speeds.

Possible Materials

paper
scissors
confetti
grass clippings
meterstick
**measuring tape*

**Alternate materials*

Safety Precautions

Data Source

Refer to Section 1 in your text for more information about anemometers and other wind speed instruments. Consult the data table for information about Beaufort's wind speed scale.

Make a Model

❑ 1. **Scan** the list of possible materials and choose the materials you will need to devise your system. Think about the influence of the size and shape of the object.

❑ 2. **Devise** a system to measure different wind speeds. Be certain the materials you use are light enough to be moved by slight breezes.

❑ **Make** a checklist of items you will need.

Check the Model Plans

❑ 1. **Describe** your plan to your teacher. Provide a sketch of your instrument or system and ask your teacher how you might improve its design.

❑ 2. **Present** your idea for measuring wind speed to the class in the form of a diagram or poster. Ask your classmates to suggest improvements in your design that will make your system more accurate or easier to use.

LAB (continued) **LAB A**

Test Your Model

❑ 1. Confetti or grass clippings that are all the same size can be used to measure wind speed by dropping them from a specific height. Measuring the distances they travel in different strength winds will provide data for devising a wind speed scale.

❑ 2. Different sizes and shapes of paper also could be dropped into the wind, and the strength of the wind would be determined by measuring the distances traveled by these different types of paper.

Beaufort's Wind Speed Scale

Description	Wind speed (km/h)
Calm—smoke drifts up	less than 1
Light air—smoke drifts with wind	1–5
Light breeze—leaves rustle	6–11
Gentle breeze—leaves move constantly	12–19
Moderate breeze—branches move	20–29
Fresh breeze—small trees sway	30–39
Strong breeze—large branches move	40–50
Moderate gale—whole trees move	51–61
Fresh gale—twigs break	62–74
Strong gale—slight damage to houses	75–87
Whole gale—much damage to houses	88–101
Storm—extensive damage	102–120
Hurricane—extreme damage	more than 120

Analyze Your Data

1. **Develop** a scale for your method.

___

___

2. **Compare** your results with Beaufort's wind speed scale.

___

___

3. **Analyze** what problems may exist in the design of your system and suggest steps you could take to improve your design.

___

___

Conclude and Apply

1. **Explain** why it is important for meteorologists to measure wind speeds.

___

___

2. **Evaluate** how well your system worked in gentle breezes and strong winds.

___

___

Communicating Your Data

Demonstrate your system for the class. Compare your results and measurements with the results of other classmates.

Name ______ Date ______ Class ______

Model and Invent

Measuring Wind Speed

LAB B

Lab Preview

Directions: *Answer these questions before you begin the Lab.*

1. Who was Admiral Beaufort?

____

2. How could different sizes and shapes of paper be used to measure wind speed?

____

When you watch a gust of wind blow leaves down the street, do you wonder how fast the wind is moving? For centuries, people could only guess at wind speeds, but in 1805, Admiral Beaufort of the British navy invented a method for estimating wind speeds based on their effect on sails. Later, Beaufort's system was modified for use on land. Meteorologists use a simple instrument called an anemometer to measure wind speeds, and they still use Beaufort's system to estimate the speed of the wind. What type of instrument or system can you invent to measure wind speed?

Real-World Question

How could you use simple materials to invent an instrument or system for measuring wind speeds? What observations do you use to estimate the speed of the wind?

Goals

- **Invent** an instrument or devise a system for measuring wind speeds using common materials.
- **Devise** a method for using your invention or system to compare different wind speeds.

Possible Materials

paper
scissors
confetti
grass clippings
meterstick
**measuring tape*

**Alternate materials*

Safety Precautions

Data Source

Refer to Section 1 in your text for more information about anemometers and other wind speed instruments. Consult the data table for information about Beaufort's wind speed scale.

Make a Model

- ❑ 1. **Scan** the list of possible materials and choose the materials you will need to devise your system.
- ❑ 2. **Devise** a system to measure different wind speeds. Be certain the materials you use are light enough to be moved by slight breezes.

Check the Model Plans

- ❑ 1. **Describe** your plan to your teacher. Provide a sketch of your instrument or system and ask your teacher how you might improve its design.
- ❑ 2. **Present** your idea for measuring wind speed to the class in the form of a diagram or poster. Ask your classmates to suggest improvements in your design that will make your system more accurate or easier to use.

Test Your Model

❑ 1. Confetti or grass clippings that are all the same size can be used to measure wind speed by dropping them from a specific height. Measuring the distances they travel in different strength winds will provide data for devising a wind speed scale.

❑ 2. Different sizes and shapes of paper also could be dropped into the wind, and the strength of the wind would be determined by measuring the distances traveled by these different types of paper.

Beaufort's Wind Speed Scale

Description	Wind speed (km/h)
Calm—smoke drifts up	less than 1
Light air—smoke drifts with wind	1–5
Light breeze—leaves rustle	6–11
Gentle breeze—leaves move constantly	12–19
Moderate breeze—branches move	20–29
Fresh breeze—small trees sway	30–39
Strong breeze—large branches move	40–50
Moderate gale—whole trees move	51–61
Fresh gale—twigs break	62–74
Strong gale—slight damage to houses	75–87
Whole gale—much damage to houses	88–101
Storm—extensive damage	102–120
Hurricane—extreme damage	more than 120

Analyze Your Data

1. **Develop** a scale for your method.

2. **Compare** your results with Beaufort's wind speed scale.

3. **Analyze** what problems may exist in the design of your system and suggest steps you could take to improve your design.

Conclude and Apply

1. **Explain** why it is important for meteorologists to measure wind speeds.

2. **Evaluate** how well your system worked in gentle breezes and strong winds.

Challenge

1. **Examine** Think about the number of categories you developed. Did you use more or fewer than Beaufort's scale uses? What difficulties did you have distinguishing between categories? What might you change to make your categories clearer?

2. **Analyze** What aspects of wind did your system measure? What aspects of wind are not measured?

3. **Apply** Think of an example in which wind speed and direction are both important.

Extension

Build Research anemometers. How does an anemometer measure wind speed? Devise a lab to create a simple anemometer. What materials would you need? How would it measure wind speed? How would this information differ from the wind-speed measurements in today's lab?

Communicating Your Data

Demonstrate your system for the class. Compare your results and measurements with the results of other classmates.

Name Date Class

Weather

I. Testing Concepts

Directions: *In the blank at the left, write the letter of the term that best completes each statement.*

_____ **1.** The amount of water vapor present in the air is called _____.
a. weather **b.** humidity **c.** air mass **d.** dew point

_____ **2.** When the _____ is 50 percent, the air contains 50 percent of the water needed for the air to be saturated.
a. relative humidity **c.** front
b. humidity **d.** dew point

_____ **3.** The _____ is the temperature at which air is saturated and condensation forms.
a. relative humidity **c.** front
b. precipitation **d.** dew point

_____ **4.** When water is cooled to its dew point, it forms a cloud on the ground called _____.
a. cumulus **b.** precipitation **c.** fog **d.** condensation

_____ **5.** Rain, snow, sleet, and hail are all forms of _____.
a. precipitation **b.** condensation **c.** evaporation **d.** climate

_____ **6.** A violently rotating column of air is called a _____ when it comes in contact with the ground.
a. hurricane **b.** tornado **c.** trade wind **d.** local wind

_____ **7.** A(n) _____ is a large body of air that has properties similar to the part of Earth's surface over which it develops.
a. tornado **b.** pressure system **c.** front **d.** air mass

_____ **8.** When two air masses meet, there is a _____, or boundary.
a. thunderstorm **b.** watch **c.** front **d.** cloud

_____ **9.** A _____ is a large, swirling, low-pressure system that forms over the Atlantic Ocean.
a. blizzard **b.** cold front **c.** tornado **d.** hurricane

_____ **10.** Winter storms are classified as _____ if the winds are high, the temperature is low, and the visibility is low.
a. blizzards **b.** hurricanes **c.** thunderstorms **d.** typhoons

_____ **11.** A(n) _____ is a line that connects points of equal temperature on a weather map.
a. station model **b.** occluded front **c.** isotherm **d.** isobar

_____ **12.** A _____ is a person who studies the weather.
a. meteorologist **b.** geologist **c.** weatherologist **d.** hydrologist

Name _______________ Date _______________ Class _______________

Chapter Test A (continued)

II. Understanding Concepts

Skill: Classifying

Directions: *Match the descriptions on the left with the terms on the right to show how clouds are classified.*

Matching Set 1

_______ **1.** high-level clouds — **a.** ciro

_______ **2.** middle-level clouds — **b.** strato

_______ **3.** low-level clouds — **c.** alto

Matching Set 2

_______ **4.** clouds appear fibrous or curly — **a.** stratus

_______ **5.** clouds form layers or smooth, even sheets — **b.** cumulus

_______ **6.** masses of puffy white clouds, often with flat bases — **c.** cirrus

Skill: Interpreting Scientific Illustrations

Directions: *Look at the partial station model in the figure. Answer each of the following questions using information from that figure.*

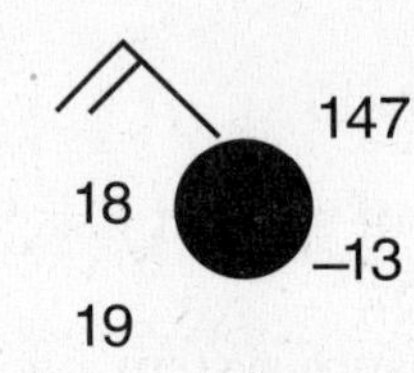

7. What is the barometric pressure? _______________

8. What is the change in barometric pressure? _______________

9. What is the current temperature? _______________

10. What is the dew point? _______________

Chapter Test A (continued)

III. Applying Concepts

Writing Skills

Directions: *Respond to the following using complete sentences.*

1. **Explain** How do tornadoes develop from thunderstorms?

2. **Generalize** Why are fronts helpful in predicting weather?

3. **Apply** What should you do if there is a storm warning?

4. **Explain** How do variations in atmospheric pressure affect the weather?

Chapter Test A (continued)

5. **List** What are some ways data are collected for weather maps and forecasts?

6. **Explain** How does solar heating affect weather?

Name ______ Date ______ Class ______

Chapter Test B — Weather

I. Testing Concepts

Directions: *For each of the following, write the letter of the term or phrase that best completes the sentence.*

______ **1.** When moisture condenses out of air and falls to the ground as rain, snow, sleet, or hail, we are experiencing ______
a. evaporation. **b.** condensation. **c.** precipitation. **d.** transpiration.

______ **2.** A(n) ______ is a large body of air that has the same properties as Earth's surface over which it develops.
a. air mass **b.** cloud **c.** tornado **d.** front

______ **3.** A violent, whirling wind that moves in a narrow path over land is ______
a. thunderstorm. **b.** tornado. **c.** hurricane. **d.** front.

______ **4.** At higher temperatures, air can hold ______ water vapor as compared to air at lower temperatures.
a. more or less, depending on the dew point **c.** more
b. less **d.** the same amount of

______ **5.** ______ humidity is a measure of the amount of water vapor that air is holding compared to the amount that it can hold at a specific temperature.
a. Total **b.** Partial **c.** Relative **d.** Saturated

______ **6.** Low, layered gray clouds that produce drizzle are ______ clouds.
a. cumulus **b.** stratus **c.** cirrus **d.** nimbus

______ **7.** A ______ forms where cold and warm air masses meet.
a. front **b.** cloud **c.** climate **d.** flood

______ **8.** A line that connects points of equal temperature is a(n) ______
a. station model. **b.** satellite map. **c.** isotherm. **d.** isobar.

______ **9.** When air holds all the water vapor it possibly can, we say it's ______
a. relative humidity. **b.** saturated. **c.** relieved. **d.** condensed.

______ **10.** The highest clouds are known as ______
a. cumulus. **b.** stratus. **c.** nimbus. **d.** cirrus.

______ **11.** High pressure air usually means good weather because ______
a. temperatures are moderate.
b. the density of the air is less.
c. the air's sinking motion makes it difficult for air to rise and clouds to form.
d. relative humidity is close to zero percent.

______ **12.** If air containing moisture is cooled, the temperature at which the air is saturated and condensation forms is known as the ______
a. dew point. **b.** rain point. **c.** wind point. **d.** wind chill factor.

______ **13.** High, white, feathery clouds usually associated with fair weather are ______ clouds.
a. cumulus **b.** stratus **c.** cirrus **d.** nimbus

Chapter Test B (continued)

______ **14.** One place where ______ form is along fronts.
a. high pressure systems
b. temperate zones
c. isotherms
d. low pressure systems

______ **15.** When water droplets form around dust particles and become heavy enough to fall out of the clouds, we have______
a. wind. **b.** fog. **c.** dew point. **d.** precipitation.

______ **16.** A ______ forecasts the weather using data collected from many sources.
a. meteorologist **b.** geologist **c.** hydrologist **d.** biologist

______ **17.** Water drops can form on surfaces at night when the air is clear because ______
a. the air near the ground is colder than the ground.
b. the air is NOT saturated.
c. the air near the ground cools to its dew point.
d. the relative humidity decreases.

______ **18.** Tornadoes often form from a type of cumulonimbus cloud called a ______
a. mainflow. **b.** mid-level. **c.** wall cloud. **d.** downdraft.

______ **19.** The interaction of air, water, and ______ results in weather.
a. sun **b.** humidity **c.** land **d.** wind

______ **20.** Thick, puffy clouds are called ______ clouds.
a. stratus **b.** cumulus **c.** nimbus **d.** cirrus

______ **21.** Violent storms generally form along a(n) ______
a. occluded front. **b.** cold front. **c.** warm front. **d.** stationary front.

______ **22.** An air mass that forms off the southeast coast of the U.S. is ______
a. cold, dry. **b.** cool, moist. **c.** hot, dry. **d.** warm, moist.

______ **23.** Hurricanes form over ______
a. grasslands.
b. mountain ranges near the coasts.
c. temperate zones.
d. tropical oceans.

______ **24.** Raindrops that pass through a layer of freezing air near the ground become ______
a. snow with a different form of flake.
b. sleet.
c. hail.
d. fog.

______ **25.** Lightning results from ______
a. high winds.
b. when air heats and expands rapidly, then cools quickly and contracts.
c. the rapid heating of the air.
d. the build-up of positive and negative electrical charges in clouds.

Chapter Test B (continued)

II. Understanding Concepts

Skill: Sequencing

Directions: *Beginning with 1 for the lowest, number the following in sequence to indicate the height of each cloud type above Earth.*

1. _______ altostratus

_______ cirrocumulus

_______ cirrus

_______ stratocumulus

Match: Interpreting Scientific Illustrations

Directions: *Look at the partial station model in the figure. Answer each of the following questions using information from that figure.*

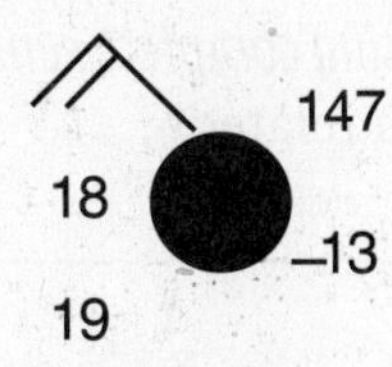

2. This station model was drawn from data collected in Ames, Iowa. Does it describe the weather in Ames only, the Midwest, or all of North America?

____

3. Is the barometric pressure rising or falling?

____

4. What is the current temperature at the station?

____

5. What is the current dew point at the station?

____

6. Given the dew point, the air temperature, and the barometric pressure, do you expect there to be precipitation at this station?

____

Match: Comparing and Contrasting

Directions: *Answer the following questions on the lines provided.*

7. What is the difference between a cold front and a warm front?

____

____

Chapter Test B (continued)

8. Compare and contrast sleet and hail.

Skill: Recognizing Cause and Effect

Directions: *Answer the following question on the line provided.*

9. Following these events, what happens next? Warm air is forced upward, expands, and cools; the air becomes saturated with water vapor; water begins to condense around small particles of dust, salt, and smoke. Eventually, millions of these drops collect.

III. Applying Concepts

Writing Skills

Directions: *Answer the following questions using complete sentences.*

1. How are thunderstorms and tornadoes related?

2. What is the relationship between high relative humidity and a feeling of discomfort in the summer?

3. What kinds of data are used to make weather maps and forecasts? How are these data collected?

4. Why does dew form on grass in the early morning?

5. What is the relationship between the presence of a stationary front and the precision of a weather prediction?

Name ____ Date ____ Class ____

Weather

I. Testing Concepts

Directions: *Identify each statement as* **true** *or* **false.** *If false, rewrite the underlined word(s) to make it true.*

_____ 1. There are <u>three</u> forms of precipitation: <u>rain, snow, and sleet</u>.

____

_____ 2. High-pressure areas are associated with fair weather and are called <u>cyclones</u>.

____

_____ 3. <u>An occluded front</u> may remain in the same place for several days, producing light wind and precipitation. _____________________

_____ 4. When air near the ground is cooled to its dew point, it forms a <u>cirrus</u> cloud near the ground called fog. _____________________

_____ 5. When a cumulus cloud grows into a thunderstorm, it is called a <u>cumulonimbus</u> cloud.

____

_____ 6. Hailstones are pellets of ice that form <u>inside</u> a cloud.

____

II. Understanding Concepts

Skill: Contrasting

Directions: *Fill in the blanks to complete each contrast.*

1. This line connects points of equal temperature. _____________________

   This line connects points of equal atmospheric pressure. _____________________

2. This storm with violent winds begins over land. _____________________

   This storm with violent winds begins over the Atlantic Ocean. _____________________

   This storm with violent winds begins over the Pacific Ocean. _____________________

   This storm with violent winds begins over the Indian Ocean. _____________________

3. This is a measure of the amount of water vapor in the air. _____________________

   This is a measure of the amount of water vapor present in the air compared to the amount needed for saturation at a specific temperature. _____________________

   This is the temperature at which air is saturated and condensation forms.

   ____

Name Date Class

Chapter Test C (continued)

Skill: Classifying

Directions: *Describe the following clouds, indicating their shape, height, and/or ability to produce precipitation.*

4. cirrostratus ______

5. cumulonimbus ______

6. altostratus ______

7. altocumulus ______

8. nimbostratus ______

9. stratocumulus ______

Skill: Interpreting Scientific Illustrations

10. Look at the partial station model in the figure. Interpret the information. Include your weather forecast.

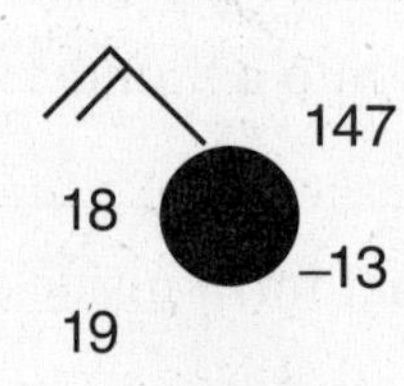

______

______

______

______

______

Skill: Interpreting Maps

Directions: *Explain what each weather map symbol represents.*

11. A blue line with triangles indicates a(n) ______.

12. A red line with red semicircles indicates a(n) ______.

13. A purple line with triangles and semicircles indicates a(n) ______.

14. An alternating red and blue line with red semicircles and blue triangles indicates a(n) ______.

Name Date Class

III. Applying Concepts

Writing Skills

Directions: *Respond to the following using complete sentences.*

1. **Compare and Contrast** Discuss the similarities and differences among rain, hail, sleet, and snow.

2. **Hypothesize** If the atmosphere were so thick that it blocked the Sun's rays, what would happen to the weather?

3. **Analyze** You are planning a school picnic. The meteorologist says that a low-pressure system will be coming through. Is this good news? Explain why or why not.

4. **Contrast** Tell about the difference between a severe weather warning and a severe weather watch. How should you respond to each?

Chapter Test C (continued)

5. **Critique** A meteorologist on television announces a tornado watch. Your friend says you are safe, because there is a thunderstorm outside, which means a tornado will not appear. Is your friend correct? Explain your answer.

Name Date Class

Microclimates

LAB A

Lab Preview

Directions: *Answer the following questions before you begin the Lab.*

1. What should you do if a thermometer breaks?

____

2. How do large cities affect local climates?

____

A microclimate is a localized climate that differs from the main climate of a region. Buildings in a city, for instance, can affect the climate of the surrounding area. Large buildings, such as the Bank of America Plaza in Dallas, Texas, can create microclimates by blocking the Sun or changing wind patterns.

Real-World Question

Does your school create microclimates?

Materials

thermometers
psychrometer
paper strip or wind sock
large cans (4 or 5)
**beakers or rain gauges (4 or 5)*
unlined paper
**Alternative materials*

Goals

- **Observe** temperature, wind speed, relative humidity, and precipitation in areas outside your school.
- **Identify** local microclimates.

Safety Precautions

WARNING: *If a thermometer breaks, do not touch it. Have your teacher dispose of the glass safely.*

Procedure

❑ 1. Select four or five sites around your school building. Also, select a control site well away from the school.

❑ 2. Attach a thermometer to an object near each of the locations you selected. Set up a rain gauge, beaker, or can to collect precipitation.

❑ 3. Visit each site at two predetermined times, one in the morning and one in the afternoon, each day for a week. Record the temperature and measure any precipitation that might have fallen.

❑ Use a wind sock or paper strip to determine wind direction.

❑ 4. To find relative humidity, you'll need to use a psychrometer. A psychrometer is an instrument with two thermometers—one wet and one dry. As moisture from the wet thermometer evaporates, it takes heat energy from its environment, and the environment immediately around the wet thermometer cools. The thermometer records a lower temperature.

❑ Relative humidity can be found by finding the difference between the wet thermometer and the dry thermometer and by using the chart on the following page. Record all of your weather data.

❑ 5. **Analyze** your data to find patterns. Make separate line graphs for temperature, relative humidity, and precipitation for your morning and afternoon data. Make a table showing wind direction data.

(continued)

LAB A

Data and Observations

Table 1

Relative Humidity										
Dry Bulb Temperature (°C)	Dry Bulb Temperature Minus Wet Bulb Temperature (°C)									
	1	2	3	4	5	6	7	8	9	10
14	90	79	70	60	51	42	34	26	18	10
15	90	80	71	61	53	44	36	27	20	13
16	90	81	71	63	54	46	38	30	23	15
17	90	81	72	64	55	47	40	32	25	18
18	91	82	73	65	57	49	41	34	27	20
19	91	82	74	65	58	50	43	36	29	22
20	91	83	74	66	59	51	44	37	31	24
21	91	83	75	67	60	53	46	39	32	26
22	92	83	76	68	61	54	47	40	34	28
23	92	84	76	69	62	55	48	42	36	30
24	92	84	77	69	62	56	49	43	37	31
25	92	84	77	70	63	57	50	44	39	33

Day	Time	Temp.	Wind
1	A.M.		
	P.M.		
2	A.M.		
	P.M.		
3	A.M.		
	P.M.		
4	A.M.		
	P.M.		
5	A.M.		
	P.M.		

Conclude and Apply

1. **Explain** Why did you take weather data at a control site away from the school building? How did the control help you analyze and interpret your data?

2. **Compare and contrast** weather data for each of your sites. What microclimates did you identify around your school building? How did these climates differ from the control site? How did they differ from each other?

3. **Infer** what conditions could have caused the microclimates that you identified. Are your microclimates similar to those that might exist in a large city? Explain.

Communicating Your Data

Use your graphs to make a large poster explaining your conclusions. Display your poster in the school building. **For more help, refer to the Science Skill Handbook.**

Name _______________ Date _______________ Class _______________

Microclimates

LAB B

Lab Preview

Directions: *Answer the following questions before you begin the Lab.*

1. What should you do if a thermometer breaks?

____

2. How do large cities affect local climates?

____

A microclimate is a localized climate that differs from the main climate of a region. Buildings in a city, for instance, can affect the climate of the surrounding area. Large buildings, such as the Bank of America Plaza in Dallas, Texas, can create microclimates by blocking the Sun or changing wind patterns.

Real-World Question

Does your school create microclimates?

Materials

thermometers
psychrometer
paper strip or wind sock
large cans (4 or 5)
**beakers or rain gauges (4 or 5)*
unlined paper

**Alternative materials*

Goals

- **Observe** temperature, wind speed, relative humidity, and precipitation in areas outside your school.
- **Identify** local microclimates.

Safety Precautions  

WARNING: *If a thermometer breaks, do not touch it. Have your teacher dispose of the glass safely.*

Procedure

❑ 1. Select four or five sites around your school building. Also, select a control site well away from the school.

❑ 2. Attach a thermometer to an object near each of the locations you selected. Set up a rain gauge, beaker, or can to collect precipitation.

❑ 3. Visit each site at two predetermined times, one in the morning and one in the afternoon, each day for a week. Record the temperature and measure any precipitation that might have fallen. Use a wind sock or paper strip to determine wind direction.

❑ 4. To find relative humidity, you'll need to use a psychrometer. A psychrometer is an instrument with two thermometers—one wet and one dry. As moisture from the wet thermometer evaporates, it takes heat energy from its environment, and the environment immediately around the wet thermometer cools. The thermometer records a lower temperature. Relative humidity can be found by finding the difference between the wet thermometer and the dry thermometer and by using the chart on the following page. Record all of your weather data.

❑ 5. **Analyze** your data to find patterns. Make separate line graphs for temperature, relative humidity, and precipitation for your morning and afternoon data. Make a table showing wind direction data.

(continued)

Data and Observations

Table 1

Relative Humidity										
Dry Bulb Temperature (°C)	Dry Bulb Temperature Minus Wet Bulb Temperature (°C)									
	1	2	3	4	5	6	7	8	9	10
14	90	79	70	60	51	42	34	26	18	10
15	90	80	71	61	53	44	36	27	20	13
16	90	81	71	63	54	46	38	30	23	15
17	90	81	72	64	55	47	40	32	25	18
18	91	82	73	65	57	49	41	34	27	20
19	91	82	74	65	58	50	43	36	29	22
20	91	83	74	66	59	51	44	37	31	24
21	91	83	75	67	60	53	46	39	32	26
22	92	83	76	68	61	54	47	40	34	28
23	92	84	76	69	62	55	48	42	36	30
24	92	84	77	69	62	56	49	43	37	31
25	92	84	77	70	63	57	50	44	39	33

Put table here:

Conclude and Apply

1. **Explain** Why did you take weather data at a control site away from the school building? How did the control help you analyze and interpret your data?

2. **Compare and contrast** weather data for each of your sites. What microclimates did you identify around your school building? How did these climates differ from the control site? How did they differ from each other?

3. **Infer** what conditions could have caused the microclimates that you identified. Are your microclimates similar to those that might exist in a large city? Explain.

Challenge

1. **Predict** Imagine you gathered data for an industrial site and a wooded park around the corner. From what you learned, what differences would you expect to find in the two sites?

2. **Explain** How might microclimates be of interest to gardeners?

3. **Analyze** What factors that you did not measure in your lab might influence the microclimate?

Extension

Apply Imagine you were asked to create a landscaping plan for the school. Use the data your class developed to come up with a set of recommendations about where to plant certain types of plants. For example, would one area be better for plants that do not require much rainfall?

Communicating Your Data

Use your graphs to make a large poster explaining your conclusions. Display your poster in the school building. **For more help, refer to the Science Skill Handbook.**

Name ______ Date ______ Class ______

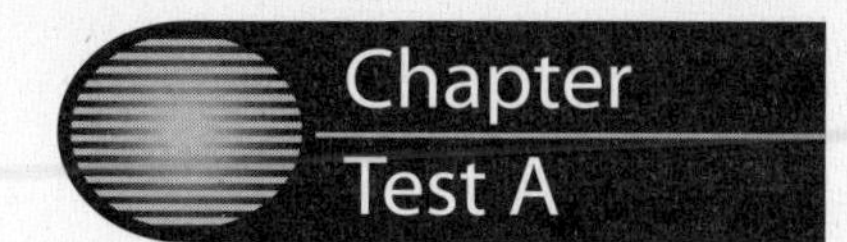

Climate

I. Testing Concepts

Directions: *In the blank at the left, write the letter of the term that best completes each statement.*

______ **1.** ______ is a pattern of weather that occurs in an area over many years.
a. Atmosphere
b. Air mass
c. Climate
d. El Niña

______ **2.** In the ______, the Sun shines almost directly on Earth, making it always hot.
a. polar zones
b. tropics
c. doldrums
d. rain shadows

______ **3.** The ______ receive little or no solar radiation, so they are never warm.
a. polar zones
b. tropics
c. doldrums
d. rain shadows

______ **4.** Most of the United States is a ______.
a. tropical zone
b. polar zone
c. temperate zone
d. temperature zone

______ **5.** ______ is an example of an adaptation.
a. A rock slide
b. Air mass
c. A tree root
d. Thick fur

______ **6.** During ______, animal activity is reduced during the winter.
a. estivation **b.** hibernation **c.** easterlies **d.** adaptations

______ **7.** Because Earth ______, we have seasons.
a. is tilted
b. rotates
c. revolves
d. is large

______ **8.** El Niño is a climatic event that involves the tropical Pacific Ocean and the ______.
a. easterlies
b. polar zones
c. trade winds
d. atmosphere

______ **9.** ______ is a natural heating process that occurs when certain gases in Earth's atmosphere trap heat.
a. Global warming
b. The greenhouse effect
c. Estivation
d. Adaptation

______ **10.** The average global surface temperature on Earth is increasing, causing ______.
a. global warming
b. greenhouse effect
c. carbon dioxide
d. fossil fuels

______ **11.** Deforestation adds to the amount of ______ in the air.
a. water vapor **b.** oxygen **c.** carbon dioxide **d.** carbon monoxide

______ **12.** During ______, glaciers covered large parts of North America.
a. the ice age
b. the greenhouse years
c. La Niña years
d. El Niño years

Name Date Class

Chapter Test A (continued)

II. Understanding Concepts

Skill: Using Charts

Directions: *Study the chart. Use the information to answer the following questions.*

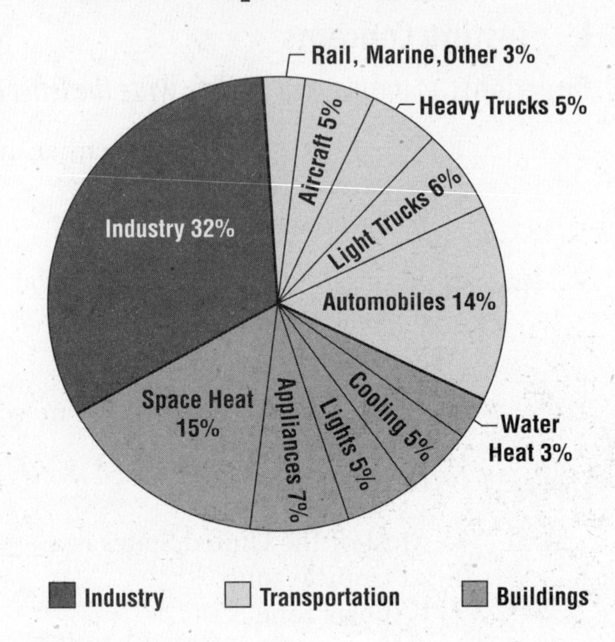

1. What category is responsible for producing the most carbon monoxide?

____

2. What is one way you could help reduce these emissions?

____

3. Given the information in this chart, would you expect to find more carbon monoxide emissions in the city or in the country? Why?

____

Skill: Cause and Effect

Directions: *Identify the cause in each pairing. Rewrite the sentences to show a cause and effect relationship.*

4. __________ A city is located next to a large body of water.
   __________ The city is warmer in the winter.

____

5. __________ The tropics have temperatures that are almost always hot.
   __________ In the tropics, the Sun shines almost directly over the area.

____

6. __________ The warmer currents warm the land areas they pass.
   __________ Warm ocean currents from the equator flow toward higher latitudes.

____

7. __________ Earth's atmosphere is thinner at higher altitudes.
   __________ The mountain air has fewer molecules to heat.

____

8. ____________ Air rises, cools, and drops moisture on the windward side of a mountain range.

____________ The windward side of a mountain receives more precipitation than the leeward side.

____

9. ____________ Temperatures in cities are hotter than in rural areas.

____________ Air pollution traps heat from sidewalks, roads, and buildings.

____

III. Applying Concepts

Writing Skills

Directions: *Respond to the following using complete sentences.*

1. **Explain** How did Köppen classify climates?

____

____

____

2. **Give an Example** What are some organisms that practice hibernation and estivation?

____

____

____

____

3. **Explain** What causes the seasons?

____

____

____

____

4. **Describe** How does El Niño affect climate?

____

____

____

____

____

Chapter Test A (continued)

5. Name What are four causes of climatic change?

____

____

____

____

6. Define What is the greenhouse effect?

____

____

____

____

____

____

Name Date Class

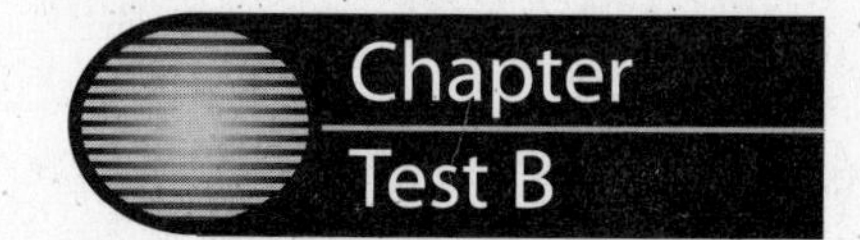

Climate

I. Testing Concepts

Directions: *For each of the following, write the letter of the term or phrase that best completes the sentence.*

_____ 1. Seasons are caused by _____.
- a. changes in the distance from Earth to the sun
- b. tropical storms
- c. the tilt of Earth's axis with respect to the sun
- d. wind patterns

_____ 2. A major influence on climate is _____.
- a. large bodies of water
- b. craters
- c. moonlight
- d. solar wind

_____ 3. When gas, oil, and coal are burned, _____ is released into the atmosphere.
- a. chlorofluorocarbon
- b. carbon dioxide
- c. hydrogen
- d. oxygen

_____ 4. Moderate temperatures are characteristic of _____.
- a. the polar zones
- b. areas at low altitude
- c. the sides of mountains that are protected from wind
- d. the temperate zones

_____ 5. Very few species can adapt to _____.
- a. warm weather conditions
- b. extreme cold, as is found in polar regions
- c. summer
- d. humidity

_____ 6. One cause of _____ may be deforestation.
- a. thunderstorms
- b. global warming
- c. clouds
- d. precipitation

_____ 7. Planetary cooling can happen because of _____.
- a. tides
- b. thunderstorms
- c. winds
- d. volcanic eruptions

_____ 8. El Niño causes _____.
- a. sea level to fall
- b. stronger trade winds
- c. ocean temperatures to increase off the coast of Peru
- d. climate changes every 100 years

_____ 9. If there are 24 consecutive hours of night, then _____.
- a. it is winter near the North Pole
- b. you are experiencing a large building's micro-climate
- c. it is the fall equinox at the equator
- d. it is a cold day in a temperate zone

Chapter Test B (continued)

_____ **10.** An animal that hibernates _____.
a. reduces its activity in hot weather
b. reduces its activity in cold weather
c. has thin fur
d. has a waxy coating

_____ **11.** Opposite extremes of day and night temperatures are associated with _____.
a. deserts
b. areas near the oceans when there are tidal waves
c. the greenhouse effect
d. the tropics

_____ **12.** Many scientists think corals are dying due to _____.
a. changes in Earth's orbit
b. global warming
c. the greenhouse effect
d. volcanic eruptions

_____ **13.** The climate classification system is based on studies of _____.
a. cities
b. mountains
c. temperature and precipitation
d. oceans

_____ **14.** Geological records indicate _____.
a. Earth was flatter in the past
b. there were no ice ages until one million years ago
c. nothing about the climate in the past
d. Earth was warmer at times in the past

_____ **15.** Carbon dioxide can be reduced in the atmosphere by _____.
a. planting trees
b. deforestation
c. burning fossil fuels
d. melting glaciers

_____ **16.** The greenhouse effect causes _____.
a. the change of the seasons
b. pollution
c. the formation of glaciers
d. Earth to be warm enough to support life

_____ **17.** With regard to the ice ages, _____.
a. we are now in an interglacial interval
b. all were of equal duration
c. the last one wiped out all living things
d. the sun almost burned out at times

_____ **18.** All of the following are examples of behavioral adaptations except _____.
a. people shivering **b.** deforestation **c.** hibernation **d.** estivation

_____ **19.** Changes in the shape of Earth's orbit around the sun _____.
a. cause the seasons to reverse each year
b. happen every 100 years
c. might have caused some of the ice ages
d. have no effect on mammals

_____ **20.** Climate is determined by averaging _____ over a long period of time.
a. tides
b. weather
c. ice ages
d. animal extinctions

Chapter Test B (continued)

II. Understanding Concepts

Skill: Classifying

Directions: *On the blank at the left, write the letter of the statement that answers the question.*

______ 1. Which of the following might be connected to "temperate climates"?
- **a.** Solar energy hits these regions at a low angle.
- **b.** Year-round temperatures are always hot.
- **c.** Weather generally changes with the seasons—hot in summer, cold in winter, and mild in spring and fall.

Directions: *Answer the following question on the lines provided.*

Skill: Comparing and Contrasting

2. Compare and contrast the greenhouse effect and global warming.

____

____

____

Skill: Using Charts

3. Study the chart. Then come up with three ideas for reducing carbon dioxide emissions.

____

____

____

____

____

____

____

____

Sources of CO_2 in the United States

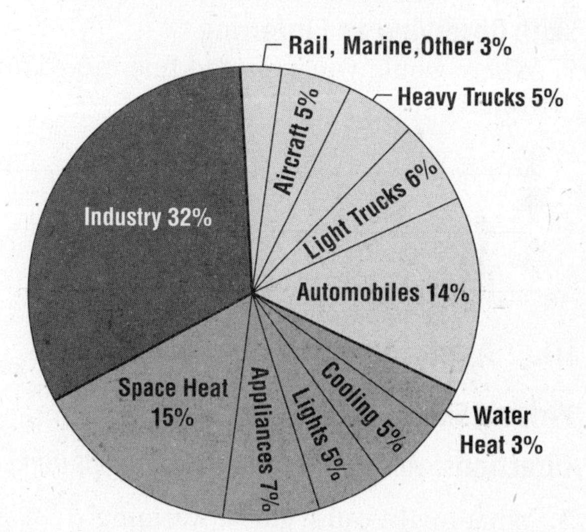

Industry 32% Transportation 33% Buildings 35%

Skill: Hypothesizing

4. There is a rain forest in the United States. It is found in a narrow strip of land on the West Coast and extends from northern California through Oregon and Washington state. On one side of this rain forest is the Pacific Ocean. On the other side are steep upthrust Cascade Mountains. Given what you know about winds that blow in off oceans and how mountains affect climate, hypothesize about why there is a rain forest in this particular place.

____

____

____

Chapter Test B (continued)

Skill: Recognizing Cause and Effect

5. How does the angle of incoming sunlight explain why temperatures tend to become cooler as one moves from the equator toward either pole?

6. What effect do large bodies of water have on climate?

7. How do some animals adapt behaviorally to a dry climate?

8. What is the relationship between global warming and deforestation?

Skill: Observing and Inferring

9. Where would you expect to find more animal and plant species—in the tropics, or in the polar zones?

III. Applying Concepts

Writing Skills

Directions: *Answer the following questions using complete sentences.*

1. What might cause global warming?

2. Why would you expect the climate of a large city to be similar to that of the area surrounding it? Why would you expect it to be different?

Name Date Class

Climate

I. Testing Concepts

Directions: *Identify each statement as* **true** *or* **false**. *If a statement is false, change the underlined term to make it true.*

______ **1.** Once adapted to an environment, animals may not be able to survive in other environments. ______________________________

______ **2.** Lungfish estivate by burrowing into mud and covering themselves with a layer of mud and mucus. ______________________________

______ **3.** La Niña may cause droughts in the southern United States and excess rainfall in the northwestern United States. ______________________________

______ **4.** Pollution particles can increase the amount of cloud cover upwind of the city. ______________________________

______ **5.** Some changes in the amount of energy given off by the Sun seem to be related to the presence of interglacial intervals. ______________________________

Directions: *Fill in the blanks to complete the sentences.*

6. The polar zones are never warm because solar radiation hits theses zones at a(n) ______________.

7. The region between 23.5°N and 23.5°S is known as the ______________.

8. Climatologists often use a system developed by ______________ to classify climate regions.

9. ______________ and ______________ are structural adaptations of cacti.

10. During the year, the high latitudes near the poles have great differences in ______________ and ______________.

11. During El Niño years, the winds ______________ and sometimes ______________.

12. ______________, ______________, and ______________ are all greenhouse gases.

13. On Venus, a(n) ______________ traps gases inside.

14. Deforestation is a concern because it increases the amount of ______________ in the air.

Name Date Class

Chapter Test C (continued)

II. Understanding Concepts

Skill: Using Charts

Directions: *Study the chart. Use the information to answer the following questions.*

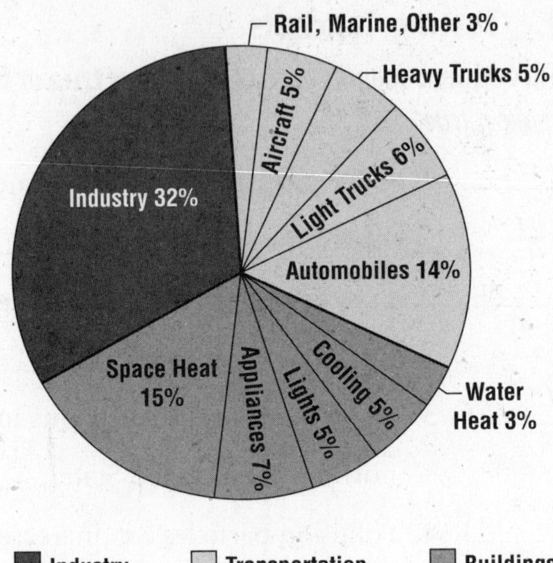

1. What generalizations can you make about the contributions of industry, transportation, and buildings to carbon dioxide emissions?

2. What is missing from this circle graph?

3. What would be a good title for the graph?

Skill: Cause and Effect

Directions: *Identify the effect for each cause.*

4. A city is located next to a large body of water.

5. In the tropics, the Sun shines almost directly over the area.

6. Warm ocean currents from the equator flow toward higher latitudes.

7. Earth's atmosphere is thinner at higher altitudes.

8. Air rises, cools, and drops moisture on the windward side of a mountain range.

9. Air pollution traps heat from sidewalks, roads, and buildings.

10. Solar radiation hits polar zones at a low angle.

11. Winds blowing from the sea are often more moist than those blowing from land.

Chapter Test C (continued)

III. Applying Concepts

Skill: Compare and Contrast

Directions: *Compare and contrast the following terms.*

1. hibernation and estivation

2. behavioral adaptations and structural adaptations

Writing Skills

Directions: *Respond to the following using complete sentences.*

3. Evaluate A friend is planning a trip to a city near the equator. He notices that the average temperature is 32°C in June. He considers going in December instead, because he believes it will be cooler then. Your friend asks for your advice.

4. Infer When studying the weather across the globe, you notice that one year Africa experienced droughts and California experienced severe flooding. What is one explanation for this? How could you know?

Design Your Own

Sink or Float?

LAB A

Lab Preview

Directions: *Answer these questions before you begin the Lab.*

1. Why is the disposal symbol used in this lab?

2. Why would you need a ruler in this lab?

As you know, ocean water contains many dissolved salts. How does this affect objects within the oceans? Why do certain objects float on top of the ocean's waves, while others sink directly to the bottom? Density is a measurement of mass per volume. You can use density to determine whether an object will float within a certain volume of water of a specific salinity. Based on what you know so far about salinity, why things float or sink, and the density of a potato, plus what it looks and feels like, formulate a hypothesis. Do you think the salinity of water has any effect on objects that are floating in water? What kind of effect? Will they float or sink?

Real-World Question

How would a dense object like a potato be different from a less dense object like a cork?

Possible Materials

small, uncooked potato
teaspoon
salt
large glass bowl
water
balance
large graduated cylinder
metric ruler

Goals

- **Design** an experiment to identify how increasing salinity affects the ability of a potato to float in water.

Safety Precautions

Test Your Hypothesis

Make a Plan

❑ 1. As a group, agree upon and write your hypothesis statement.

❑ 2. **Devise** a method to test how salinity affects whether a potato floats in water.

❑ 3. **List** the steps you need to take to test your hypothesis. Be specific, describing exactly what you will do at each step.

❑ 4. **Read** over your plan for testing your hypothesis.

❑ 5. How will you determine the densities of the potato and the different water samples? How will you measure the salinity of the water? How will you change the salinity of the water? Will you add teaspoons of salt one at a time?

❑ 6. How will you measure the ability of an object to float? Could you somehow measure the displacement of the water? Perhaps you could draw a line somewhere on your bowl and see how the position of the potato changes.

 (continued)

LAB A

❑ 7. **Copy** the data table on a separate sheet of paper. Include columns/rows for the salinity and float/sink measurements.

Amount of Salt	Position in Water

Follow Your Plan

❑ 1. Make sure your teacher approves your plan before you start.

❑ 2. Carry out the experiment.

❑ 3. While conducting the experiment, record your data and any observations that you or other group members make.

Analyze Your Data

1. **Compare** how the potato floated in water with different salinities.

2. How does the ability of an object to float change with changing salinity?

Conclude and Apply

1. Did your experiment support the hypothesis you made?

2. A heavily loaded ship barely floats in the Gulf of Mexico. Based on what you learned, infer what might happen to the ship if it travels into the freshwater of the Mississippi River.

Communicating Your Data

Prepare a large copy of your data table and share the results of your experiment with members of your class. **For more help, refer to the Science Skill Handbook.**

Name Date Class

Design Your Own
Sink or Float?

LAB B

Lab Preview

Directions: *Answer these questions before you begin the Lab.*

1. Why is the disposal symbol used in this lab?

2. Why would you need a ruler in this lab?

As you know, ocean water contains many dissolved salts. How does this affect objects within the oceans? Why do certain objects float on top of the ocean's waves, while others sink directly to the bottom? Density is a measurement of mass per volume. You can use density to determine whether an object will float within a certain volume of water of a specific salinity. Based on what you know so far about salinity, why things float or sink, and the density of a potato, plus what it looks and feels like, formulate a hypothesis. Do you think the salinity of water has any effect on objects that are floating in water? What kind of effect? Will they float or sink?

Real-World Question

How would a dense object like a potato be different from a less dense object like a cork?

Possible Materials

small, uncooked potato
teaspoon
salt
large glass bowl
water
balance
large graduated cylinder
metric ruler

Goals

- **Design** an experiment to identify how increasing salinity affects the ability of a potato to float in water.

Safety Precautions

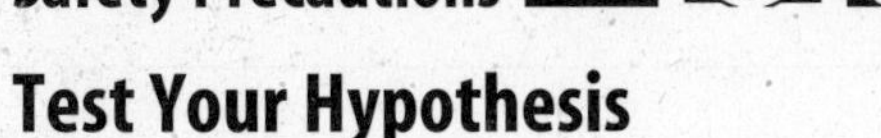

Test Your Hypothesis

Make a Plan

❑ 1. As a group, agree upon and write your hypothesis statement.

❑ 2. **Devise** a method to test how salinity affects whether a potato floats in water.

❑ 3. **List** the steps you need to take to test your hypothesis. Be specific, describing exactly what you will do at each step.

❑ 4. **Read** over your plan for testing your hypothesis.

❑ 5. How will you determine the densities of the potato and the different water samples? How will you measure the salinity of the water? How will you change the salinity of the water? Will you add teaspoons of salt one at a time?

❑ 6. How will you measure the ability of an object to float? Could you somehow measure the displacement of the water? Perhaps you could draw a line somewhere on your bowl and see how the position of the potato changes.

(continued)

LAB B

❑ 7. **Design** a data table where you can record your results. Include columns/rows for the salinity and float/sink measurements. What else should you include?

Put table here:

Follow Your Plan

❑ 1. Make sure your teacher approves your plan before you start.
❑ 2. Carry out the experiment.
❑ 3. While conducting the experiment, record your data and any observations that you or other group members make.

Analyze Your Data

1. **Compare** how the potato floated in water with different salinities.

____

____

2. How does the ability of an object to float change with changing salinity?

____

____

Conclude and Apply

1. Did your experiment support the hypothesis you made?

____

____

2. A heavily loaded ship barely floats in the Gulf of Mexico. Based on what you learned, infer what might happen to the ship if it travels into the freshwater of the Mississippi River.

____

____

Challenge

1. **Hypothesize** Is the temperature of the water a factor? What might have happened if you had boiled the water?

____

____

LAB (continued) **LAB B**

2. **Hypothesize** Imagine you compared your results with those of another class. Their results showed that it took much more salt to get the potato to float. What could account for the difference?

3. **Analyze** Do you think the salt water weighed less than, more than, or the same as the tap water? Why?

Extension

Support One friend thinks that the size of an object is more important in determining its buoyancy. Another friend argues that it is the density of the object. What is your hypothesis? Design a lab that tests the buoyancy of several objects of the same size to discover the relationships between size and buoyancy and density and buoyancy.

Communicating Your Data

Prepare a large copy of your data table and share the results of your experiment with members of your class. **For more help, refer to the Science Skill Handbook.**

Name _______________ Date _______________ Class _______________

Ocean Motion

I. Testing Concepts

Directions: *Match each description on the left with the correct term on the right. Write the letter of the correct term in the blank at the left.*

______ 1. the difference between the levels of the ocean at high tide and low tide

______ 2. the rise and fall of sea level

______ 3. a collapsing wave

______ 4. the shifting of winds and surface currents from their expected paths that is caused by Earth's rotation

______ 5. low areas of Earth

______ 6. a measure of the amount of salts dissolved in seawater

a. breaker

b. tide

c. tidal range

d. salinity

e. Coriolis effect

f. basins

Directions: *In the blank at the left, write the letter of the term that best completes each statement.*

______ 7. Ocean water contains dissolved ______, such as nitrogen.
a. gases b. solids c. liquids d. ions

______ 8. The most abundant elements in water are ______ and oxygen.
a. nitrogen b. halite c. hydrogen d. helium

______ 9. Nutrients brought to the surface from upwelling help ______ to grow.
a. ions b. gases c. winds d. plankton

______ 10. Density currents ______ circulate deep ocean water.
a. rarely b. slowly c. rapidly d. never

______ 11. A wave changes ______ in the shallow area near the shore.
a. texture b. amplitude c. shape d. volume

______ 12. Waves continue moving for long distances, even if the ______ stops.
a. wind b. energy c. crest d. tide

Chapter Test A (continued)

II. Understanding Concepts

Skill: Labeling a Diagram

Directions: *Write the letter from the wave diagram that matches each term.*

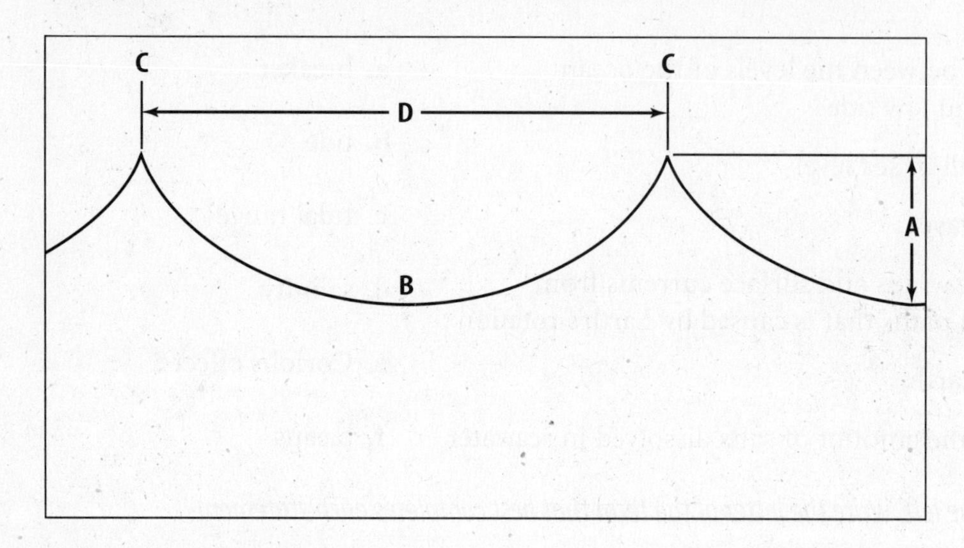

_____ 1. trough

_____ 2. wavelength

_____ 3. wave height

_____ 4. crest

Skill: Classifying

Directions: *Classify the following by identifying the type of current. Use the following terms:* **surface current, Gulf Stream, upwelling,** *and* **density current.**

_______________ 5. forms when a mass of seawater becomes denser than the surrounding water

_______________ 6. a surface current flowing between North America and Europe

_______________ 7. currents that move horizontally, parallel to Earth's surface

_______________ 8. a vertical circulation in the ocean that brings deep, cold water to the ocean surface

Chapter Test A (continued)

Skill: Sequencing

Directions: *Put the following steps in order for each set.*

Set I

______ **9.** The sun heats and evaporates the water.

______ **10.** Ocean water is piped into a glass-roofed building.

______ **11.** The water vapor is collected, and the salt is left behind.

Set II

______ **12.** The salty, unfrozen water is separated from the ice.

______ **13.** The ice can be washed and melted to produce freshwater.

______ **14.** As water freezes, ice crystals, which have less salt than unfrozen water, form.

III. Applying Concepts

Writing Skills

Directions: *Respond to the following using complete sentences.*

1. Explain What is the origin of the water in Earth's oceans?

2. Describe How do oxygen and carbon dioxide enter the oceans?

3. Restate A ship takes longer to sail from Europe to the United States than it does to sail back to Europe. Give a possible explanation.

Chapter Test A (continued)

4. **Explain** Why are the waters off the coast of California cold?

5. **Describe** How does a density current form?

6. **Describe** What happens to a wave when it moves away from the shore?

Name ____________ Date ____________ Class ____________

Ocean Motion

I. Testing Concepts

Directions: *In the blank at the left, write the letter of the term or phrase that correctly completes each statement.*

______ **1.** Water particles of ocean waves move ______.
a. toward shore **b.** in circles **c.** sideways **d.** up and down

______ **2.** As a wave slows and its crest and trough come closer together, the ______ increases.
a. wave height **b.** wavelength **c.** circular motion **d.** speed

______ **3.** The difference between the level of the ocean at high tide and low tide is called ______.
a. a neap tide **b.** a crest **c.** a trough **d.** the tidal range

______ **4.** The rise and fall in sea level caused by gravity is called a(n)______.
a. upwelling **b.** crest **c.** current **d.** tide

______ **5.** When the Sun, the Moon, and Earth form a right angle, we have ______ tides.
a. spring **b.** neap **c.** giant **d.** fall

______ **6.** The horizontal distance between the crests or troughs of two adjacent waves is called ______.
a. wave height **b.** a breaker **c.** wavelength **d.** a tide

______ **7.** Currents that are powered by wind are called ______ currents.
a. density **b.** cold water **c.** warm water **d.** surface

______ **8.** The lowest point of a wave is the ______.
a. trough **b.** crest **c.** wave height **d.** wavelength

______ **9.** In some places, vertical circulation in the ocean brings deep, cold water to the ocean surface. These ______ bring nutrients to the surface, resulting in good fishing areas.
a. upwellings **b.** density currents **c.** tides **d.** surface currents

______ **10.** When more dense seawater sinks under less dense seawater, a(n) ______ forms.
a. surface current **b.** density current **c.** upwelling **d.** tide

______ **11.** In a wave, only the ______ move(s) forward.
a. water particles **b.** energy **c.** wind **d.** deep water

______ **12.** Most of the salt in seawater is made up of the ions ______.
a. calcium and sulfate
b. chloride and sodium
c. sodium and magnesium
d. chloride and potassium

______ **13.** ______ move water parallel to Earth's surface.
a. Density currents **b.** Crests **c.** Upwellings **d.** Surface currents

______ **14.** The oceans originally formed from water vapor that condensed, fell as rain, and then collected in ______.
a. basins **b.** upwellings **c.** crests **d.** tidal ranges

______ **15.** The Coriolis effect is caused by ______.
a. density currents **b.** surface currents **c.** surface winds **d.** Earth's rotation

Chapter Test B (continued)

Directions: *Identify whether the following statements are true or false. If the statement is true, write* **true** *in the space. If the statement is false, change the word in italics to make the statement true.*

______ **16.** The density of seawater can be increased by a *decrease* in temperature.

______ **17.** Tides are caused by a giant wave produced by *friction.*

______ **18.** The highest tides are *neap* tides.

______ **19.** As a water wave approaches shore, its wave height *increases.*

______ **20.** Some of the substances dissolved in seawater come from *volcanoes.*

______ **21.** Density currents spread *rapidly* along the bottom of the ocean.

______ **22.** Some marine animals use calcium from ocean water to form *shells.*

______ **23.** The Coriolis effect causes most currents north of the equator to *turn to the left.*

______ **24.** Most of the currents that are south of the equator *turn to the left.*

______ **25.** Currents on the western coasts of continents are usually *cold* because they begin near the poles.

Directions: *Write the letter from the wave diagram that matches each term.*

______ **26.** trough

______ **27.** wavelength

______ **28.** wave height

______ **29.** crest

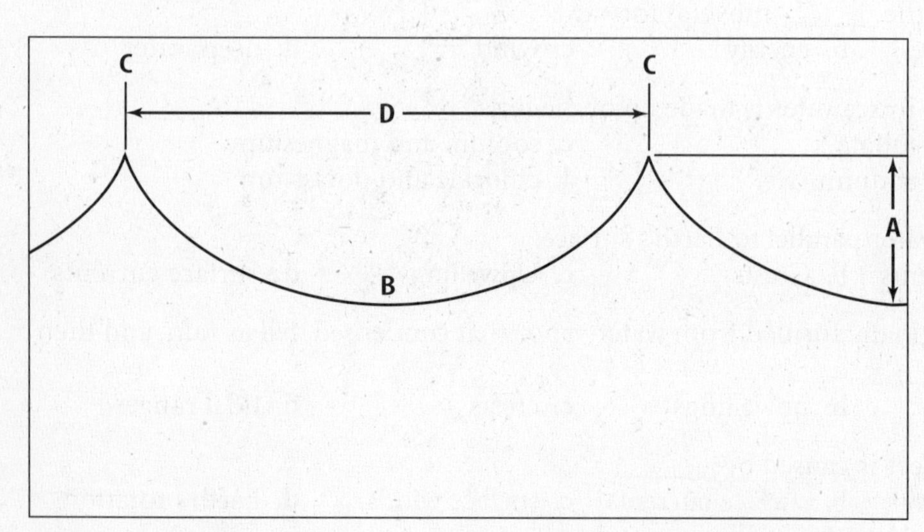

II. Understanding Concepts

Directions: *Answer the following questions on the lines provided.*

Skill: Classifying

1. Would you classify the Gulf Stream as a surface or a density current? Explain why.

______

______

Skill: Comparing and Contrasting

2. Compare and contrast spring and neap tides.

______

______

______

III. Applying Concepts

Directions: *Write the letter of the word or phrase in Column II that correctly completes the statement in Column I.*

	Column I	Column II
______	1. Salt may be removed from seawater through ______.	a. heat
______	2. Surface currents distribute ______ from equatorial regions to other areas of Earth.	b. sea level
______	3. Dense, cold water around Norway, Greenland, and Labrador sink to the seafloor and form the lower layers of ______.	c. desalination
______	4. The density of seawater is affected by temperature and ______.	d. gravitational forces
______	5. ______ occurs when the crest of a wave thousands of kilometers long approaches the shore.	e. high tide
______	6. Scientists think that water in the oceans is from vapor released by ______ into the atmosphere.	f. salinity
______	7. As the trough of a wave thousands of kilometers long approaches the shore, ______ appears to drop.	g. the shore
______	8. Tides are essentially the result of ______.	h. North Atlantic Deep Water
______	9. If you see breakers, you know you are looking at waves near ______.	i. volcanoes
______	10. When dense water from the Mediterranean reaches the Atlantic, it flows to depths of 1,000 m to 2,000 m, forming the ______.	j. Mediterranean Intermediate Water

IV. Writing Skills

Directions: *Answer the following questions using complete sentences.*

1. How does wind create a wave?

2. **Explain** why upwellings help the fishing industry.

3. **Explain** why a knowledge of tides is important for people who live and work on the edge of a large body of water.

4. Why did it take sailing ships in the 1700s longer to sail from England to America than from America to England?

5. What happens to the density current that forms in the Mediterranean Sea?

Name Date Class

Chapter Test C

Ocean Motion

I. Testing Concepts

Directions: *Fill in the blanks to complete the sentences.*

1. Many years ago, the oceans were created when torrential rains filled Earth's ____________________.

2. Ocean water consists of dissolved ____________________ and ____________________.

3. The Coriolis effect causes currents north of the equator to turn to the ____________________.

4. Half the distance of a wave is called its ____________________.

5. During a storm, wave ____________________ increases, and waves carry a lot more ____________________.

6. As waves approach the shore, wavelength ____________________ and wave height ____________________.

7. Tides result from the gravitational pull of ____________________ on Earth.

8. The shape of the seacoast and the shape of the ____________________ affect the ranges of tides.

9. ____________________ containing messages and numbered cards can be released from coastal locations to track surface currents.

10. Elements are added to the ocean at about the same rate they are removed, keeping it in a(n) ____________________.

11. Surface currents move only the upper ____________________ of seawater.

12. When wind blows across a body of water, ____________________ is transferred to the water.

Skill: Contrasting

Directions: *Contrast the two terms.*

1. high tide and low tide

____

____

2. spring tide and neap tide

____

____

Chapter Test C (continued)

II. Understanding Concepts

Skill: Labeling a Diagram

Directions: *Fill in the wave diagram with the correct terms.*

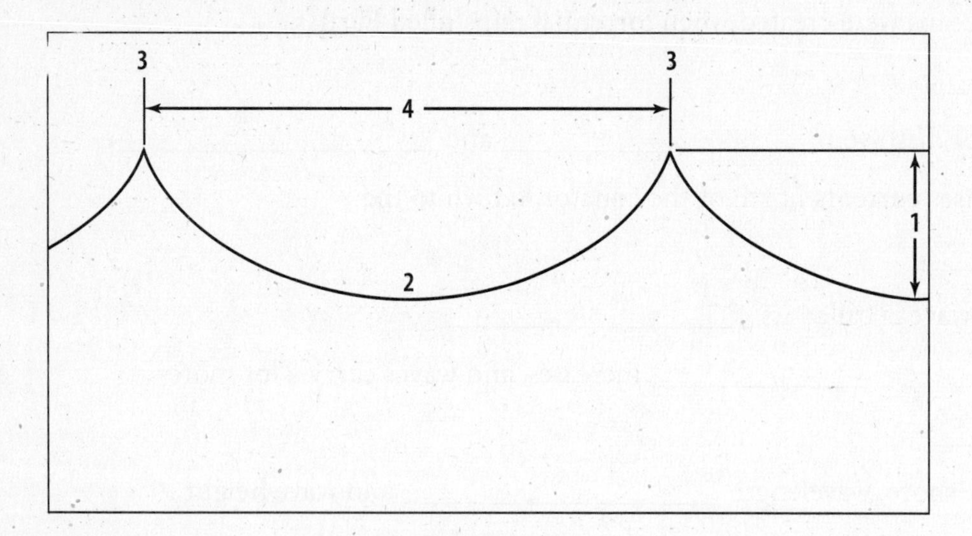

1. ______________________________

2. ______________________________

3. ______________________________

4. ______________________________

Skill: Classifying

Directions: *Classify the following by identifying the type of current.*

______________ **5.** forms when a mass of seawater becomes denser than the surrounding water

______________ **6.** a vertical circulation in the ocean that brings cold water to the ocean surface

______________ **7.** currents that move horizontally, parallel to Earth's surface

______________ **8.** cold, dense water that forms around Norway, Greenland, and Labrador

______________ **9.** a cold-water current that flows along the West Coast of the United States

______________ **10.** a surface current flowing between North America and Europe

______________ **11.** a density current in the Mediterranean Sea that forms a middle layer of water

Chapter Test C (continued)

Skill: Sequencing

12. Choose one process of desalination. Write the steps for desalination in order.

III. Applying Concepts

Writing Skills

Directions: *Respond to the following using complete sentences.*

1. **Analyze** Scientists wonder if the salt water in Earth's oceans is in balance. What could they test? Why?

2. **Contrast** Explain the differences between the temperatures of water off the East Coast and West Coast of the United States.

3. **Predict** Where would you expect density currents to be stronger? Explain your answer.

Chapter Test C (continued)

4. **Infer** The coast guard places a buoy in the deep sea, requesting ships to slow down to protect a marine habitat. They place another near the shore to warn the ships of a shallow area. The deep-sea buoy floats in one place. The shallow buoy needs to be anchored to the ground. Why do the two buoys behave differently?

5. **Analyze** Scientists want to develop a model to predict wave height. What factors should they include?

Use the Internet

Resources from the Oceans

LAB A

Oceans cover most of Earth's surface. Humans get many things from oceans, such as seafood, medicines, oil, and diamonds. Humans also use oceans for recreation and to transport materials from place to place. What else comes from oceans? Scientists continue to discover and research new uses for ocean resources. You might not realize that you probably use many products every day that are made from organisms that live in oceans. Think about the plants and animals that live in the oceans. How could these organisms be used to make everyday products? Form a hypothesis about the types of products that could be manufactured from these organisms.

Real-World Question

What products do you use that come from the oceans?

Goals

- **Research and identify** organisms that are used to make products.
- **Explain** why it is important to keep oceans clean.

Data Source

Science Online Visit **msscience.com/internet_lab** for Web links to more information about resources from the oceans, hints on which products come from the oceans, and data from other students.

Make a Plan

❑ 1. **Identify** Web links shown in the Data Source section above and identify other resources that will help you complete the data table shown below.
Hint: *What resources are available in your school library?*

❑ 2. **Observe** that to complete the table you must identify 1) products made from marine organisms, 2) where the organisms are collected or harvested, and 3) alternative products.

❑ 3. **Plan** how and when you will locate the information.

Follow Your Plan

❑ 1. Make sure your teacher approves your plan and your resource list before you begin.

❑ 2. **Describe** at least three ocean organisms that are used to make products you use every day.

❑ 3. **Identify** the name and any uses of the product.

❑ 4. **Research** where each organism lives and the method by which it is collected or harvested.

❑ 5. **Identify** alternative products.

Ocean Resources Data

Organism	Location Where Collected or Harvested	Product (name and use)	Alternatives

LAB (continued) **LAB A**

Analyze Your Data

1. **Describe** the different ways in which ocean organisms are useful to humans.

2. **Explain** Are there any substitutes or alternatives available for the ocean organisms in the products?

Conclude and Apply

1. **Infer** How might the activities of humans affect any of the ocean organisms you researched?

2. **Determine** Are the substitute or alternative products more or less expensive?

3. **Describe** Can you tell whether the ocean-made product is better than the substitute product?

4. **Explain** why it is important to conserve ocean resources and keep oceans clean.

Communicating Your Data

Find this lab using the link below. Post your data in the table provided. Compare your data to those of other students.

Science Online msscience.com/internet_lab

Name Date Class

Use the Internet

Resources from the Oceans

LAB B

Oceans cover most of Earth's surface. Humans get many things from oceans, such as seafood, medicines, oil, and diamonds. Humans also use oceans for recreation and to transport materials from place to place. What else comes from oceans? Scientists continue to discover and research new uses for ocean resources. You might not realize that you probably use many products every day that are made from organisms that live in oceans. Think about the plants and animals that live in the oceans. How could these organisms be used to make everyday products? Form a hypothesis about the types of products that could be manufactured from these organisms.

Real-World Question

What products do you use that come from the oceans?

Goals

- **Research and identify** organisms that are used to make products.
- **Explan** why it is important to keep oceans clean.

Data Source

Science Online Visit **msscience.com/ internet_lab** for Web links to more information about resources from the oceans, hints on which products come from the oceans, and data from other students.

Make a Plan

❑ 1. **Identify** Web links shown in the Data Source section above and identify other resources that will help you complete the data table shown below.

❑ 2. **Observe** that to complete the table you must identify products made from marine organisms, where the organisms are collected or harvested, and alternative products.

❑ 3. **Plan** how and when you will locate the information.

Follow Your Plan

❑ 1. Make sure your teacher approves your plan and your resource list before you begin.

❑ 2. **Describe** at least three ocean organisms that are used to make products you use every day.

❑ 3. **Identify** the name and any uses of the product.

❑ 4. **Research** where each organism lives and the method by which it is collected or harvested.

❑ 5. **Identify** alternative products.

Ocean Resources Data

Organism	Location Where Collected or Harvested	Product (name and use)	Alternatives

Name Date Class

LAB (continued)

LAB B

Analyze Your Data

1. **Describe** the different ways in which ocean organisms are useful to humans.

2. **Explain** Are there any substitutes or alternatives available for the ocean organisms in the products?

Conclude and Apply

1. **Infer** How might the activities of humans affect any of the ocean organisms you researched?

2. **Determine** Are the substitute or alternative products more or less expensive?

3. **Describe** Can you tell whether the ocean-made product is better than the substitute product?

4. **Explain** why it is important to conserve ocean resources and keep oceans clean.

Challenge

1. **Infer** From which area of the ocean do you think most of these products were mined? Why?

2. **Predict** Do you think that more or fewer products will be harvested from the ocean in the future? Explain your answer.

(continued)

3. **Compare** How are the issues surrounding mining and harvesting of minerals and organisms from the ocean similar to the issues surrounding the mining and harvesting of land minerals and organisms?

Extension

Hypothesize Does the mining of one organism affect others? Choose one of the organisms you researched. Create a food chain showing how this organism gets and transfers energy from the Sun. Use the food chain to explain why overharvesting of this organism could affect other organisms.

Communicating Your Data

Find this lab using the link below. Post your data in the table provided. Compare your data to those of other students.

Science Online msscience.com/internet_lab

Name ____________________ Date ____________ Class ____________

Oceanography

I. Testing Concepts

Directions: *Match each description on the left with the correct term on the right. Write the letter of the correct term in the blank at the left.*

______ **1.** rigid, wave-resistant structure built by corals from skeletal material

______ **2.** carbon dioxide and water changed to sugar and oxygen in the presence of sunlight

______ **3.** sulfur and nitrogen compounds used as an energy source to produce food

______ **4.** an area where the mouth of a river opens into an ocean

a. photosynthesis

b. chemosynthesis

c. estuary

d. reef

Directions: *Identify each statement as* **true** *or* **false**. *If a statement is false, change the underlined term to make it true.*

______ **5.** Material that is lost overboard accidentally is <u>not</u> considered pollution.

____

______ **6.** At a trench, one crustal plate <u>slides past</u> another.

____

______ **7.** At each stage of the food chain, <u>energy</u> obtained by one organism is used by other organisms.

____

______ **8.** Most marine animals live in the waters above or on the floor of the <u>continental slope</u>.

____

______ **9.** <u>Trenches</u> contain an abundance of food and offer protection from larger predators.

____

______ **10.** Each coral animal builds a hard capsule around its body from the <u>calcium</u> it removes from seawater.

____

______ **11.** Sea turtles may mistakenly eat <u>plastic bags</u> thinking they are jellyfish.

____

Name Date Class

II. Understanding Concepts

Skill: Interpreting Scientific Illustrations

Directions: *Write the name of each feature on the line to correspond to each term. Use the following terms:* **abyssal plain, continental shelf, continental slope, ocean trench,** *and* **mid-ocean ridge.**

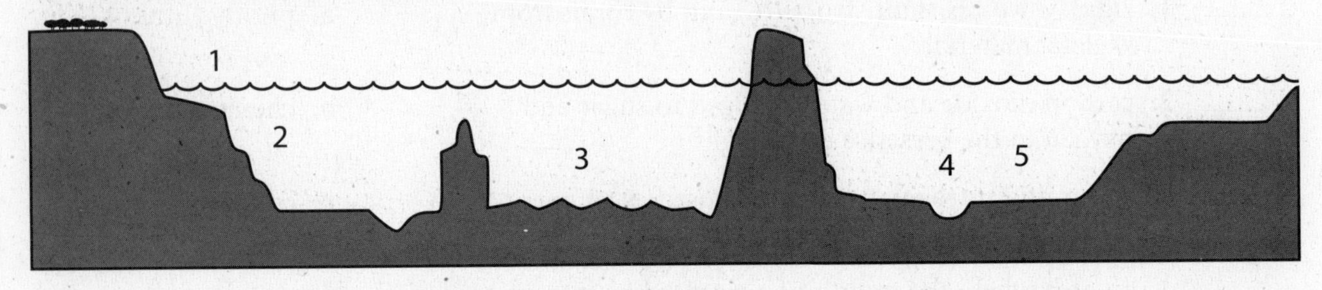

1. ______________________
2. ______________________
3. ______________________
4. ______________________
5. ______________________

Skill: Categorizing

Directions: *Decide if each of these statements describes* **plankton, nekton,** *or* **benthos.**

______________________ **6.** animals that actively swim in the ocean currents

______________________ **7.** marine organisms that drift with the currents

______________________ **8.** plants and animals living on the seafloor

______________________ **9.** animals such as crabs, snails, and sponges

______________________ **10.** range from microscopic algae and animals to organisms as large as jellyfish

______________________ **11.** animals such as sharks, whales, and flounder

Skill: Sequencing

Directions: *Sequence the events to show the cause and effect of a toxic bloom of Pfiesteria.*

______ **12.** The algae die.

______ **13.** The fertilizers cause the algae to reproduce rapidly, causing a toxic bloom.

______ **14.** Fertilizer and other waste materials run off from land and ships.

______ **15.** Fish die due to lack of oxygen.

______ **16.** Bacteria decompose algae, depleting water and oxygen.

______ **17.** People can be sick from contaminated fish and water.

III. Applying Concepts

Writing Skills

Directions: *Respond to the following using complete sentences.*

1. **Explain** What happens at a mid-ocean ridge?

2. **List** Identify three products that can be found in the continental shelf and three products that can be found in deep water.

3. **Restate** What are the five main types of ocean pollution?

4. **Apply** What are some things you can do to help prevent ocean pollution?

5. **Analyze** How would an oceanographer know where a subduction zone was located?

6. **Analyze** How are abyssal plains formed?

7. **Contrast** How is the shape of the continental shelf different from that of the continental slope?

Name Date Class

Oceanography

I. Testing Concepts

Directions: *Replace the italicized word or phrase with one that will make each statement correct. Write the new word or phrase on the blank provided.*

______________ 1. The *abyssal plain* extends from the outer edge of the continental shelf down to the ocean floor.

______________ 2. A *chemical* is a substance that damages organisms by interfering with life processes.

______________ 3. *Manganese nodules* result when dense mineral grains transported by rivers concentrate in one place.

______________ 4. In the ocean, *consumers* make food by undergoing photosynthesis.

______________ 5. Diatoms are a tiny but abundant form of *nekton* found in the ocean.

______________ 6. *Continental shelves* are the flat, seafloor areas in the deep ocean formed by deposits of sediment that fill in valleys.

______________ 7. *Plankton* include crabs, snails, clams, sea urchins, and bottom-dwelling fish.

______________ 8. *Solid waste* results from human activities that tear up the soil.

Directions: *Write the number of each feature in the appropriate circle on the drawing.*

9. abyssal plain
10. continental shelf
11. continental slope
12. ocean trench
13. mid-ocean ridge

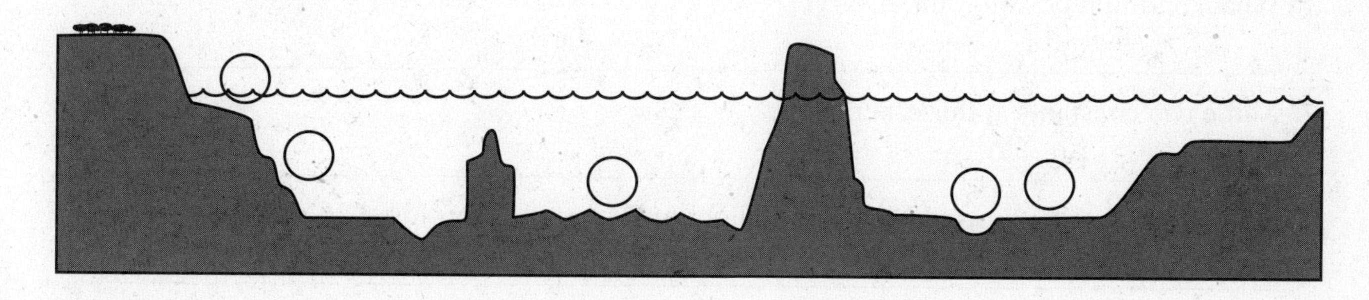

Chapter Test B (continued)

Directions: *For each of the following, write the letter of the term or phrase that best completes the sentence.*

_____ **14.** Bacteria that perform chemosynthesis using sulfur compounds live _____.
a. in ocean trenches
b. along shorelines
c. in coral reefs
d. along portions of mid-ocean ridges

_____ **15.** _____ are formed on the seafloor when one crustal plate is forced under another plate.
a. Continental shelves
b. Trenches
c. Mid-ocean ridges
d. Abyssal plains

_____ **16.** Plants and animals that live on the ocean floor are _____.
a. nekton **b.** plankton **c.** benthos **d.** diatoms

_____ **17.** The continental slope is located at the end of the _____.
a. shoreline **b.** continental shelf **c.** mid-ocean ridge **d.** abyssal plain

_____ **18.** Tide pools are most characteristic of _____.
a. beaches **b.** rocky shore areas **c.** estuaries **d.** coral reefs

_____ **19.** Petroleum, natural gas, sand, metals, and diamonds are mined from deposits found in _____.
a. deep water deposits
b. continental slopes
c. ocean trenches
d. continental shelves

_____ **20.** Food webs in the ocean consist of _____.
a. fishing nets
b. the feet of marine ducks
c. light, water, and minerals
d. interconnected food chains

_____ **21.** Most ocean pollution comes from _____.
a. ships **b.** land **c.** fish **d.** none of these

II. Understanding Concepts

Skill: Using Variables, Constants, and Controls

Directions: *Read the following sentences, then answer the questions on the lines provided.*

Suppose you want to know how light affects a certain plant in the ocean. You fill three jars with ocean water and put three plants in each jar.

1. What condition do you want to vary?

____

2. Name two constants in this experiment.

____

3. How many jars, if any, would you shine a light on 24 hours a day? Just 12 hours a day?

____

4. If you added plant food to one of the jars, what would you be introducing—another constant, another control, or another variable?

____

Chapter Test B (continued)

5. How could you judge the results of this experiment?

____

6. If you varied both light and plant food, what could you conclude from this experiment?

____

Skill: Concept Mapping

Directions: *The following events occur in chemosynthesis. Number the events in the order they occur.*

______ 7. Organisms feed on the bacteria.

______ 8. Bacteria produce food.

______ 9. Bacteria take in sulfur compounds for energy.

______ 10. Superheated water seeps or blasts from Earth's crust.

Skill: Comparing and Contrasting

Directions: *Compare and contrast plankton, nekton, and benthos by putting the letter of the statement in the correct column. If a statement refers to more than one form of life, put its letter in each column that it refers to.*

11. Plankton	12. Nekton	13. Benthos

a. Plants and animals that depend on currents to move them are included in this group.
b. These live on the bottom of the ocean floor.
c. The animals in this group can swim.
d. These are forms of life in the ocean.
e. This group includes kelp, which grows from depths of up to 30 m.
f. Animals in this group can control their buoyancy.
g. Some members, such as sea urchins, can move or swim; others, such as sponges, are permanently attached to the seafloor.
h. These find necessary conditions for life in the ocean.
i. Whales are a member of this group.
j. This group includes jellyfish, newly hatched crabs, and copepods.

Name Date Class

III. Applying Concepts

Writing Skills

Directions: *Answer the following questions using complete sentences.*

1. How is Sun energy the basis for many of the ocean's food chains?

2. What might happen if one link of a food chain is destroyed?

3. **Compare** the landforms on the ocean floor with landforms on Earth's dry surfaces.

4. **Explain** the differences between photosynthesis and chemosynthesis.

5. What are four things that oceans provide for organisms?

6. **Name** four ways that pollutants may be introduced into the ocean.

7. How does sewage in the ocean cause fish kills?

Name _______________ Date _______________ Class _______________

Chapter Test C

Oceanography

I. Testing Concepts

Directions: *Fill in the blanks to complete the sentences.*

1. In the deep ocean, sediment deposits fill in valleys, creating _______________.
2. _______________ are underwater inactive volcanic peaks.
3. Seafloor spreading occurs at a(n) _______________.
4. Most trenches are found in the _______________ Basin.
5. _______________ occur when the energy of ocean waves and currents causes denser mineral grains that have been brought in by rivers to concentrate in one place.
6. The greatest source of food is located in the waters of the _______________.
7. Energy from the Sun is transferred to animals through _______________.
8. Many ocean animals have a special organ filled with gas that helps them control their _______________.
9. Corals thrive in clear, warm water that receives a lot of _______________.
10. Sewage is a pollutant that acts like _______________.
11. _______________ are called "the nurseries of the ocean" because many creatures spend their early lives there.
12. The _______________ is the part of the intertidal zone that is splashed by high waves and is usually covered by water only during the highest tides each month.
13. Submerged at most high tides and exposed at most low tides, the _______________ is populated by sponges, barnacles, and sea stars.
14. Some deep-dwelling nekton have adapted special _______________ organs that are used to attract prey and mates.
15. Diatoms and phytoplankton are the source of food for _______________, animals that drift with ocean currents.

Name Date Class

Chapter Test C (continued)

II. Understanding Concepts

Skill: Interpreting Scientific Illustrations

Directions: *Identify each area on the ocean floor.*

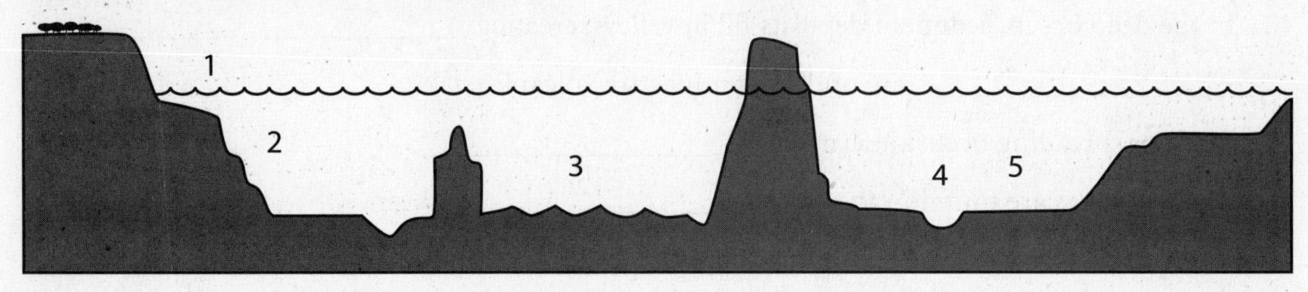

1. ______________________

2. ______________________

3. ______________________

4. ______________________

5. ______________________

Skill: Making a Chart

6. **Make** a chart to describe characteristics of plankton, nekton, or benthos.

7. **Create** an events-chain concept map to show the cause and effect of a toxic bloom of Pfiesteria.

III. Applying Concepts

Writing Skills

Directions: *Respond to the following using complete sentences.*

1. **Contrast** What are the differences between continental shelves and continental slopes?

2. **Generalize** Name the types of products found on the continental shelf and in deep water. Why are more minerals and other products mined from the continental shelf than from deep water?

3. **Analyze** Explain the differences between photosynthesis and chemosynthesis.

4. **Compare and Contrast** How are ocean margin habitats alike and different?

5. **Evaluate** A group promises to get rid of ocean pollution by promoting a major cleanup of solid waste along the beaches and shores. Will this solve the problem?

Name Date Class

A World Full of People

LAB A

Lab Preview

Directions: *Answer these questions before you begin the Lab.*

1. What will you be showing in this lab?

____

2. How many people does each object represent?

____

Every second, five people are born on Earth and two or three people die. As a result, there is a net increase of two or three people in the world every second of every day. That amounts to about 81 million new people every year. This is nearly equal to the population of Central Africa. What effects will this rapid increase in human population have on Earth?

Real-World Question

How crowded will different regions of Earth become in the next ten years?

Materials

small objects such as popcorn kernels or dried beans (1,000)
large map of the world (the map must show the countries of the world)
clock or watch
calculator

Goals

- **Demonstrate** the world's human population increase in the next decade.
- **Predict** the world's population in 50 years.
- **Record, graph,** and **interpret** population data.

Safety Precautions 

Never eat or taste anything in the lab, even if you are confident that you know what it is.

Procedure

❑ **1. Lay** the map out on a table. The map represents Earth and the people already living here.

❑ **2.** Each minute of time will represent one year. During your first minute, place 78 popcorn kernels on the continents of your map. Each kernel represents 1 million new people.

❑ **3. Place** one kernel inside the borders of developed countries such as the United States, Canada, Japan, Australia, and countries in Europe.

❑ **Place** 77 kernels inside the borders of developing nations located in South America, Africa, and Asia.

❑ **4.** Continue adding 78 kernels to your map in the same fashion each minute for 10 min.

❑ **Record** the total population increase for each year (each minute of the lab) in the data table in the Data and Observation section.

Name Date Class

LAB (continued) **LAB A**

Data and Observations

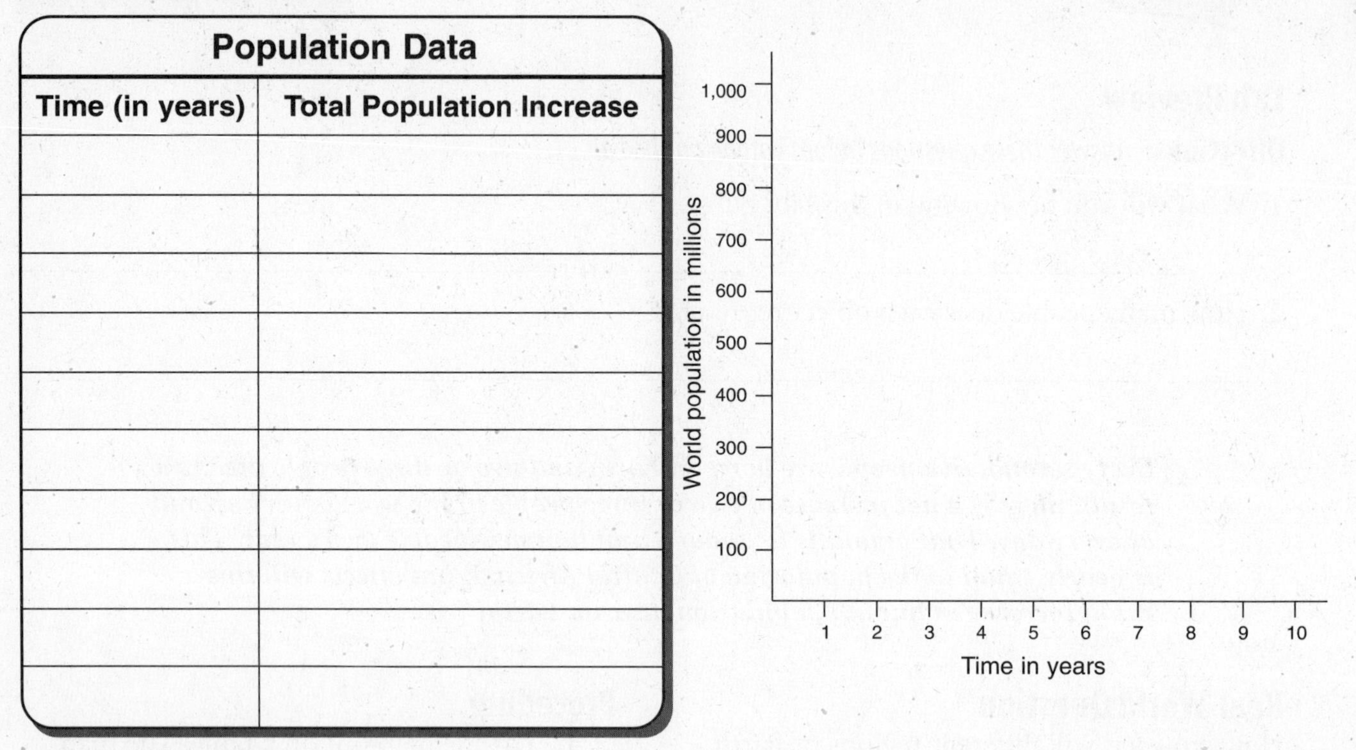

Population Data

Time (in years)	Total Population Increase

Analyze Your Data

1. **Draw and label** a graph like the one above showing the time in years on the horizontal axis and the world population on the vertical axis.
2. **Calculate** the world's population in 50 years by using an average rate of 71 million people per year.
3. **Determine** world population in ten years if only 4.5 million people are added each year.

Conclude and Apply

1. **Infer** how many people will be added to Earth in the next ten years. Determine the world's population in ten years. ____________________
2. **Compare** the population growth in developed countries to the growth of developing countries.
____
3. **Discuss** ways the increase in the human population will affect Earth's resources in the future.
____

Communicating Your Data

Draw your graph on a computer and present your findings to the class. **For more help, refer to the Science Skill Handbook.**

Name Date Class

A World Full of People

LAB B

Lab Preview

Directions: *Answer these questions before you begin the Lab.*

1. What will you be showing in this lab?

____

2. How many people does each object represent?

____

Every second, five people are born on Earth and two or three people die. As a result, there is a net increase of two or three people in the world every second of every day. That amounts to about 81 million new people every year. This is nearly equal to the population of Central Africa. What effects will this rapid increase in human population have on Earth?

Real-World Question

How crowded will different regions of Earth become in the next ten years?

Materials

small objects such as popcorn kernels or dried beans (1,000)
large map of the world (the map must show the countries of the world)
clock or watch
calculator

Goals

- **Demonstrate** the world's human population increase in the next decade.
- **Predict** the world's population in 50 years.
- **Record, graph,** and **interpret** population data.

Safety Precautions 

Never eat or taste anything in the lab, even if you are confident that you know what it is.

Procedure

❑ **1. Lay** the map out on a table. The map represents Earth and the people already living here.

❑ **2.** Each minute of time will represent one year. During your first minute, place 78 popcorn kernels on the continents of your map. Each kernel represents 1 million new people.

❑ **3. Place** one kernel inside the borders of developed countries such as the United States, Canada, Japan, Australia, and countries in Europe. Place 77 kernels inside the borders of developing nations located in South America, Africa, and Asia.

❑ **4.** Continue adding 78 kernels to your map in the same fashion each minute for 10 min. **Record** the total population increase for each year (each minute of the lab) in the data table in the Data and Observation section.

(continued)

LAB B

Data and Observations

Population Data	
Time (in years)	Total Population Increase

Put graph here:

Analyze Your Data

1. **Draw and label** a graph of your data showing the time in years on the horizontal axis and the world population on the vertical axis.
2. **Calculate** the world's population in 50 years by using an average rate of 71 million people per year.
3. **Determine** world population in ten years if only 4.5 million people are added each year.

Conclude and Apply

1. **Infer** how many people will be added to Earth in the next ten years. Determine the world's population in ten years. ______
2. **Compare** the population growth in developed countries to the growth of developing countries. ______
3. **Discuss** ways the increase in the human population will affect Earth's resources in the future. ______

Challenge

1. **Infer** What will happen to other populations as the human population increases? ______

LAB (continued) **LAB B**

2. **Hypothesize** What might have happened if the population growth had leveled off or decreased?

____

____

3. **Infer** Why do you think there is more growth in the developing countries?

____

____

____

Extension

Analyze Look at population data from your city or state for the past ten years. Create a graph to display the data. How does the graph compare to the data from your lab? Is the growth rapid, slow, or negative?

Communicating Your Data

Draw your graph on a computer and present your findings to the class. **For more help, refer to the Science Skill Handbook.**

Name ______ Date ______ Class ______

Our Impact on Land

I. Testing Concepts

Directions: *In the blank at the left, write the letter of the term that best completes each statement.*

______ **1.** ______ is a group of individuals of one species occupying a particular area.
a. A habitat
b. Carrying capacity
c. Niche
d. A population

______ **2.** ______ is the largest number of individuals of a particular species that the environment can support.
a. Niche
b. Carrying capacity
c. Habitat
d. Population

______ **3.** ______ are substances that contaminate the environment.
a. Pollutants **b.** Populations **c.** Enzymes **d.** Niches

______ **4.** During a storm, people monitor the ______, or the volume of water flowing past a point per unit of time.
a. carrying capacity
b. enzymes
c. stream discharge
d. niches

______ **5.** One way of safely disposing of waste is in a ______ where the garbage is covered with soil.
a. stream discharge
b. sanitary landfill
c. niche
d. pollutant

______ **6.** ______ are substances that make chemical reactions go faster.
a. Enzymes
b. Pollutants
c. Hazardous wastes
d. Stream discharges

______ **7.** We promote ______ when we carefully use Earth's materials.
a. pollution
b. hazardous wastes
c. conservation
d. environmental impact

II. Understanding Concepts

Skill: Categorizing

Directions: *Categorize each activity as* **reducing, recycling,** *or* **reusing.**

______ **1.** collecting aluminum cans to make new cans

______ **2.** composting yard waste

______ **3.** using both sides of printer paper

______ **4.** riding a bicycle to school instead of driving

______ **5.** building a bird feeder from a milk carton

______ **6.** making steel from scrap metal

Chapter Test A (continued)

Skill: Concept Mapping

Directions: *Complete the concept map showing how phytoremediation can remove contaminants from the soil. Use the following terms:* **composting, ash disposal, metal absorbed, burning,** *and* **metal recovered.**

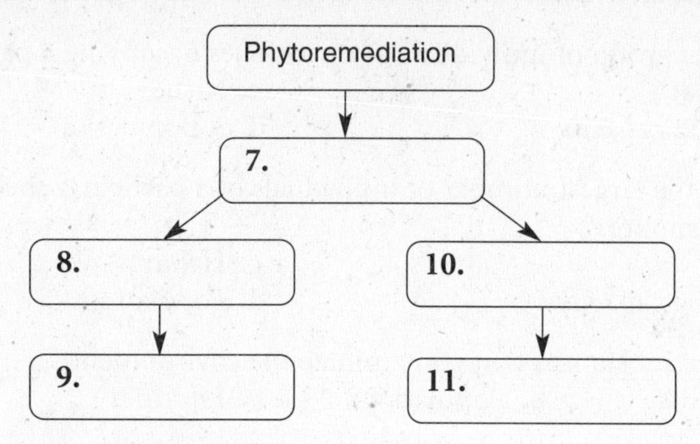

Skill: Using Diagrams, Charts, and Tables

Directions: *Use the graph below, which shows the population growth of modern humans, to answer the questions.*

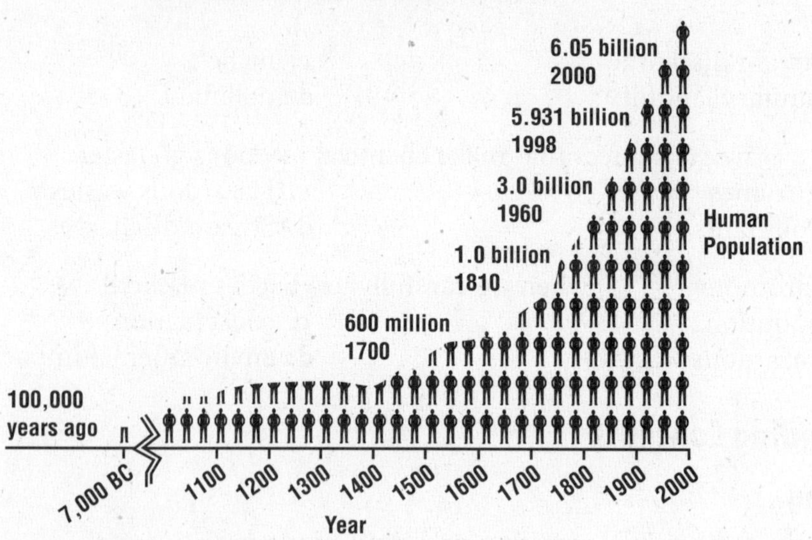

12. What was the population in 1960? ______________________

13. What was the population in 2000? ______________________

14. How has the population changed in that time? ______________________

15. Predict how the population in 2010 will compare to the population in 2000.

____

16. What does the zigzag line between 7000 B.C. and A.D. 1100 represent? ______________________

Chapter Test A (continued)

III. Applying Concepts

Skill: Cause and Effect

Directions: *Write each of the following negative effects under the corresponding human action listed below.*

- Trees are cut down, and oil is used to transport them.
- Earth is changed when fossil fuels are mined.
- More trash is created.
- Refining oil to make this product can produce pollutants.
- Pesticides used to grow plants can get into the water supply.

1. You pack a single-serving packaged cheese slice and a single-serving packaged juice drink in your lunch.

____

2. You use paper.

____

3. You make a salad.

____

4. You buy plastic forks.

____

5. You turn on a light.

____

Writing Skills

Directions: *Respond to the following using complete sentences.*

6. List What are four ways that land is used?

____

____

7. Explain Why can it be dangerous to throw away paint and some chemicals?

____

____

____

8. Compare Why is recycling better than throwing materials away?

____

____

____

Name ______________________ Date ______________________ Class ______________________

Our Impact on Land

I. Testing Concepts

Directions: *Identify each statement as* **true** *or* **false.** *Rewrite false statements to make them correct.*

______ **1.** Each day about 500,000 people are added to Earth's population.

______ **2.** Paving over land causes little damage to the environment.

______ **3.** Recycling saves natural resources and reduces damage to the environment.

______ **4.** Sanitary landfills are lined to help lessen groundwater pollution.

______ **5.** When forests disappear, animal species may also disappear.

______ **6.** A container law requires a refundable deposit on all trash.

______ **7.** Because sanitary landfills are lined, hazardous substances cannot leak into the soil.

______ **8.** The average person in the United States uses several times the energy used by the average person elsewhere in the world.

______ **9.** Developed countries use more resources than developing countries.

______ **10.** The term *composting* means piling up grass and leaves so they can be collected.

Directions: *For each of the following, write the letter of the term or phrase that best completes the sentence.*

______ **11.** Population explosion refers to the _____.
a. estimated world population in 2025
b. number of people who live in poverty
c. world population in 1810
d. increased rate at which the population is growing

______ **12.** One example of a program that encourages recycling is _____.
a. the development of paper products made of recycled material
b. a five-cent refundable deposit is made on beverage containers
c. people pay higher trash collection fees if they recycle
d. new jobs are created in "reuse" industries

______ **13.** One disadvantage to recycling is _____.
a. more trucks and people needed to haul materials
b. a five-cent refundable deposit on beverage cans
c. a growing population
d. a lower trash collection fee

______ **14.** One cause of the population explosion is _____.
a. air pollution **b.** poor nutrition **c.** better nutrition **d.** water pollution

______ **15.** Reduced vegetation on Earth may result in _____.
a. a localized decrease in rainfall
b. increased habitats
c. less room for humans
d. more oxygen in the atmosphere

______ **16.** The ways each person in a developed country affects the environment include _____.
a. generating waste
b. using fossil fuels for energy
c. treating water to clean it
d. all of the above

______ **17.** A land use that **DOES NOT** change the environment _____.
a. grazing livestock
b. using herbicides
c. setting aside natural preserves
d. cutting trees

______ **18.** Recycling materials helps save _____.
a. energy **b.** landfill space **c.** both a and b **d.** neither a nor b

______ **19.** A growing population puts demands on the land for _____.
a. food **b.** living space **c.** landfills for trash **d.** all of these

______ **20.** A person in a developed country can help protect the environment by _____.
a. using more energy
b. using less energy
c. cutting down trees
d. creating trash for landfills

Chapter Test B (continued)

II. Understanding Concepts

Skill: Making an Outline

Directions: *Insert the number of the correct phrase below to complete the outline at the right.*

How People Affect Earth

I. Farming the land

A. ______

B. ______

II. Paving over the land

A. ______

B. ______

III. Cutting trees

A. ______

B. ______

1. Erosion from tilling the soil
2. Habitat destruction
3. Species extinction
4. Pollution from herbicides
5. Reduction of water in underground supplies
6. Increased risk of flooding

Skill: Using Graphs

Directions: *Use the graph below, which shows the population growth of modern humans, to answer the questions.*

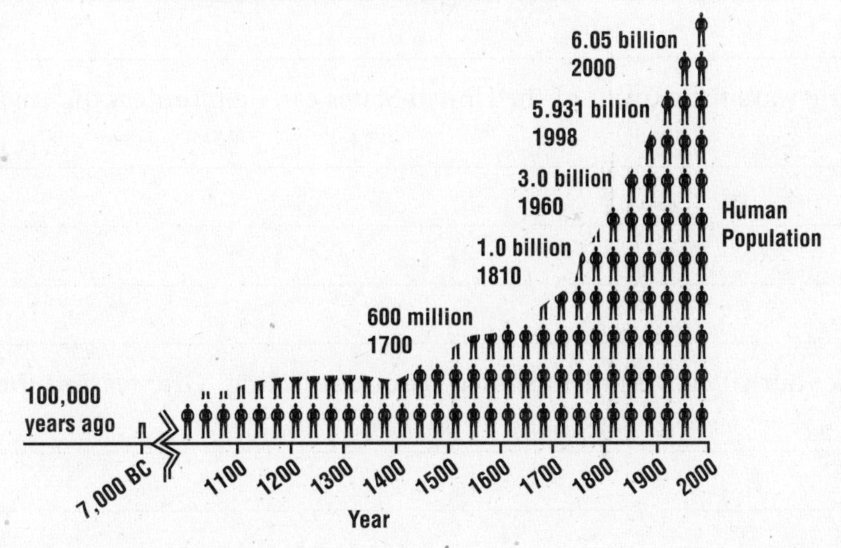

7. What was the population in 1960? ______

8. How many years did it take for the population to grow from 1 billion to 3 billion? ______

9. By how many more people did the population increase between 1700 and 1810? ______

10. About when did the human species first appear? ______

Chapter Test B (continued)

III. Applying Concepts

Writing Skills

Directions: *Answer the following questions using complete sentences.*

1. People who live in the United States use several times as much energy as an average person elsewhere in the world. Explain some ways the activities of a person in the United States may affect the environment.

2. If a law required all newspapers in the nation to use recycled paper for Sunday issues, and it takes 500,000 trees for one Sunday's issues nationwide, how many trees would be saved in one year? How would this affect the environment?

3. How can the design of a sanitary landfill reduce air, soil, and water pollution?

4. What are some ways the citizens of the United States can help protect the environment?

5. Do you think your city government should require recycling? Give reasons for your answer.

Name _______________ Date _______________ Class _______________

Our Impact on Land

I. Testing Concepts

Directions: *Determine whether the statements below are* **true** *or* **false**. *If a statement is false, change the underlined term to make it true.*

______ **1.** In <u>contour plowing</u>, rows are tilled across hills and valleys to help reduce water erosion.

____

______ **2.** <u>Deforestation</u> is the clearing of forested land for agriculture, grazing, development, or logging.

____

______ **3.** Sanitary landfills are designed to prevent <u>gases</u> from draining into the soil and groundwater below.

____

______ **4.** Covering the land with roads, sidewalks, and parking lots <u>reduces</u> the chances of flooding.

____

______ **5.** By 2050, the population of Earth is predicted to be about <u>9 billion</u>, which is about double what it is now.

____

Directions: *Fill in the blanks to complete the sentences.*

6. During a flood, city officials monitor _______________ to determine the amount of water flowing past a point in a given unit of time.

7. Some plant roots release _______________, which help(s) make chemical reactions go faster.

8. A neighbor is _______________ when she piles up yard waste to let it gradually decompose.

9. Three methods of reducing wind erosion are _______________,

_______________, and _______________.

10. When soil is exposed, several _______________ of topsoil a year may be lost due to erosion.

11. _______________ is the largest number of individuals of a particular species that the environment can support.

Chapter Test C (continued)

II. Understanding Concepts

Skill: Using Diagrams, Charts, and Tables

Directions: *Use the graph below, which shows the population growth of modern humans, to answer the questions.*

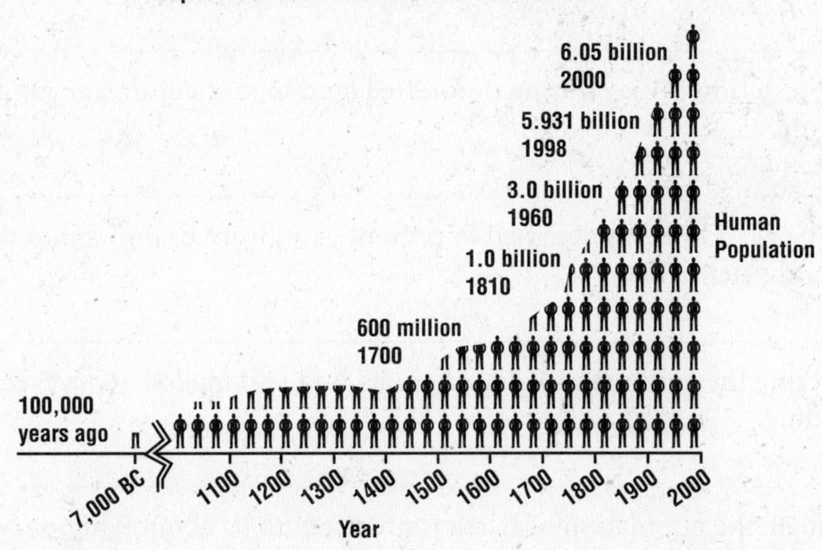

1. **Describe** the time intervals measured on the graph. How are they indicated?

____

____

2. Why do you think these intervals were chosen?

____

____

3. **Provide** a possible explanation for the trend shown on the graph.

____

____

Chapter Test C (continued)

Skill: Concept Mapping

4. Create a concept map showing how phytoremediation can remove contaminants from the soil.

III. Applying Concepts

Skill: Cause and Effect

Directions: *Write a negative effect that each of the following human actions can have on Earth.*

1. You pack a single-serving packaged cheese slice and a single-serving packaged juice drink in your lunch.

____

2. You use paper.

____

3. You make a salad.

____

4. You buy plastic forks.

____

5. You turn on a light.

____

Chapter Test C (continued)

Skill: Categorizing

Directions: *Give an example for each category of conserving resources.*

6. reducing ______________________________

7. recycling ______________________________

8. reusing ______________________________

Writing Skills

Directions: *Respond to the following using complete sentences.*

9. Recommend What are three things that could be done at your school or home to conserve natural resources?

____

____

____

10. Assess The city wants to build a sanitary landfill next to your school. List some advantages and disadvantages for this type of waste storage.

____

____

____

____

____

11. Support The city wants to create a "greenway" park, which will link green areas to ring the city. Support the city's proposition.

____

____

____

Name _______________ Date _______________ Class _______________

Design Your Own

What's in the air?

LAB A

Lab Preview

Directions: *Answer these questions before you begin the Lab.*

1. Why should you wear a thermal mitt in this experiment?

____

2. What is the purpose of the plastic lids in this experiment?

____

When you dust items in your household, you are cleaning up particles that settled out of the air. How often do you have to dust to keep your furniture clean? Just imagine how many pieces of particulate matter the air must hold.

Real-World Question

Do some areas of your environment have more particulates than other areas?

Form a Hypothesis

Based on your knowledge of your neighborhood, form a hypothesis to explain whether all areas in your community contain the same types and amounts of particulate matter.

Possible Materials

small box of plain gelatin
hot plate
pan or pot
water
marker
refrigerator
plastic lids (4)
microscope
**magnifying lens*

**Alternate materials*

Goals

- **Design** an experiment to collect and analyze particulate matter in the air in your community.
- **Observe and describe** the particulate matter you collect.

Safety Precautions

WARNING: *Wear a thermal mitt, safety goggles, and an apron while working with a hot plate and while pouring the gelatin from the pan or pot into the lids. Never eat anything in the lab.*

Test Your Hypothesis

Make a Plan

- ❑ **1.** As a group, agree upon your hypothesis and decide how you will test it. **Hint:** *What could you observe from particulate in the air?*
- ❑ **2. List** the steps you need to take to test your hypotheses.
  - ❑ **Describe** exactly what you will do at each step. List your materials.
- ❑ **3. Record** your observations in the data table on the next page.
- ❑ **4. Label** your lids with the location where you decide to place them.
- ❑ **5. Mix** the gelatin according to the directions on the box.
  - ❑ Carefully pour a thin layer of gelatin into each lid. Use this to collect air particulate matter.
- ❑ **6. Read** over your entire experiment to make sure that all steps are in a logical order.
- ❑ **7. Identify** any constants, variables, and controls of the experiment.

LAB (continued)

LAB A

Follow Your Plan

- ❑ **1.** Make sure your teacher approves your plan.
- ❑ **2.** Carry out the experiment as planned.
- ❑ **3. Record** any observations that you make and complete the data table below.

Data and Observations

Lid Number	Type of Material	Number of Particles	Description of Material
1			
2			
3			
4			

Analyze Your Data

1. **Describe** the types of materials you collected in each lid.

2. **Calculate** the number of particles on each lid.

3. **Compare and contrast** your controls and your variables in this experiment.

4. **Graph** Record your results using a bar graph. Place the number of particulates on the *y*-axis and the test-site location on the *x*-axis.

Conclude and Apply

1. **Determine** if the results support your hypothesis.

2. **Explain** why different sizes of particulate matter may be found at different locations.

3. **Infer** why some test-site locations showed more particulates than other sites did.

Communicating Your Data

Develop Multimedia Presentations Give an oral presentation of your experiment on air pollution in your community to another class. **For more help, refer to the Science Skills Handbook.**

Name Date Class

Design Your Own

What's in the air?

LAB B

Lab Preview

Directions: *Answer these questions before you begin the Lab.*

1. Why should you wear a thermal mitt in this experiment?

____

2. What is the purpose of the plastic lids in this experiment?

____

When you dust items in your household, you are cleaning up particles that settled out of the air. How often do you have to dust to keep your furniture clean? Just imagine how many pieces of particulate matter the air must hold.

Real-World Question

Do some areas of your environment have more particulates than other areas?

Form a Hypothesis

Based on your knowledge of your neighborhood, form a hypothesis to explain whether all areas in your community contain the same types and amounts of particulate matter.

Possible Materials

small box of plain gelatin
hot plate
pan or pot
water
marker
refrigerator
plastic lids (4)
microscope
**magnifying lens*
**Alternate materials*

Goals

- **Design** an experiment to collect and analyze particulate matter in the air in your community.
- **Observe and describe** the particulate matter you collect.

Safety Precautions

WARNING: *Wear a thermal mitt, safety goggles, and an apron while working with a hot plate and while pouring the gelatin from the pan or pot into the lids. Never eat anything in the lab.*

Test Your Hypothesis

Make a Plan

- ❑ **1.** As a group, agree upon your hypothesis and decide how you will test it.
- ❑ **2. List** the steps you need to take to test your hypotheses. Describe exactly what you will do at each step. List your materials.
- ❑ **3. Record** your observations in the data table on the next page.
- ❑ **4. Label** your lids with the location where you decide to place them.
- ❑ **5. Mix** the gelatin according to the directions on the box. Carefully pour a thin layer of gelatin into each lid. Use this to collect air particulate matter.
- ❑ **6. Read** over your entire experiment to make sure that all steps are in a logical order.
- ❑ **7. Identify** any constants, variables, and controls of the experiment.

(continued)

LAB B

Follow Your Plan

❑ 1. Make sure your teacher approves your plan.
❑ 2. Carry out the experiment as planned.
❑ 3. **Record** any observations that you make and complete the data table below.

Put graph here:

Data and Observations

Lid Number	Type of Material	Number of Particles	Description of Material
1			
2			
3			
4			

Analyze Your Data

1. **Describe** the types of materials you collected in each lid.

2. **Calculate** the number of particles on each lid.

3. **Compare and contrast** your controls and your variables in this experiment.

4. **Graph** your results using a bar graph. Place the number of particulates on the *y*-axis and the test-site location on the *x*-axis.

Conclude and Apply

1. **Determine** if the results support your hypothesis.

2. **Explain** why different sizes of particulate matter may be found at different locations.

3. **Infer** why some test-site locations showed more particulates than other sites did.

Name Date Class

(continued) **LAB B**

Challenge

1. **Infer** Do you think you were able to count all of the particulate? Why or why not?

2. **Apply** Some people are allergic to dust and pollen in the air. What types of precautions could they take to reduce exposure to these particulate sources?

3. **Hypothesize** Based on your results, in what areas of your classroom or home would you expect to find the most particulate matter in the air?

Extension

Create Your nose uses filters (hairs and mucus) to keep particulate out of your lungs. Design a filter for your sample collection container. What characteristics would make a good filter? How would it keep the particles out of the sample while still allowing the sample to get air? How would the filter be attached? Test your filter to see how well it filters out particulate.

Communicating Your Data

Develop Multimedia Presentations Give an oral presentation of your experiment on air pollution in your community to another class. **For more help, refer to the Science Skills Handbook.**

Name _______________ Date _______________ Class _______________

Our Impact on Water and Air

I. Testing Concepts

Directions: *Match each description on the left with the correct term. Write the letter of the correct term in the blank.*

Matching Set I

_____ 1. a measure of the acidity or alkalinity of a substance

_____ 2. substance with a pH lower than 7

_____ 3. substance with a pH above 7

_____ 4. precipitation with a pH below 5.6

a. acid

b. base

c. pH scale

d. acid rain

Matching Set II

_____ 5. chemical that helps plants grow

_____ 6. pollution that enters water from a large area, such as a lawn or construction site

_____ 7. pollution that enters water from a specific location, such as a drainpipe or ditch

_____ 8. substance that destroys pests

a. pesticide

b. fertilizer

c. point source pollution

d. nonpoint source pollution

Directions: *Circle the word or words that complete the sentence.*

9. Human waste, detergents, and soaps that go down drains are called (discharge, sewage).

10. The hazy, yellowish-brown blanket of smog that is sometimes found over cities is called (photochemical smog, particulate matter).

11. The (nitrogen, carbon monoxide) gas found in car exhaust can make people ill.

12. Some coal-burning power plants have (drizzle basins, scrubbers) that remove carbon dioxide from the smoke.

13. (Acid rain, Particulate matter) consists of fine particles such as dust, pollen, mold, ash, and soot that are in the air.

Name Date Class

Chapter Test A (continued)

II. Understanding Concepts

Skill: Concept Mapping

1. Use these sentences to complete the events-chain map showing how fertilizers can cause water pollution.

Algae grow and multiply.
Algae decompose and use up oxygen.
Without enough oxygen, fish may die.
Fertilizer runs off into the water.

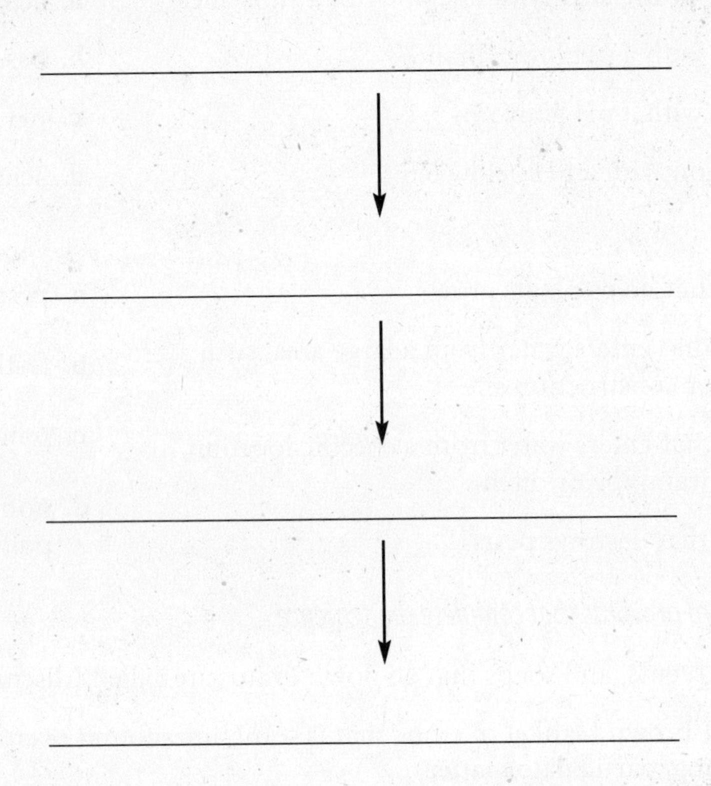

Skill: Categorizing

Directions: *Place an* **X** *by the sources of air pollution.*

_______ 2. car exhaust

_______ 3. burning fuels in factories

_______ 4. scrubbers

_______ 5. dust from plowed fields

_______ 6. the generation of electricity

_______ 7. volcanic eruptions

_______ 8. dust from construction sites

_______ 9. radon gas

Chapter Test A (continued)

Skill: Sequencing

Directions: *Number the sentences below to show the steps followed in a sewage treatment plant.*

_______ **10.** The sewage flows into the primary settling tank.

_______ **11.** Bacteria are killed by adding chlorine, ultraviolet rays, or ozone.

_______ **12.** Metal screens remove large solids.

_______ **13.** The water flows to a trickling bed and sand filter before it is discharged.

_______ **14.** The wastewater is pumped from the primary tank to a bed of gravel.

_______ **15.** The sewage flows to a secondary settling tank.

Skill: Cause and Effect

Directions: *Identify the cause in each pairing.*

16. _______________ Exposure to pollutants causes cancer.

_______________ Oil and gasoline run off roads into streams and rivers when it rains.

17. _______________ At gas stations, old gasoline tanks were made of steel.

_______________ Tanks rusted and leaked, damaging the water supply.

18. _______________ Hot water reduces the amount of oxygen available for plants and animals.

_______________ A factory releases hot water into a stream.

III. Applying Concepts

Writing Skills

Directions: *Respond to the following using complete sentences.*

1. Identify What are three things you can do to conserve water and reduce water pollution?

____

____

____

2. Explain How can air pollution affect your health?

____

____

____

____

____

Chapter Test A (continued)

3. **Restate** What are two ways you can help reduce air pollution?

4. **Explain** The weather report indicates that the smog level is high. What does this mean?

5. **Describe** Tell about one way the United States has worked toward reducing water pollution.

Name Date Class

Chapter Test B

Our Impact on Water and Air

I. Testing Concepts

Directions: *For each of the following, write the letter of the term or phrase that best completes the sentence.*

______ **1.** One cause of air pollution is ______.
a. acid rain
b. burning fossil fuels
c. water pollution
d. bases

______ **2.** A combination of smoke and fog is ______.
a. oxygen **b.** acid rain **c.** fossil fuels **d.** smog

______ **3.** A brown smog formed with the aid of sunlight is ______ smog.
a. nitrogen **b.** photochemical **c.** natural gas **d.** oxygen

______ **4.** In the US, ______ are responsible for much of the makeup of smog.
a. cars **b.** factories **c.** farms **d.** fertilizers

______ **5.** Burning fossil fuels in electrical power plants helps create ______.
a. ozone
b. ultraviolet radiation
c. sulfurous smog
d. trapped air layers

______ **6.** Smog development is affected naturally by ______.
a. the pH scale
b. the greenhouse effect
c. landforms
d. all of these

______ **7.** Sunlight reacts with waste gases to form ______.
a. carbon dioxide
b. ultraviolet radiation
c. ozone
d. none of these

______ **8.** Acid rain is created when emissions from coal-burning power plants combine with moisture to form ______.
a. sulfur dioxide
b. sulfuric acid
c. cooler air
d. photochemical smog

______ **9.** A consequence of acid rain is ______.
a. damage to buildings
b. lower pH in lakes and streams
c. damage to forests
d. all of these

______ **10.** A measure of the strength of an acid can be obtained using ______.
a. an acid **b.** a base **c.** a pH scale **d.** all of these

______ **11.** Air pollution affects people's ______.
a. lungs **b.** eyes **c.** blood **d.** all of these

______ **12.** Diplomats from around the world have focused on eliminating the use of ______.
a. fossil fuels
b. chlorofluorocarbons
c. sulfur dioxide
d. none of these

Chapter Test B (continued)

______ **13.** Ways to support the Clean Air Act include ______.
a. using less electricity
b. driving more frequently
c. cutting down on public transportation
d. developing more coal-burning power plants

______ **14.** Mountains may contribute to smog formation by ______.
a. emitting sulfurous compounds
b. blocking clouds
c. blocking air circulation
d. limiting water runoff

______ **15.** Air pollution can be controlled by ______.
a. permitting more storm water runoff
b. burning more coal
c. eliminating hard water
d. putting scrubbers on power plants

______ **16.** A way for individuals to reduce water pollution is to ______.
a. plant forests
b. reduce electricity use
c. drive everywhere
d. add to the acidity of garden soil

______ **17.** Inhaling the humid air of acid rain can ______.
a. damage your lungs
b. sting your eyes
c. cause a headache
d. interfere with oxygen absorption

______ **18.** A way for individual citizens to improve air quality is to ______.
a. reduce industrial pollution
b. take fewer showers
c. burn trash
d. use public transportation

______ **19.** Some coal contains a high amount of ______.
a. oxygen **b.** nitrogen **c.** sulfur **d.** none of these

______ **20.** Acid rain is more of a problem in ______.
a. the desert **b.** cities **c.** humid areas **d.** rural areas

______ **21.** Water pollutants include ______.
a. bacteria
b. oil and gasoline
c. runoff from mines
d. all of these

______ **22.** Farms often pollute water through the use of ______.
a. pesticides and fertilizers
b. hospital waste
c. motor oil
d. all of these

______ **23.** An example of a polluted water source that has improved because of cooperation between the United States and Canada is ______.
a. the Colorado River
b. Lake Erie
c. the Atlantic Ocean
d. the Mississippi River

Name Date Class

Chapter Test B (continued)

II. Understanding Concepts

Skill: Concept Mapping

Directions: *Complete the concept map using the terms in the list below.*

coal	**gasoline**	**ozone**
sunlight	**nitrogen**	**oxygen**

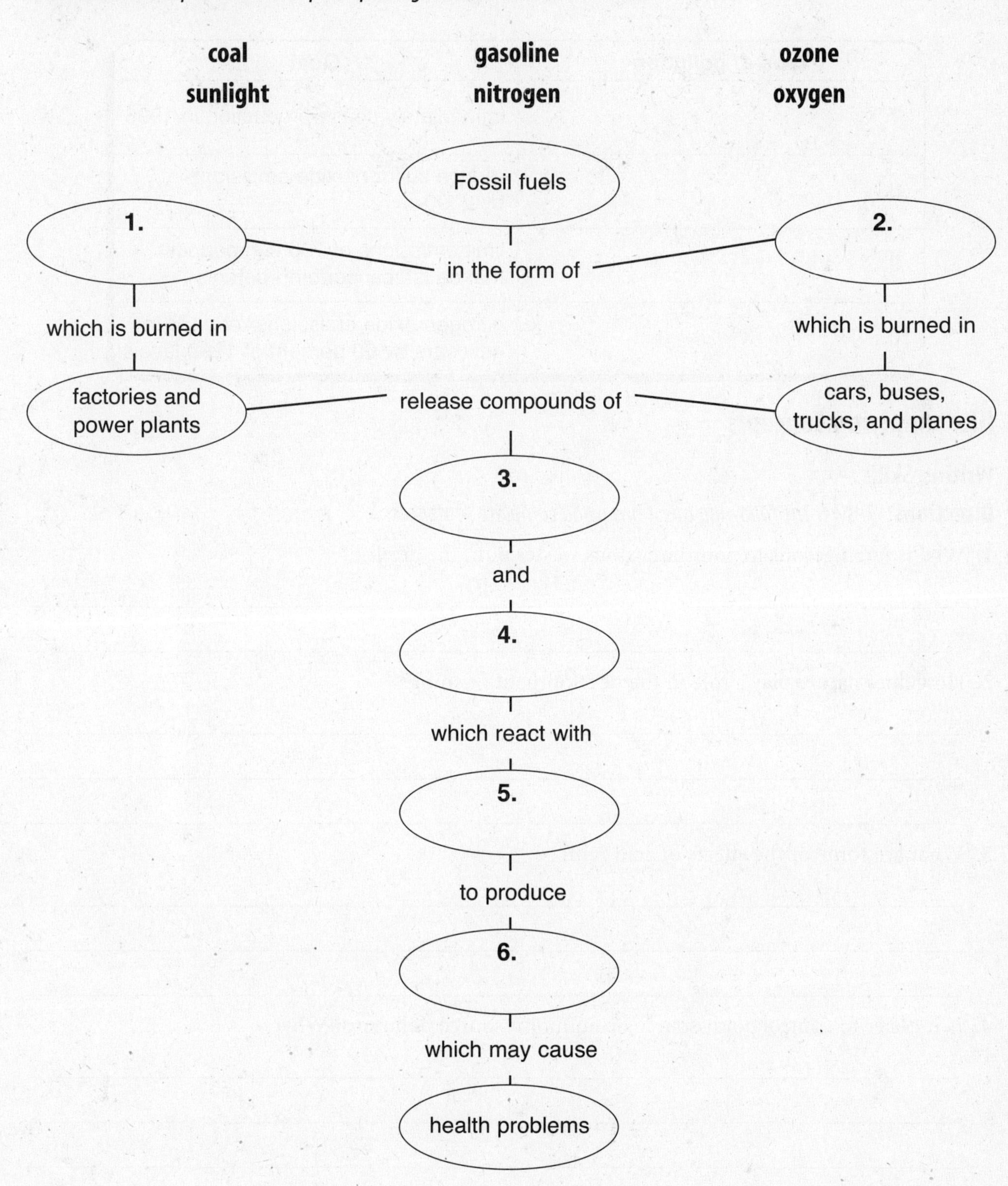

Name Date Class

Chapter Test B (continued)

Skill: Using Tables

Directions: *Complete the table below that shows the goals of the 1990 Clean Air Act using the terms below.*

acid rain **airborne toxins** **urban air pollution** **ozone-depleting chemicals**

Type of pollution	Goal
7.	immediately cease production in 1996
8.	reduce sulfur dioxide emissions by 2000
9.	limit emissions of 200 compounds that cause cancer/birth defects
10.	nitrogen oxide emissions reduced in new cars by 60 percent of 1990 levels

III. Applying Concepts

Writing Skills

Directions: *Answer the following questions using complete sentences.*

1. Why is it dangerous to pour hazardous wastes onto the ground?

____

____

2. How does nature play a role in the development of smog?

____

____

____

3. What are some of the effects of acid rain?

____

____

____

4. Is it easier to control point source or nonpoint source pollution? Why?

____

____

____

Chapter Test C

Our Impact on Water and Air

I. Testing Concepts

Directions: *Fill in the blank(s) to complete the sentences.*

1. The ______________________________, written in 1971, provided funds to build sewage-treatment facilities.
2. Conserving water reduces ______________________ and ______________________.
3. Water from your home containing ____________________ must be purified before being returned to the environment.
4. During a(n) ______________________, warm air traps cool air near the ground.
5. Acid rain is precipitation with a pH below ____________________.
6. Smaller ____________________ are more dangerous because they can travel deeper into the lungs.
7. ____________________ in coal-burning power plants can be removed by passing smoke through a(n) ____________________.
8. Newer cars are equipped with ______________________, which reduce automobile emissions.

II. Understanding Concepts

Skill: Contrasting

Directions: *Contrast the two terms.*

1. point source pollution and nonpoint source pollution

____

____

2. pesticides and fertilizers

____

____

3. acids and bases

____

____

Chapter Test C (continued)

Skill: Cause and Effect

Directions: *Write an effect for each cause.*

4. Oil and gasoline run off roads into streams and rivers when it rains.

5. A gas station has an old gasoline tank made of steel.

6. A mine uses mercury to trap gold and separate it from sediment.

Skill: Sequencing

7. Write the steps of sewage treatment.

Skill: Concept Mapping

8. Create an events-chain map to show how fertilizers can cause water pollution.

Skill: Creating a Table

9. Create a table explaining the 1990 Clean Air Act, with a column for the type of pollution targeted and a column for the goal associated with that target.

Chapter Test C (continued)

III. Applying Concepts

Writing Skills

Directions: *Respond to the following using complete sentences.*

1. **Infer** A new housing development is being built on a previously wooded area. The new residents notice that the water in the neighboring stream is becoming increasingly cloudy. What could be the cause? Should the residents be concerned?

2. **Infer** Fish are dying in a pond near a city's power plant. The water has been tested for metals and other pollutants, and none were detected. What else should be tested? Why?

3. **Analyze** There are two cities of similar size and amount of industrial activity. One has higher smog levels than the other. What might explain the difference?

4. **Analyze** Why is it sometimes challenging to create legislation to limit air pollution?

Chapter Test C (continued)

5. **Critique** Suppose you read an article that claims that air pollution is a human-made problem. How would you respond to this?

Name Date Class

Use the Internet
Star Sightings

LAB A

For thousands of years, people have measured their position on Earth using the position of Polaris, the North Star. At any given observation point, it always appears at the same angle above the horizon. For example, at the North Pole, Polaris appears directly overhead, and at the equator, it is just above the northern horizon. Other locations can be determined by measuring the height of Polaris above the horizon using an instrument called an astrolabe. Could you use Polaris to determine the size of Earth?

Real-World Question
You know that Earth is round. Knowing this, do you think you can estimate the circumference of Earth based on star sightings?

Form a Hypothesis
Think about what you have learned about sightings of Polaris. How does this tell you that Earth is round? Knowing that Earth is round, form a hypothesis about how you can estimate the circumference of Earth based on star sightings.

Goals
- **Record** your sightings of Polaris.
- **Share** the data with other students to calculate the circumference of Earth.

Safety Precautions
WARNING: *Do not use the astrolabe during the daytime to observe the Sun.*

Data Sources
Science Online Go to **msscience.com** for more information about health risks from heavy metals, hints on health risks, and data from other students.

Make a Plan
❑ 1. Obtain an astrolabe or construct one using the instructions posted by visiting the link below.

❑ 2. **Record** your information in the Data and Observations table.

❑ 3. Decide as a group how you will make your observations. Does it take more than one person to make each observation? When will it be easiest to see Polaris?

Follow Your Plan
❑ 1. Make sure your teacher approves your plan before you start.

❑ 2. Carry out your observations.

❑ 3. **Record** your observations in the data table in the Data and Observations section.

❑ 4. Average your readings and post them in the table provided at the link shown below.

 (continued)

LAB A

Analyze Your Data

1. **Research** the names of cities that are at approximately the same longitude as your hometown. Gather astrolabe readings at **msscience.com** from students in one of those cities.
2. **Compare** your astrolabe readings. Subtract the smaller reading from the larger one.

____

3. **Determine** the distance between your star sighting location and the other city.

____

____

4. **Calculate** the circumference of Earth using the following relationship:

$$\text{Circumference} = (360°) \times \frac{\text{(distance between locations)}}{\text{difference between readings}}$$

____

Data and Observations

Polaris Observations		
Your Location:		
Date	Time	Astrolabe Reading

Conclude and Apply

1. **Analyze** how the circumference of Earth that you calculated compares with the accepted value of 40,079 km.

____

____

____

2. **Determine** some possible sources of error in this method of establishing the size of Earth. What improvements would you suggest?

____

____

____

____

LAB (continued)

LAB A

Communicating Your Data

Find this lab using the link below. **Create** a poster that includes a table of your data and data from students in other cities. **Perform** a sample circumference calculation for your class.

Science Online **msscience.com**

Use the Internet

Star Sightings

LAB B

For thousands of years, people have measured their position on Earth using the position of Polaris, the North Star. At any given observation point, it always appears at the same angle above the horizon. For example, at the North Pole, Polaris appears directly overhead, and at the equator, it is just above the northern horizon. Other locations can be determined by measuring the height of Polaris above the horizon using an instrument called an astrolabe. Could you use Polaris to determine the size of Earth?

Real-World Question

You know that Earth is round. Knowing this, do you think you can estimate the circumference of Earth based on star sightings?

Form a Hypothesis

Think about what you have learned about sightings of Polaris. How does this tell you that Earth is round? Knowing that Earth is round, form a hypothesis about how you can estimate the circumference of Earth based on star sightings.

Goals

- **Record** your sightings of Polaris.
- **Share** the data with other students to calculate the circumference of Earth.

Safety Precautions

WARNING: *Do not use the astrolabe during the daytime to observe the Sun.*

Data Sources

Science Online Go to **msscience.com** for more information about health risks from heavy metals, hints on health risks, and data from other students.

Make a Plan

❑ **1.** Obtain an astrolabe or construct one using the instructions posted by visiting the link below.

❑ **2.** Record your information in the Data and Observations table.

❑ **3.** Decide as a group how you will make your observations. Does it take more than one person to make each observation? When will it be easiest to see Polaris?

Follow Your Plan

❑ **1.** Make sure your teacher approves your plan before you start.

❑ **2.** Carry out your observations.

❑ **3.** **Record** your observations in the data table in the Data and Observations section.

❑ **4.** Average your readings and post them in the table provided at the link shown below.

(continued)

Analyze Your Data

1. **Research** the names of cities that are at approximately the same longitude as your hometown. Gather astrolabe readings at **msscience.com** from students in one of those cities.
2. **Compare** your astrolabe readings. Subtract the smaller reading from the larger one.

   ____

3. **Determine** the distance between your star sighting location and the other city.

   ____

4. **Calculate** the circumference of Earth using the following relationship:

$$\text{Circumference} = (360°) \times \frac{\text{(distance between locations)}}{\text{difference between readings}}$$

   ____

Data and Observations

Polaris Observations		
Your Location:		
Date	Time	Astrolabe Reading

Conclude and Apply

1. **Analyze** how the circumference of Earth that you calculated compares with the accepted value of 40,079 km.

   ____

2. **Determine** some possible sources of error in this method of establishing the size of Earth. What improvements would you suggest?

   ____

   ____

   ____

Challenge

1. **Reason** The closest star to our own, Proxima Centauri, is 4.2 light-years away from Earth. Light travels at 300,000 km/sec in a vacuum, and one light-year is the distance light covers in a year's time. When we look at Proxima Centauri in a telescope, how old is the image we are seeing?

   ____

LAB (continued) **LAB B**

2. **Deduce** Why is there a North Star and a South Star but not an East Star or a West Star?

3. **Reason** If an astronomical object put out no visible light at all, would we know it was there? Why or why not?

Extension

Visualize yourself standing on the North Pole and looking at the North Star. How far south can you go while still being able to see it? Make a drawing to help you figure out the answer. Use a ruler to draw straight lines to represent the line of sight possible from different positions on the globe.

Communicating Your Data

Find this lab using the link below. **Create** a poster that includes a table of your data and data from students in other cities. **Perform** a sample circumference calculation for your class.

Science Online msscience.com

Name Date Class

Chapter Test A — Exploring Space

I. Testing Concepts

Directions: *Use the following words and phrases to identify the numbered parts of the illustration:* **space station, space shuttle, space probe, Earth,** *and* **Moon.**

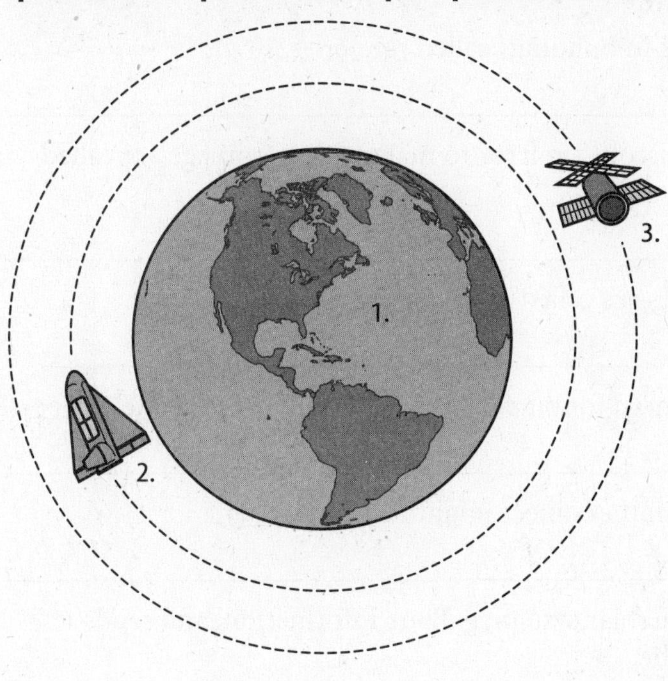

1. ______________________
2. ______________________
3. ______________________
4. ______________________
5. space probe

Directions: *In the blank on the left, write the letter of the term that best completes each statement.*

______ 6. Two types of telescopes are optical and ______.
 a. radio b. audio c. visual d. vertical

______ 7. When you look out into space, you are also looking ______ in time.
 a. back b. forward c. at yourself d. faster

______ 8. Sound waves can't travel ______.
 a. underwater b. in air c. in a vacuum d. through wood

______ 9. Light moves at ______ km/sec in a vacuum.
 a. 3,000 b. 30,000 c. 300,000 d. 3,000,000

______ 10. If it uses a convex lens to gather light, it must be a(n) ______ telescope.
 a. reflecting b. refracting c. recycling d. orbital

Chapter Test A (continued)

______ **11.** If it uses a concave mirror to gather light, it must be a(n) ______ telescope.
a. reflecting **b.** refracting **c.** recycling **d.** orbital

Directions: *Identify each statement as* **true** *or* **false**. *Rewrite the underlined words in the false statements to make them true.*

______ **12.** Most optical telescopes are housed in buildings called refineries.

____

______ **13.** Computers rapidly adjusting a telescope's mirror to make a clearer image are called active optics.

____

______ **14.** Telescopes that pick up radio waves are called radio telescopes.

____

______ **15.** Engines that have everything they need for burning their own fuel are called telescopes.

____

______ **16.** Any object that revolves around another object might be called a star.

____

______ **17.** An instrument that travels into the solar system, gathers information, and sends it back to Earth is called a space probe.

____

II. Understanding Concepts

Skill: Comparing and Contrasting

Directions: *Answer the following questions on the lines provided.*

1. Compare and contrast a land-based telescope with the Hubble Space Telescope.

____

____

____

____

____

Chapter Test A (continued)

2. Compare exploring a planet with a telescope and exploring it with a space probe.

______

______

______

______

______

Directions: *Match each term on the left with the correct description.*

Matching Set 1

______	3. space shuttle	a. orbits Earth with no people on board
______	4. space probe	b. orbits Earth with people on board
______	5. space telescope	c. orbits other planets

Matching Set 2

______	6. the Moon	d. closest to Earth
______	7. Mars	e. farthest from Earth
______	8. the Sun	f. not as close to Earth as one, not as far from Earth as the other

III. Applying Concepts

Writing Skills

Directions: *Answer the following questions.*

1. **Differentiate** How is a space station different from a space shuttle?

______

______

______

______

______

2. **Rearrange** Put the following in order from largest to smallest: ***Saturn***, ***the Sun***, ***the Moon***, ***a space station***, ***Earth***, and ***an astronaut***.

______

______

Chapter Test B

Exploring Space

I. Testing Concepts

Directions: *Circle the term that correctly completes the sentence.*

1. The Moon orbiting Earth is an example of a(n) (artificial, natural) satellite.

2. In a (reflecting, refracting) telescope, light passes through convex lenses.

3. The *Hubble Space Telescope* is an example of a (reflecting, refracting) telescope.

4. The space probe (*Cassini, Voyager*) was launched in 1997 to study Saturn.

5. The arrangement of electromagnetic radiation according to wavelengths is the (electromagnetic spectrum, electromagnetic waves).

6. (Project Mercury, Project Apollo) was the first stage in the space program designed to send Americans to the Moon.

7. The *Voyagers* are (satellites, space probes) that have traveled beyond our solar system.

8. On a (space shuttle, space station), astronauts can live and work in space for long periods of time.

9. (Optical, Radio) telescopes allow us to study the visible light radiated by the stars.

10. A(n) (artificial, natural) satellite is one that is built and launched by humans.

11. As part of (Project Gemini, Project Apollo), Neil Armstrong and Edwin Aldrin became the first humans to walk on the Moon.

12. A goal of (Project Mercury, Project Gemini) was to link two spacecraft together while they were in orbit.

13. Most (radio, optical) telescopes used by professional astronomers are housed in observatories.

14. A (reflecting, refracting) telescope uses concave mirrors to focus light.

15. Space stations are (satellites, space probes).

16. Because it can be used more than once to send people into space, the (space station, space shuttle) saves resources.

17. (Radio, Optical) telescopes are useful under most weather conditions and at all times of night and day.

18. In the future, the (space shuttle, space station) could be a construction site for ships traveling to the Moon and Mars.

19. A (space shuttle, space station) is able to land like an airplane.

Name Date Class

Chapter Test B (continued)

Directions: *Use these words and phrases to identify the numbered parts of the illustration:* **space station, space shuttle, space probe, Earth, Moon.**

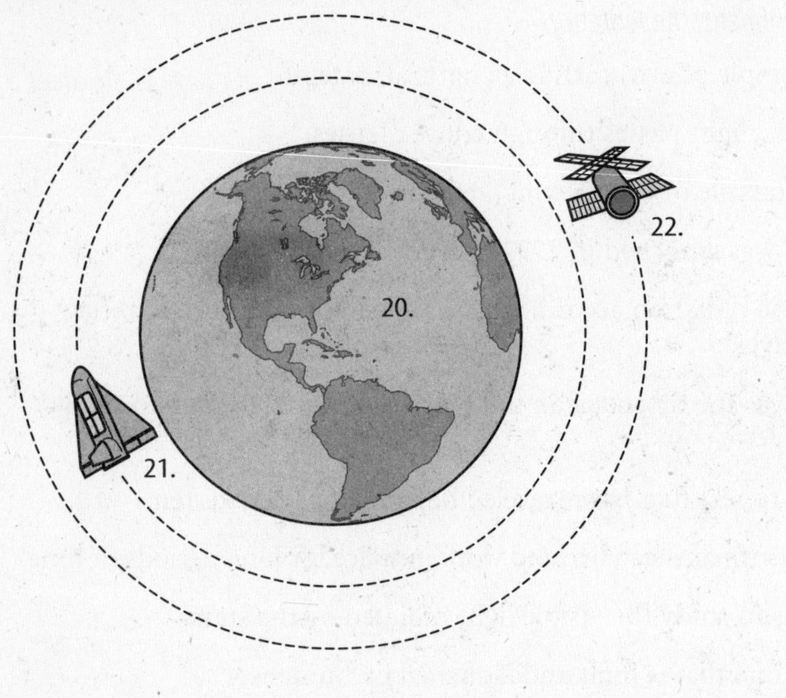

20. ______________________________

21. ______________________________

22. ______________________________

23. ______________________________

24. ______________________________

II. Understanding Concepts

Skill: Sequencing

1. Place the various forms of radiant energy in the electromagnetic spectrum in sequence from longest to shortest wavelength. Number the radiant energy with the longest wavelength *1*.

______ **a.** infrared waves

______ **b.** ultraviolet waves

______ **c.** visible light

______ **d.** microwaves

______ **e.** gamma rays

______ **f.** radio waves

______ **g.** X rays

Name ______ Date ______ Class ______

Chapter Test B (continued)

Skill: Concept Mapping

Directions: *Write* **true** *in the blank if the statement is true. If the statement is false, change the boldfaced term to make the statement true and write the new term in the blank.*

______ 2. In an events-chain concept map of the race to the Moon, Project Gemini would follow **Project Mercury.**

______ 3. In a network-tree concept map of the race for space, *Sputnik* would be listed under the **U.S.** space program.

Skill: Outlining

Directions: *Answer the following questions on the lines provided.*

4. In an outline of the American space program, John Glenn orbiting Earth would be listed under which space project?

______

5. How would an entry for space shuttles be included in an outline for an article about spacecraft?

______

______

III. Applying Concepts

Writing Skills

Directions: *Answer the following questions using complete sentences.*

1. Can you study visible light using a radio telescope? Explain your answer.

______

______

______

2. How are orbital space stations useful?

______

______

______

______

Name Date Class

Chapter Test B (continued)

3. **Compare** and **contrast** refracting and reflecting telescopes.

4. **Summarize** the importance of Projects Mercury, Gemini, and Apollo.

5. Should the government of the United States continue to finance the space shuttle program? Why or why not?

6. What are some of the exciting things planned for future space missions?

7. **Describe** the difference between solid-propellant rockets and liquid-propellant rockets.

Name ______________________ Date ______________________ Class ______________________

Chapter Test C

Exploring Space

I. Testing Concepts

Directions: *In the blank, write the term that best completes each statement or answers the question.*

1. All forms of electromagnetic radiation, arranged according to wavelength, make up the electromagnetic ____________________.

2. What is the speed of light in a vacuum? ____________________

3. Electromagnetic waves with frequencies between 10^{14} and 10^{15} Hz make up what we call ____________________.

4. If it uses a convex lens to gather light, it must be a(n) ____________________ telescope.

5. If it uses a concave mirror to gather light, it must be a(n) ____________________ telescope.

6. Using lasers to probe the atmosphere for turbulence and adjust the telescope accordingly is called ____________________.

Directions: *Use these words and phrases to identify the numbered parts of the illustration:* **space station**, **space shuttle**, **space probe**, **Earth**, *and* **Moon**.

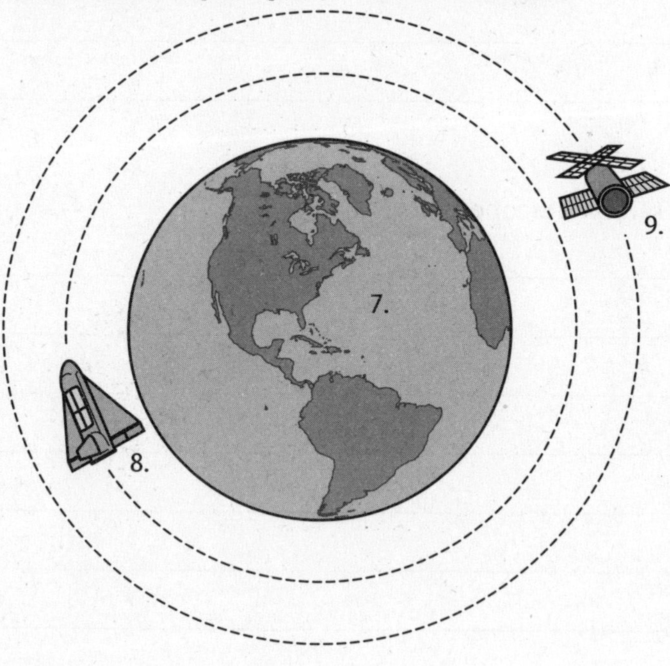

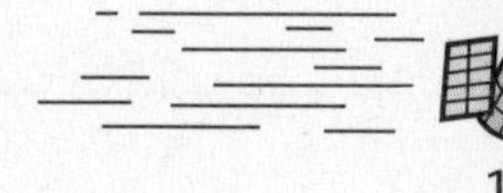

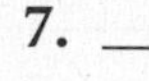
7. ____

8. ____

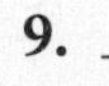
9. ____

10. ____

11. ____

Chapter Test C (continued)

II. Understanding Concepts

Directions: *Answer the following questions on the lines provided.*

Skill: Making Generalizations

1. Suppose someone said, "The only thing a telescope really sees is light." How would you respond?

2. Suppose that when your friend learned about radio waves, she decided to call them "light you can't see." How would you respond to this odd-sounding claim?

Skill: Comparing and Contrasting

3. Compare and contrast light telescopes with radio telescopes.

Chapter Test C (continued)

III. Applying Concepts

Writing Skills

Directions: *Answer the following question on the lines provided.*

1. **Suppose** a friend says he has invented a time machine. Excited, you go over to his house, where he unveils . . . a telescope. How would you respond?

Directions: *Write a multiparagraph essay on the following question. Use additional sheets of paper if necessary.*

2. **Suppose** The Hubble Space Telescope has given us many of the best images of outer space ever seen. Do you think moving a telescope even farther away would make for even better images? Why or why not?

Name Date Class

Tilt and Temperature

LAB A

Lab Preview

Directions: *Answer these questions before you begin the Lab.*

1. Why are the particular safety precautions suggested?

____

2. At what possible angle do you think your paper will be the hottest?

____

If you walk on blacktop pavement at noon, you can feel the effect of solar energy. The Sun's rays hit at the highest angle at midday. Now consider the fact that Earth is tilted on its axis. How does this tilt affect the angle at which light rays strike an area on Earth? How is the angle of the light rays related to the amount of heat energy and the changing seasons?

Real-World Question

How does the angle at which light strikes Earth affect the amount of heat energy received by any area on Earth?

Materials

tape
black construction paper (one sheet)
gooseneck lamp with 75-watt bulb
Celsius thermometer
watch
protractor

Goals

- **Measure** the temperature change in a surface after light strikes it at different angles.
- **Describe** how the angle of light relates to seasons on Earth.

Safety Precautions

WARNING: *Do not touch the lamp without safety gloves. The lightbulb and shade can be hot even when the lamp has been turned off. Handle the thermometer carefully. If it breaks, do not touch anything. Inform your teacher immediately.*

Procedure

❏ 1. **Choose** three angles that you will use to aim the light at the paper.

❏ 2. **Determine** how long you will shine the light at each angle before you measure the temperature. You will measure the temperature at two times for each angle. Use the same time periods for each angle.

❏ 3. In the table on the next page, record the temperature the paper reaches at each angle and time.

❏ 4. **Form** a pocket out of a sheet of black construction paper and tape it to a desk or the floor.

❏ 5. Using the protractor, set the gooseneck lamp so that it will shine on the paper at one of the angles you chose.

❏ 6. Place the thermometer in the paper pocket. Turn on the lamp.
- ❏ Use the thermometer to measure the temperature of the paper at the end of the first time period.
- ❏ Continue shining the lamp on the paper until the second time period has passed. Measure the temperature again.
- ❏ **Record** your data in your data table.

(continued)

❑ 7. Turn off the lamp until the paper cools to room temperature. Repeat steps 5 and 6 using your other two angles.

Data and Observations

Temperature Data

Angle of Lamp	Initial Temperature (°C)	Temperature at ___ Minutes/Seconds	Temperature at ___ Minutes/Seconds
First angle			
Second angle			
Third angle			

Conclude and Apply

1. **Describe** your experiment. Identify the variables in your experiment. Which were your independent and dependent variables?

____

____

____

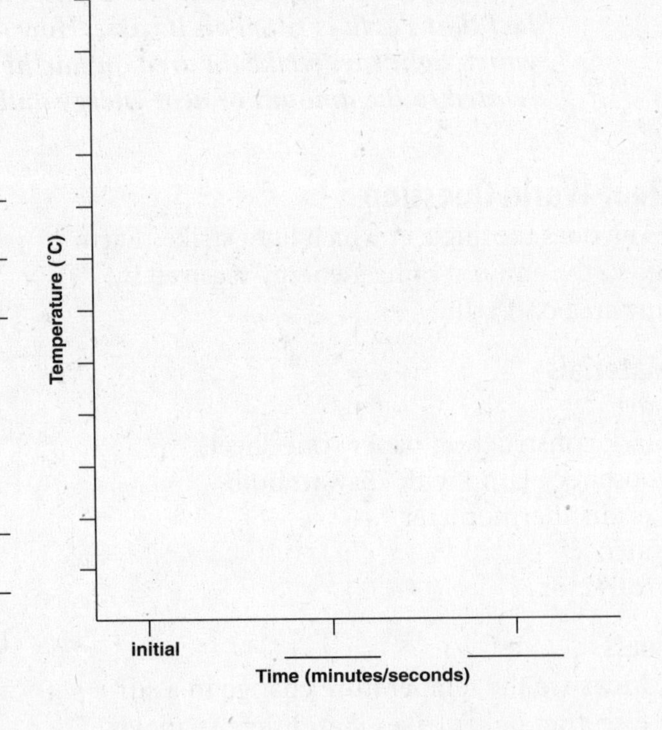

2. **Graph** Record your data using a line graph. Use a different color for each angle. Describe what your graph tells you about the data.

____

____

3. **Describe** what happened to the temperature of the paper as you changed the angle of light.

____

____

4. **Predict** how your results might have been different if you used white paper. Explain why.

____

____

(continued) **LAB A**

5. **Describe** how the results of this experiment apply to seasons on Earth.

Communicating Your Data

Compare your results with those of other students in your class. **Discuss** how the different angles and time periods affected the temperatures.

Tilt and Temperature

LAB B

Lab Preview

Directions: *Answer these questions before you begin the Lab.*

1. Why are the particular safety precautions suggested?

____

2. At what possible angle do you think your paper will be the hottest?

____

If you walk on blacktop pavement at noon, you can feel the effect of solar energy. The Sun's rays hit at the highest angle at midday. Now consider the fact that Earth is tilted on its axis. How does this tilt affect the angle at which light rays strike an area on Earth? How is the angle of the light rays related to the amount of heat energy and the changing seasons?

Real-World Question

How does the angle at which light strikes Earth affect the amount of heat energy received by any area on Earth?

Materials

tape
black construction paper (one sheet)
gooseneck lamp with 75-watt bulb
Celsius thermometer
watch
protractor

Goals

- **Measure** the temperature change in a surface after light strikes it at different angles.
- **Describe** how the angle of light relates to seasons on Earth.

Safety Precautions

WARNING: *Do not touch the lamp without safety gloves. The lightbulb and shade can be hot even when the lamp has been turned off. Handle the thermometer carefully. If it breaks, do not touch anything. Inform your teacher immediately.*

Procedure

- ❑ 1. **Choose** three angles that you will use to aim the light at the paper.
- ❑ 2. **Determine** how long you will shine the light at each angle before you measure the temperature. You will measure the temperature at two times for each angle. Use the same time periods for each angle.
- ❑ 3. In the table on the next page, record the temperature the paper reaches at each angle and time.
- ❑ 4. **Form** a pocket out of a sheet of black construction paper and tape it to a desk or the floor.
- ❑ 5. Using the protractor, set the gooseneck lamp so that it will shine on the paper at one of the angles you chose.
- ❑ 6. Place the thermometer in the paper pocket. Turn on the lamp. Use the thermometer to measure the temperature of the paper at the end of the first time period. Continue shining the lamp on the paper until the second time period has passed. Measure the temperature again. Record your data in your data table.

(continued)

❑ 7. Turn off the lamp until the paper cools to room temperature. Repeat steps 5 and 6 using your other two angles.

Data and Observations

Temperature Data

Angle of Lamp	Initial Temperature (°C)	Temperature at ___ Minutes/Seconds	Temperature at ___ Minutes/Seconds
First angle			
Second angle			
Third angle			

Conclude and Apply

1. **Describe** your experiment. Identify the variables in your experiment. Which were your independent and dependent variables?

2. **Graph** your data using a line graph. Describe what your graph tells you about the data.

3. **Describe** what happened to the temperature of the paper as you changed the angle of light.

Put graph here:

4. **Predict** how your results might have been different if you used white paper. Explain why.

Name Date Class

 (continued)

LAB B

5. **Describe** how the results of this experiment apply to seasons on Earth.

___

___

___

Challenge

1. **Compare** How did your graph compare to others? Analyze the differences.

___

___

___

2. **Critique** Is this an accurate model of what causes unequal distribution of heat? Why or why not?

___

___

___

3. **Explain** Would you expect other planets to have similar temperature variations?

___

___

___

Extension

Revise Rewrite your lab to use a spherical surface for recording heat. Make marks at three different locations to record the heat at each angle. What new materials will you need? How will you need to revise your procedures? Do you expect to see differences in the heat? Why or why not? Share your findings with your class.

Communicating Your Data

Compare your results with those of other students in your class. **Discuss** how the different angles and time periods affected the temperatures.

The Sun-Earth-Moon System

I. Testing Concepts

Directions: *Match each description on the left with the correct term on the right. Write the letter of the correct term in the blank at the left.*

______ **1.** the spinning of Earth on its axis — **a.** rotation

______ **2.** Earth's yearly orbit around the Sun — **b.** revolution

______ **3.** day when the Sun reaches its farthest points north or south of the equator — **c.** solstice

______ **4.** point when the Sun is directly over the equator — **d.** equinox

Directions: *In the blank at the left, write the letter of the term that best completes each statement.*

______ **5.** The ______ axis of Earth differs from its rotational axis.
a. equinox **b.** polar **c.** tilted **d.** magnetic

______ **6.** The Moon revolves around Earth about once every ______ days.
a. 27.3 **b.** 21.3 **c.** 28.3 **d.** 30.3

______ **7.** During ______ phases, the illuminated portion of the Moon grows larger.
a. waning **b.** waxing **c.** crescent **d.** gibbous

______ **8.** The Moon's surface is covered with depressions called ______.
a. penumbra **b.** abrasions **c.** impact craters **d.** umbra

______ **9.** Flat, dark regions within craters are called ______.
a. clouds **b.** seas **c.** depressions **d.** maria

______ **10.** It takes around ______ days for the Moon to complete its cycle of phases.
a. 20.5 **b.** 29.5 **c.** 30.5 **d.** 21.5

______ **11.** Earth's magnetic field resembles a(n) ______.
a. bar magnet **c.** circular magnet
b. horseshoe magnet **d.** ellipse

______ **12.** Earth revolves around the Sun in a(n) ______ orbit.
a. linear **b.** spherical **c.** elliptical **d.** unpredictable

Name ____________ Date ____________ Class ____________

Chapter Test A (continued)

II. Understanding Concepts

Skill: Sequencing

Directions: *Place the following phases of the Moon during its cycle in order. Begin with the new moon.*

waning gibbous	**waxing gibbous**	**third quarter**	**first quarter**
waxing crescent	**waning crescent**	**new moon**	**full moon**

1. ____________
2. ____________
3. ____________
4. ____________
5. ____________
6. ____________
7. ____________
8. ____________

Skill: Cause and Effect

Directions: *Fill in the blanks to complete the cause and effect relationship.*

9. ____________ passing directly between ____________ and ____________ causes a lunar eclipse.

10. ____________ passing between ____________ and ____________ causes a solar eclipse.

Skill: Completing a Table

Directions: *Use the following to complete the table describing important events in the history of moon exploration.*

Apollo 8	***Luna 3***	***Surveyor 1***
Crew deploys first lunar roving vehicle.	**The last crewed Moon mission launches.**	**Neil Armstrong is the first human to walk on the Moon.**

History of Moon Exploration

11.	October 7, 1959	Russian space probe returns first pictures of the Moon's far side.
12.	June 2, 1966	The first of seven U.S. missions makes a perfect soft landing on the Moon.
13.	December 24, 1968	The first manned mission orbits the Moon.
Apollo 11	July 20, 1969	**14.**
Apollo 15	July 30, 1971	**15.**
Apollo 17	December 11, 1972	**16.**

Chapter Test A (continued)

III. Applying Concepts

Writing Skills

Directions: *Respond to the following using complete sentences.*

1. **Explain** What causes the changing seasons on Earth?

2. **Describe** What is impact theory?

3. **Explain** Why does the Moon appear to shine?

4. **Describe** Why does the Moon's appearance change at night?

5. **Interpret** Why is there more daylight at certain times of the year?

6. **Generalize** Why is Earth's magnetic pole important?

Name ______________________ Date ______________ Class ______________

The Sun-Earth-Moon System

I. Testing Concepts

Directions: *Match the terms in Column I with their definitions in Column II. Write the letter of the correct definition in the blank at the left.*

Column I	Column II
______ **1.** full moon	**a.** when the amount of the Moon's lighted surface seen on Earth increases
______ **2.** axis	**b.** an elongated, closed curve
______ **3.** rotation	**c.** waning Moon phase in which only one-half of the lighted side of the Moon can be seen from Earth
______ **4.** revolution	**d.** a round, three-dimensional object whose surface is the same distance from its center at all points
______ **5.** third quarter	**e.** the changing appearances of the Moon as seen from Earth
______ **6.** equinox	**f.** when all of the Moon's surface that faces Earth is lit up
______ **7.** solstice	**g.** dark-colored, relatively flat regions of the Moon
______ **8.** Moon phases	**h.** when the Moon temporarily blocks the sunlight reaching Earth
______ **9.** ellipse	**i.** waxing Moon phase in which one-half of the Moon's lighted side can be seen from Earth
______ **10.** waxing	**j.** reached when the Sun's position is directly over Earth's equator
______ **11.** first quarter	**k.** the imaginary line around which a planet such as Earth spins
______ **12.** new moon	**l.** when the Moon is between Earth and the Sun and cannot be seen
______ **13.** waning	**m.** the spinning of Earth on its axis
______ **14.** sphere	**n.** when Earth's shadow falls on the Moon
______ **15.** solar eclipse	**o.** when the amount of the Moon's lighted side that can be seen becomes smaller
______ **16.** lunar eclipse	**p.** the point at which the Sun reaches its greatest distance north or south of the equator
______ **17.** maria	**q.** Earth's yearly orbit around the Sun
______ **18.** impact basin	**r.** hollow area formed on the Moon by an object striking its surface

Name ____________________ Date ____________ Class ____________

Chapter Test B (continued)

Directions: *Identify each statement as true or false by writing* **T** *or* **F** *in the blank. Change the italicized words and phrases to make the false statements true.*

______ **19.** A total solar eclipse can only be seen by people in the area of Earth within the Moon's *umbra.* ______________________________

______ **20.** Earth rotates on its axis about once every *year.* ______________________________

______ **21.** Night and day on Earth are caused by Earth's *revolution around the Sun.*

____

______ **22.** The *Clementine* spacecraft provided data for a detailed map of the Moon's *surface.*

____

______ **23.** By studying moonquakes, scientists have been able to develop a model of the Moon's *interior* structure. ______________________________

______ **24.** The *summer solstice* begins in June in the northern hemisphere and in December in the southern hemisphere. ______________________________

______ **25.** Daylight hours are *shorter* for the hemisphere tilted toward the Sun. ______________

______ **26.** People are *more* likely in their lifetime to see a total lunar eclipse than they are to see a total solar eclipse. ______________________________

______ **27.** If you followed a compass needle, pointing north, you would end up at the *geographical* north pole of Earth. ______________________________

______ **28.** Impacting comets may have left *ice deposits* at the bottom of craters.

____

______ **29.** According to the *Impact Theory,* the Moon formed from gas and debris thrown off Earth after a collision. ______________________________

______ **30.** Earth is *farthest* from the Sun in January. ______________________________

Directions: *Circle the term in parentheses that makes each statement correct.*

31. Earth's orbit is a(n) (ellipse, circle) and the Sun is offset from its center, meaning that the distance between Earth and the Sun changes during the year.

32. Hours of daylight and nighttime are equal during the (solstice, equinox).

33. The Moon appears to shine because it reflects (ice, sunshine) from its surface.

34. During a solstice the Sun is (north or south of, directly above) the equator.

35. The Moon revolves around (on its axis, Earth) every 27.3 days.

Name _______________ Date _______________ Class _______________

Chapter Test B (continued)

II. Understanding Concepts

Skill: Recognizing Cause and Effect

Directions: *For each effect given, identify the cause by placing a ✓ in the blank.*

1. Scientists chose the Moon's South Pole, Aitken Basin, as the possible location for a solar-powered Moon colony.

______ **a.** Scientists discovered that the Moon's crust is thinner at Aitken Basin.

______ **b.** A large plateau that is always in sunlight was discovered in Aitken Basin. There may be ice nearby.

2. The seasons occur on Earth.

______ **a.** Earth is tilted as it revolves around the Sun.

______ **b.** Earth rotates.

3. A lunar eclipse occurs.

______ **a.** The Moon moves directly between the Sun and Earth and casts a shadow on Earth.

______ **b.** Earth is between the Moon and the Sun and casts a shadow on the Moon.

4. Spring begins in the southern hemisphere.

______ **a.** The Sun is directly above the equator.

______ **b.** The Sun has reached its northernmost point.

Skill: Measuring in SI

5. Find the volume of Earth. Earth's mass is 5.98×10^{24} kg and its average density is about 5.52 g/cm^3. Use the formula volume = $\frac{\text{mass}}{\text{density}}$. Show your work and answer in the space below.

Chapter Test B (continued)

III. Applying Concepts

Writing Skills

Directions: *Answer the following questions in complete sentences on the lines provided.*

1. **Describe** how a solar eclipse occurs.

2. How do the Moon's phases depend on the relative positions of the Sun, the Moon, and Earth?

3. What does the presence of maria on the Moon tell us about the Moon's history?

4. What would be an advantage of locating a Moon colony in an area where ice deposits from impacting comets may have collected?

Name ____________________ Date ____________________ Class ____________________

The Sun-Earth-Moon System

I. Testing Concepts

Directions: *Fill in the blanks to complete the sentences.*

1. A person standing within the ____________________ experiences a total solar eclipse.
2. A person standing within the ____________________ experiences a partial solar eclipse.
3. The *Lunar Prospector* confirmed that the Moon has a small ____________________ core.
4. *Clementine*'s cameras discovered that the Moon's crust is thinnest ____________________.
5. Sometimes sunlight bends through Earth's atmosphere, causing the eclipsed Moon to appear ____________________.
6. It takes about ____________________ days for the Moon to complete its cycle of phases and ____________________ days for the Moon to revolve around Earth.
7. The discrepancy between the two numbers above is because of ____________________.
8. The Moon seems to shine because its surface ____________________.

II. Understanding Concepts

Skill: Contrasting

Directions: *Contrast the following terms as they relate to the Sun-Earth-Moon system.*

1. rotation and revolution

____

____

2. mare and impact basin

____

____

3. solstice and equinox

____

____

4. waxing phase and waning phase

____

____

Chapter Test C (continued)

Skill: Sequencing

Directions: *Sequence the phases of the Moon during its cycle. Begin with the new moon.*

5. ______________________
6. ______________________
7. ______________________
8. ______________________
9. ______________________
10. ______________________
11. ______________________
12. ______________________

Skill: Cause and Effect

Directions: *Write a sentence to show the cause for each type of eclipse.*

13. lunar eclipse

____

14. solar eclipse

____

Skill: Creating a Table

15. Create a table showing the milestones in the history of exploration of the Moon.

Chapter Test C (continued)

III. Applying Concepts

Writing Skills

Directions: *Respond to the following using complete sentences.*

1. **Critique** A friend states that Earth's seasons are a result of Earth being farther away from the Sun at certain times of the year. How would you respond to this?

2. **Reason** A moon probe collects samples that show that the composition of the Moon's soil is similar, but not identical, to Earth's surface. Does this support the impact theory? Why or why not?

3. **Consider** If you were studying possible colonization on the Moon, which recent discoveries would be of most interest to you? Why?

4. **Evaluate** If you were exploring the north pole, would a compass be useful in identifying its exact location? Explain.

Name Date Class

Model and Invent

Solar System Distance Model

LAB A

Lab Preview

Directions: *Answer these questions before you begin the Lab.*

1. What safety precaution should you take while completing this lab?

____

2. Would it be a good idea to determine your scale by starting with the planet Mercury and giving it a diameter equal to the width of a sheet of notebook paper? Explain.

____

Distances between the Sun and the planets of the solar system are large. These large distances can be difficult to visualize.

Real-World Question

Can you design and create a model that will demonstrate the distances in the solar system?

Possible Materials

meterstick
scissors
pencil
string (several meters)
notebook paper (several sheets)

Safety Precautions  

Use care when handling scissors.

Goals

- **Design** a table of scale distances and model the distances between and among the Sun and the planets.

Data Source

SCIENCE *Online* Go to the Glencoe Science Web site at **msscience.com** to find information about the distances in the solar system.

Make a Model

❑ 1. **List** the steps that you need to take in making your model. Be specific, describing exactly what you will do at each step.

❑ 2. **List** the materials that you will need to complete your model.

❑ 3. **Describe** the calculations that you will use to get scale distances from the Sun for all planets. **Hint:** *Which planet is farthest from the Sun?*

❑ 4. **Make a table** of scale distances you will use in your model. Show your calculations in your table.

❑ 5. **Write** a description of how you will build your model, explaining how it will demonstrate relative distances between and among the Sun and planets of the solar system.

Test Your Model

❑ 1. **Compare** your scale distances with those of other students. Discuss why each of you chose the scale you did.

❑ 2. Make sure your teacher approves your plan before you start.

❑ 3. **Construct** the model using your scale distances.

❑ 4. While constructing the model, write any observations that you or other members of your group make, and complete the data table in your Science Journal. Calculate the scale distances that would be used in your model if 1 AU = 2 m.

LAB (continued) **LAB A**

Data and Observations

Planet	Distance to Sun (km)	Distance to Sun (AU)	Scale Distance	Scale Distance (1 AU = 2 m)
1. Mercury	5.97×10^7	0.39		
2. Venus	1.08×10^8	0.72		
3. Earth	1.50×10^8	1.00		
4. Mars	2.28×10^8	1.52		
5. Jupiter	7.78×10^8	5.20		
6. Saturn	1.43×10^9	9.54		
7. Uranus	2.87×10^9	19.19		
8. Neptune	4.50×10^9	30.07		

Analyze and Your Data

1. **Explain** how a scale distance is determined.

2. Was it possible to work with your scale? Explain why or why not.

3. How much string would be required to construct a model with a scale distance of 1 AU = 2 m?

4. Proxima Centauri, the closest star to the Sun, is about 270,000 AU from the Sun. Based on your scale, how much string would you need to place this star on your model?

Conclude and Apply

1. **Summarize** your observations about distances in the solar system. How are distances between the inner planets different from distances between the outer planets?
2. Using your scale distances, determine which planet orbits closest to Earth. Which planet's orbit is second closest?

Communicating Your Data

Compare your scale models with those of other students. Discuss any differences.
For more help refer to the Science Skill Handbook.

Name Date Class

Model and Invent
Solar System Distance Model

LAB B

Lab Preview

Directions: *Answer these questions before you begin the Lab.*

1. What safety precaution should you take while completing this lab?

____

2. Would it be a good idea to determine your scale by starting with the planet Mercury and giving it a diameter equal to the width of a sheet of notebook paper? Explain.

____

Distances between the Sun and the planets of the solar system are large. These large distances can be difficult to visualize.

Real-World Question

Can you design and create a model that will demonstrate the distances in the solar system?

Possible Materials

meterstick
scissors
pencil
string (several meters)
notebook paper (several sheets)

Safety Precautions 

Use care when handling scissors.

Goals

- **Design** a table of scale distances and model the distances between and among the Sun and the planets.

Data Source

SCIENCE *Online* Go to the Glencoe Science Web site at **msscience.com** to find information about the distances in the solar system.

Make a Model

❑ 1. **List** the steps that you need to take in making your model. Be specific, describing exactly what you will do at each step.

❑ 2. **List** the materials that you will need to complete your model.

❑ 3. **Describe** the calculations that you will use to get scale distances from the Sun for all nine planets.

❑ 4. **Make a table** of scale distances you will use in your model. Show your calculations in your table.

❑ 5. **Write** a description of how you will build your model, explaining how it will demonstrate relative distances between and among the Sun and planets of the solar system.

Test Your Model

❑ 1. **Compare** your scale distances with those of other students. Discuss why each of you chose the scale you did.

❑ 2. Make sure your teacher approves your plan before you start.

❑ 3. **Construct** the model using your scale distances.

(continued)

LAB B

❑ **4.** While constructing the model, write any observations that you or other members of your group make, and complete the data table in your Science Journal. Calculate the scale distances that would be used in your model if 1 AU = 2 m.

Data and Observations

Planet	Distance to Sun (km)	Distance to Sun (AU)	Scale Distance	Scale Distance (1 AU = 2 m)
1. Mercury	5.97×10^7	0.39		
2. Venus	1.08×10^8	0.72		
3. Earth	1.50×10^8	1.00		
4. Mars	2.28×10^8	1.52		
5. Jupiter	7.78×10^8	5.20		
6. Saturn	1.43×10^9	9.54		
7. Uranus	2.87×10^9	19.19		
8. Neptune	4.50×10^9	30.07		

Analyze and Your Data

1. **Explain** how a scale distance is determined.

2. Was it possible to work with your scale? Explain why or why not.

3. How much string would be required to construct a model with a scale distance of 1 AU = 2 m?

4. Proxima Centauri, the closest star to the Sun, is about 270,000 AU from the Sun. Based on your scale, how much string would you need to place this star on your model?

Conclude and Apply

1. **Summarize** your observations about distances in the solar system. How are distances between the inner planets different from distances between the outer planets?
2. Using your scale distances, determine which planet orbits closest to Earth. Which planet's orbit is second closest?

(continued)

Challenge

1. **Analyze** Do you notice any pattern in the distances between the planets? Explain your answer.

2. **Hypothesize** Given what you have learned and the distances of the planets from Earth, which planet(s) will humans most likely visit in the near future? Explain your answer.

3. **Consider** If you were planning a mission to Mars or to another planet, what would you need to consider in factoring the distance?

Extension

Create The model you used today compared the distances of the objects. Can you create a scale model that would compare the circumferences of the planets? Once you devise a scale, use clay to create models. Place your planet models on your distance model to compare the sizes of the planets.

Communicating Your Data

Compare your scale models with those of other students. Discuss any differences. **For more help refer to the Science Skill Handbook.**

The Solar System

I. Testing Concepts

Directions: *Match each description on the left with the correct term on the right. Write the letter of the correct term in the blank at the left.*

______ **1.** a piece of rock similar to the material that formed planets

______ **2.** a meteor that strikes Earth's surface

______ **3.** a meteoroid that burns up in Earth's atmosphere

______ **4.** an object composed of dust and rock particles mixed with frozen water, methane, and ammonia

a. asteroid
b. meteor
c. comet
d. meteorite

Directions: *Identify each statement as* **true** *or* **false**. *If a statement is false, change the underlined term to make it true.*

______ **5.** Billions of <u>asteroids</u> surround the solar system in the Oort cloud.

____

______ **6.** Meteor showers occur when Earth crosses the orbital path of <u>an asteroid</u>.

____

______ **7.** The asteroid belt is located between the planets <u>Mars and Jupiter</u>.

____

______ **8.** The <u>galaxy</u> formed from a piece of a nebula of gas, ice, and dust.

____

______ **9.** As a piece of the nebula <u>expanded</u>, nuclear fusion began and the Sun was born.

____

______ **10.** The planets' orbits are <u>elliptical</u>.

____

______ **11.** Planets that are closer to the Sun revolve <u>more slowly</u> than those that are farther away from the Sun. ______________________________

______ **12.** <u>Johannes Kepler</u> discovered that the planets travel at different speeds.

____

______ **13.** <u>Johannes Kepler</u> proposed an Earth-centered view of the solar system.

____

Chapter Test A (continued)

II. Understanding Concepts

Skill: Sequence

Directions: *Number the inner planets in order, beginning with the planet nearest the Sun.*

1. ______ Mars

2. ______ Venus

3. ______ Mercury

4. ______ Earth

Skill: Interpreting Data

Directions: *Match the descriptions of the planets on the left with the planet names on the right. Write the letter of the correct planet in the blank at the left.*

Matching Set I

______ **5.** has no atmosphere and is smallest planet

______ **6.** has a yellowish color and a thick atmosphere made mostly of carbon dioxide

______ **7.** appears reddish-yellow and has frozen polar ice caps

______ **8.** has one large moon and an atmosphere that protects life

a. Mercury
b. Earth
c. Venus
d. Mars

Matching Set II

______ **9.** has a complex ring system and is second largest planet

______ **10.** has a bluish-green color

______ **11.** has thin, dark rings and an axis of rotation nearly parallel to its orbit

______ **12.** has a storm called the Great Red Spot and is the largest planet

a. Uranus
b. Saturn
c. Jupiter
d. Neptune

Chapter Test A (continued)

Skill: Interpreting Scientific Illustrations

Directions: *Use the following to identify each model and the person or people credited with originating the model.*

Earth-centered
Nicholas Copernicus

Sun-centered
early Greek astronomers

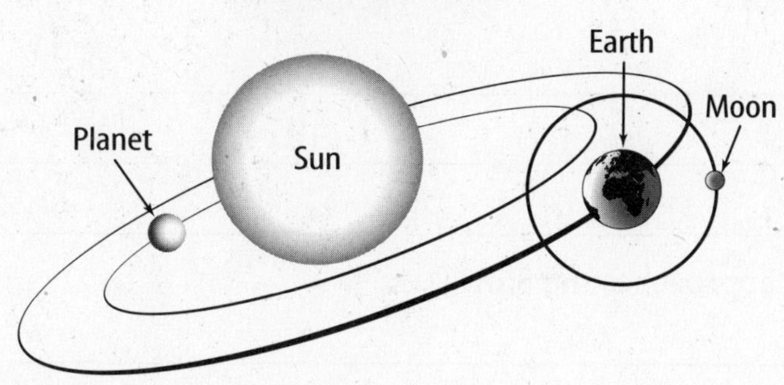

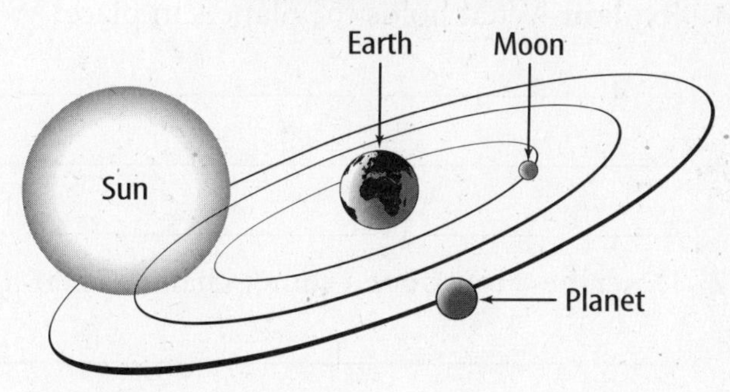

13. This is a(n) ______________________

model, first described by

______________________.

14. This is a(n) ______________________

centered model, first described by

______________________.

Skill: Comparing and Contrasting

Directions: *Fill in the blanks to compare and contrast Venus and Earth.*

15. Venus and Earth have similar ______________ and ______________.

16. Venus and Earth both have atmosphere with a(n) ______________, which traps heat near the surface.

17. Temperatures on ______________ are much higher than they are on

______________.

18. ______________ has water in all three states of matter.

Chapter Test A (continued)

III. Applying Concepts

Writing Skills

Directions: *Respond to the following using complete sentences.*

1. **Explain** What holds the planets in place? Why?

2. **Describe** How does a comet change when it approaches the Sun?

Name Date Class

Chapter Test B

The Solar System

I. Testing Concepts

Directions: *For each of the following, write the letter of the term or phrase that best completes the sentence.*

______ **1.** The planet with the lowest density and hundreds of thin rings is ______.
a. Jupiter **b.** Uranus **c.** Saturn **d.** Neptune

______ **2.** Johannes Kepler discovered that the orbits of planets are ______.
a. parabolic **b.** circular **c.** elliptical **d.** spherical

______ **3.** A planet that is very hot and has sulfuric acid in its clouds is ______
a. Mars **b.** Venus **c.** Mercury **d.** Earth

______ **4.** The closest moon to Jupiter, ______, is volcanically active.
a. Io **b.** Callisto **c.** Ganymede **d.** Europa

______ **5.** ______ axis of rotation is nearly parallel to the plane of its orbit.
a. Mars's **b.** Uranus's **c.** Mercury's **d.** Earth's

______ **6.** Two planets with similar mass and size are ______.
a. Mercury and Jupiter **c.** Earth and Pluto
b. Saturn and Uranus **d.** Venus and Earth

______ **7.** The planet that averages 150 million km, or one AU, from the Sun is ______.
a. Mars **b.** Jupiter **c.** Mercury **d.** Earth

______ **8.** ______ is the largest moon in the solar system.
a. Callisto **b.** Ganymede **c.** Earth's moon **d.** Io

______ **9.** The largest known volcano in the solar system is an extinct volcano known as Olympus Mons found on the planet ______.
a. Mars **b.** Jupiter **c.** Mercury **d.** Venus

______ **10.** The second smallest planet and the one closest to the sun is ______.
a. Mars **b.** Venus **c.** Mercury **d.** Jupiter

______ **11.** A planet that appears reddish-yellow due to iron oxide in its rocks is ______.
a. Mercury **b.** Jupiter **c.** Uranus **d.** Mars

______ **12.** The largest of ______ moons, Titan, is larger than the planet Mercury.
a. Neptune's **b.** Pluto's **c.** Uranus' **d.** Saturn's

______ **13.** At times, the planet ______ is actually the farthest planet from the Sun.
a. Uranus **b.** Saturn **c.** Neptune **d.** Jupiter

______ **14.** The Great Red Spot, a continuous storm, is located on the planet ______.
a. Saturn **b.** Uranus **c.** Jupiter **d.** Neptune

______ **15.** Methane gives ______ their blue-green color.
a. Mars and Earth **c.** Saturn and Jupiter
b. Uranus and Neptune **d.** Neptune and Venus

Chapter Test B (continued)

_____ **16.** The solid portion of a comet is called its _____.
a. coma **b.** core **c.** heart **d.** nucleus

_____ **17.** A cloud of gases around the solid portion of a comet is known as the _____.
a. coma **b.** core **c.** heart **d.** nucleus

_____ **18.** _____ are small pieces of rock moving through space.
a. Comets **b.** Meteors **c.** Meteoroids **d.** Meteorites

_____ **19.** Two of the inner planets are _____.
a. Mars and Jupiter
b. Mercury and Mars
c. Earth and Saturn
d. Uranus and Neptune

_____ **20.** The planet least like its close neighbor is _____.
a. Neptune **b.** Pluto **c.** Uranus **d.** Saturn

_____ **21.** _____ published the Sun-centered model of the solar system in 1543.
a. Kepler **b.** Magellan **c.** Copernicus **d.** Galileo

_____ **22.** When small pieces of rock moving through space enter Earth's atmosphere and completely burn up, they are called _____.
a. comets **b.** meteors **c.** meteorites **d.** asteroids

_____ **23.** Pieces of rock that actually strike Earth's surface are called _____.
a. meteoroids **b.** comets **c.** meteors **d.** meteorites

_____ **24.** Most asteroids are located in an area between the orbits of _____.
a. Earth and Mars
b. Jupiter and Saturn
c. Mars and Jupiter
d. Mercury and Venus

_____ **25.** Scientists theorize that the asteroid belt did not form a planet because _____
a. Jupiter's gravity kept it from forming
b. some of the particles were too large
c. it was too rocky
d. some of the particles moved too slowly

II. Understanding Concepts

Skill: Concept Mapping

Directions: *Think about a network-tree concept map that shows the routes of the* Voyager *space probes and the information they gathered while touring the outer planets. Then answer the following questions.*

1. Which planet would you list first? _____
2. What is one piece of information the *Voyager's* gathered about this planet?

_____

3. Which planet would you list last? _____
4. What is one piece of information the *Voyager's* gathered about this planet?

_____

Name ____________________ Date ____________ Class ____________

Chapter Test B (continued)

Skill: Interpreting Data

Directions: *Determine which planet is being described from the data given below.*

5. This planet is second largest in the solar system, is the sixth planet from the Sun, and has the lowest density. It has the most complex ring system of all the outer gaseous planets and has at least 31 moons. The planet may have a rocky core. It has a liquid ocean and an atmosphere, both composed mostly of hydrogen and helium.

   The planet is ____________________.

Skill: Recognizing Cause and Effect

Directions: *Answer the following question on the lines provided.*

6. Why can't we see the surface of Titan?

7. What causes the greenhouse effect on Venus and Earth?

8. What is one theory about the formation of the Sun?

Skill: Interpreting Scientific Illustrations

Directions: *Complete the following item on the lines provided.*

9. **Identify** which figure is an Earth-centered model of the solar system. Explain.

Figure 1

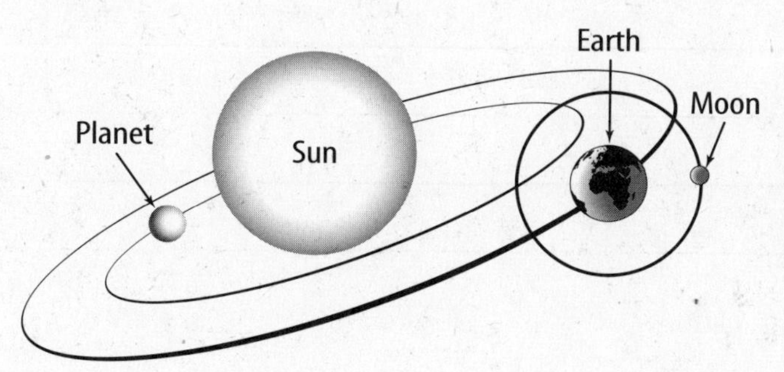

Figure 2

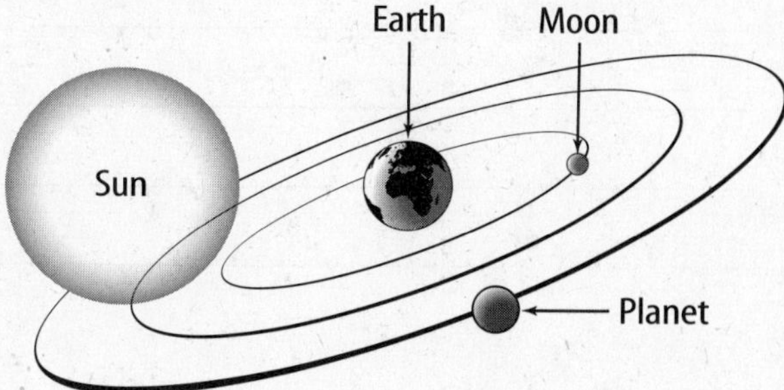

Chapter Test B (continued)

III. Applying Concepts

Writing Skills

Directions: *Answer the following questions using complete sentences.*

1. Some think that Pluto should be classified as an ice comet or an asteroid. Why?

2. Why do scientists study comets, meteoroids, and asteroids?

3. What is the difference in the formation of the inner and outer planets?

4. What are shooting stars?

5. Why do the planets orbit the Sun?

Name ____________________ Date ____________________ Class ____________________

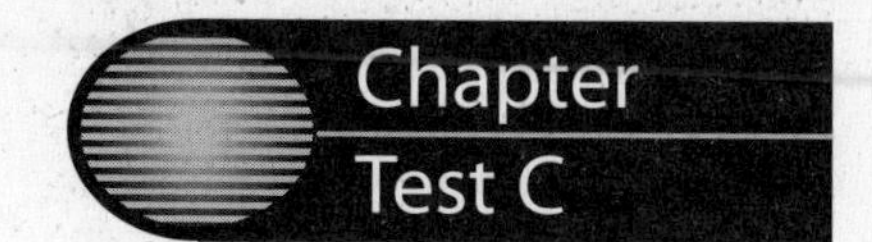

The Solar System

I. Testing Concepts

Directions: *Fill in the blanks to complete the sentences.*

1. Billions of comets surround the solar system in the ____________________.

2. The gravity of ____________________ may have kept a planet from forming in the area where the asteroid belt is now located.

3. ____________________ published a paper explaining the Sun-centered view of the solar system.

4. Galileo Galilei observed that, like the Moon, ____________________ goes through a full cycle of phases.

5. Scientists hypothesize that the solar system formed from part of a(n) ____________________ of gas, ice, and dust.

6. Johannes Kepler discovered that the orbit of planets is ____________________.

7. Planets that are closer to the Sun revolve ____________________ than those that are farther away from the Sun.

8. As a piece of a nebula contracted, ____________________ began at its center, creating the Sun.

9. The ____________________ probes touched down on Mars' surface.

10. The Mars ____________________ carried a robot rover with equipment that analyzed samples of rock and soil.

11. The *Mariner 10* detected a weak ____________________ around Mercury.

12. Olympus Mons, located on ____________________, is the largest volcano in the solar system.

13. Contrast Explain the differences between a meteor, a meteorite, and a meteoroid.

____

____

Name Date Class

Chapter Test C (continued)

II. Understanding Concepts

Skill: Creating a Chart

1. Create a chart showing the planets in order, starting with the one closest to the Sun. Include two facts about each planet.

Skill: Interpreting Scientific Illustrations

2. Describe what is illustrated in each diagram.

Figure 1

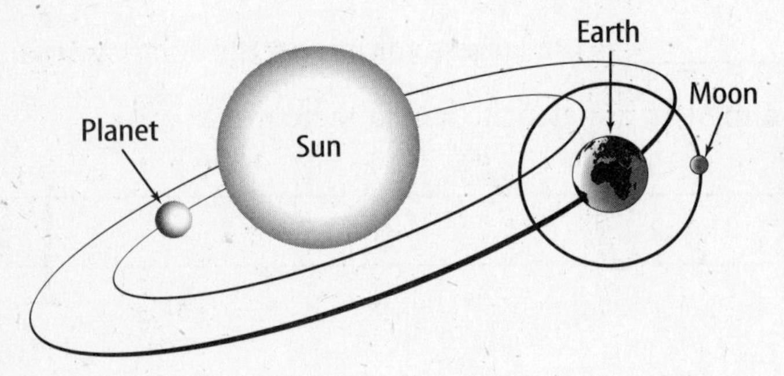

Figure 2

Chapter Test C (continued)

Skill: Comparing and Contrasting

3. Create a Venn diagram to compare and contrast Venus and Earth.

III. Applying Concepts

Writing Skills

Directions: *Respond to the following using complete sentences.*

1. **Hypothesize** What would have happened if the Sun had considerably less mass?

2. **Analyze** You are looking at photographs of comets. How would you distinguish between a comet farther from the Sun and one approaching the Sun? What would a comet look like after many trips around the Sun?

3. **Explain** How do objects from space sometimes impact Earth?

Name Date Class

Design Your Own

Measuring Parallax

LAB A

Lab Preview

Directions: *Answer these questions before you begin the Lab.*

1. Why is the safety symbol for eye protection used in this lab?

____

2. What is parallax?

____

Parallax is the apparent shift in the position of an object when viewed from two locations.

Real-World Question

How can you build a model to show the relationship between distance and parallax?

Form a Hypothesis

State a hypothesis about how parallax varies with distance.

Possible Materials

meterstick
metric ruler
masking tape
pencil

Goals

- **Design** a model to show how the distance from an observer to an object affects the object's parallax shift.
- **Describe** how parallax can be used to determine the distance to a star.

Safety Precautions 

WARNING: *Be sure to wear goggles to protect your eyes.*

Test Your Hypothesis

Make a Plan

❑ **1.** As a group, agree upon and write your hypothesis statement.

❑ **2.** **List** the steps you need to take to build your model. Be specific, describing exactly what you will do at each step.

❑ **3.** **Devise** a method to test how distance from an observer to an object, such as a pencil, affects the parallax of the object.

❑ **4.** **List** the steps you will take to test your hypothesis. Be specific, describing exactly what you will do at each step.

❑ **5.** Read over your plan for the model to be used in this experiment.

❑ **6.** How will you determine changes in observed parallax? Remember, these changes should occur when the distance from the observer to the object is changed.

❑ **7.** You should measure shifts in parallax from several different positions. How will these positions differ?

❑ **8.** How will you measure distances accurately and compare relative position shift? **Hint:** *The position of the observer is important.*

Follow Your Plan

❑ **1.** Make sure your teacher approves your plan before you start.

❑ **2.** **Construct** the model your team has planned.

❑ **3.** Carry out the experiment as planned.

❑ **4.** While conducting the experiment, record any observations that you or other members of your group make in the **Data and Observations** section.

(continued)

Data and Observations

Analyze Your Data

1. **Compare** what happened to the object when it was viewed with one eye closed, then the other.

2. At what distance from the observer did the object appear to shift the most?

3. At what distance did it appear to shift the least?

Conclude and Apply

1. **Infer** what happened to the apparent shift of the object's location as the distance from the observer was increased or decreased.

2. **Describe** how astronomers might use parallax to study stars.

Communicating Your Data

Prepare a chart showing the results of your experiment. Share the chart with members of your class. **For more help, refer to the Science Skill Handbook.**

Name Date Class

Design Your Own

Measuring Parallax

LAB B

Lab Preview

Directions: *Answer these questions before you begin the Lab.*

1. Why is the safety symbol for eye protection used in this lab?

____

2. What is parallax?

____

Parallax is the apparent shift in the position of an object when viewed from two locations.

Real-World Question

How can you build a model to show the relationship between distance and parallax?

Form a Hypothesis

State a hypothesis about how parallax varies with distance.

Possible Materials

meterstick | masking tape
metric ruler | pencil

Goals

- **Design** a model to show how the distance from an observer to an object affects the object's parallax shift.
- **Describe** how parallax can be used to determine the distance to a star.

Safety Precautions 

WARNING: *Be sure to wear goggles to protect your eyes.*

Test Your Hypothesis

Make a Plan

❑ **1.** As a group, agree upon and write your hypothesis statement.

❑ **2.** **List** the steps you need to take to build your model. Be specific, describing exactly what you will do at each step.

❑ **3.** **Devise** a method to test how distance from an observer to an object, such as a pencil, affects the parallax of the object.

❑ **4.** **List** the steps you will take to test your hypothesis. Be specific, describing exactly what you will do at each step.

❑ **5.** Read over your plan for the model to be used in this experiment.

❑ **6.** How will you determine changes in observed parallax? Remember, these changes should occur when the distance from the observer to the object is changed.

❑ **7.** You should measure shifts in parallax from several different positions. How will these positions differ?

❑ **8.** How will you measure distances accurately and compare relative position shift?

Follow Your Plan

❑ **1.** Make sure your teacher approves your plan before you start.

❑ **2.** **Construct** the model your team has planned.

❑ **3.** Carry out the experiment as planned.

❑ **4.** While conducting the experiment, record any observations that you or other members of your group make in the **Data and Observations** section.

LAB (continued) **LAB B**

Data and Observations

Analyze Your Data

1. **Compare** what happened to the object when it was viewed with one eye closed, then the other.

2. At what distance from the observer did the object appear to shift the most?

3. At what distance did it appear to shift the least?

Conclude and Apply

1. **Infer** what happened to the apparent shift of the object's location as the distance from the observer was increased or decreased.

2. **Describe** how astronomers might use parallax to study stars.

Challenge

1. **Infer** Based on your findings, would parallax be a useful tool for measuring distance for all stars? Explain your answer.

LAB (continued) **LAB B**

2. **Analyze** How does this experiment differ from the way parallax is computed?

3. **Apply** How can parallax be used to measure the difference between neighboring stars?

Extension

Analyze Now that you have explored one way scientists determine distance in space, use that information to find out about a constellation. Research the stars in the constellation you choose, and find their distances from Earth in light-years. Develop a scale model to show the distance of each star from Earth.

Communicating Your Data

Prepare a chart showing the results of your experiment. Share the chart with members of your class. **For more help, refer to the Science Skill Handbook.**

Name ______ Date ______ Class ______

Stars and Galaxies

I. Testing Concepts

Directions: *In the blank at the left, write the letter of the term that best completes each statement.*

______ 1. ______ is the closest star to Earth.
a. The Sun b. Vega c. Betelgeuse d. Polaris

______ 2. The distance that light travels in one year is called a(n) ______.
a. astronomical unit c. kilometer
b. parsec d. light-year

______ 3. The ______ states that the universe began with an explosion about 13.7 billion years ago.
a. steady state theory c. oscillating universe theory
b. big bang theory d. flux theory

______ 4. The three main types of galaxies are spiral, ______, and irregular.
a. spherical b. linear c. elliptical d. contracting

______ 5. Stars shine because of a process called ______.
a. fission b. fusion c. convection d. radiation

______ 6. ______ occur when charged particles from the Sun interact with Earth's magnetic field.
a. Auroras b. Sunspots c. Prominences d. Radiation zones

______ 7. Stars form in regions of gas and dust called ______.
a. spectrums b. constellations c. galaxies d. nebulae

Directions: *Match each description on the left with the correct term.*

Matching Set I

______ 8. areas of the Sun's surface that appear dark because they are cooler than surrounding areas

______ 9. violent eruptions on the Sun that shoot outward at high speeds

______ 10. huge, arching columns of gas on the Sun

a. sunspots
b. prominences
c. solar flares

Matching Set II

______ 11. pattern of stars in the night sky

______ 12. large group of stars, gas, and dust held together by gravity

______ 13. the closest star system to the Sun

______ 14. the name of Earth's galaxy

a. galaxy
b. Milky Way
c. constellation
d. Alpha Centauri

Name Date Class

Chapter Test A (continued)

II. Understanding Concepts

Skill: Concept Mapping

Directions: *Complete the concept map showing the relationship between a star's mass and its life cycle. Use the following terms:* **neutron star, red supergiant, white dwarf, nebula, red giant, supernova,** *and* **black hole.**

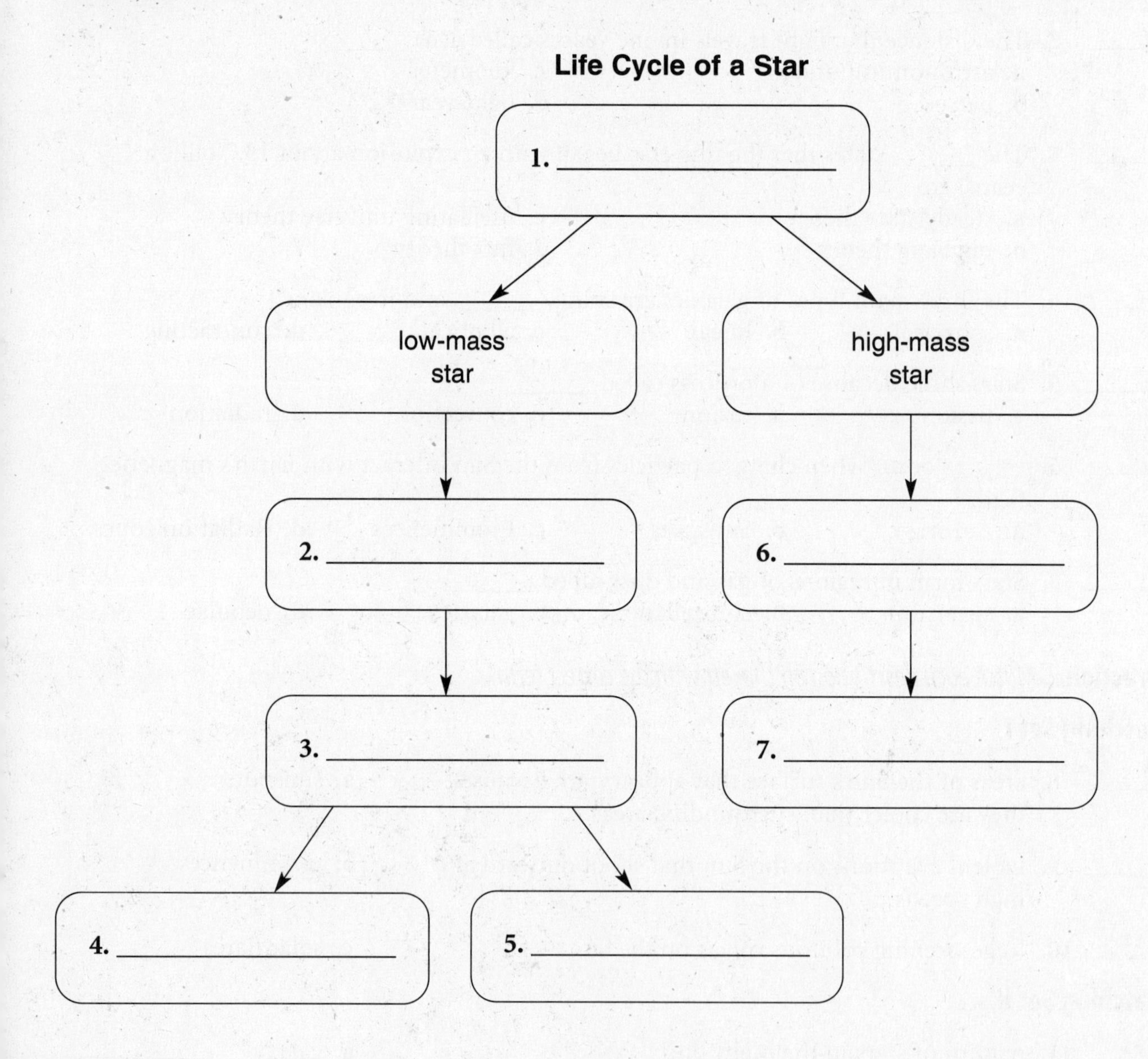

Name Date Class

Chapter Test A (continued)

Skill: Interpreting Scientific Illustrations

Directions: *Use the diagram to help you answer the following questions.*

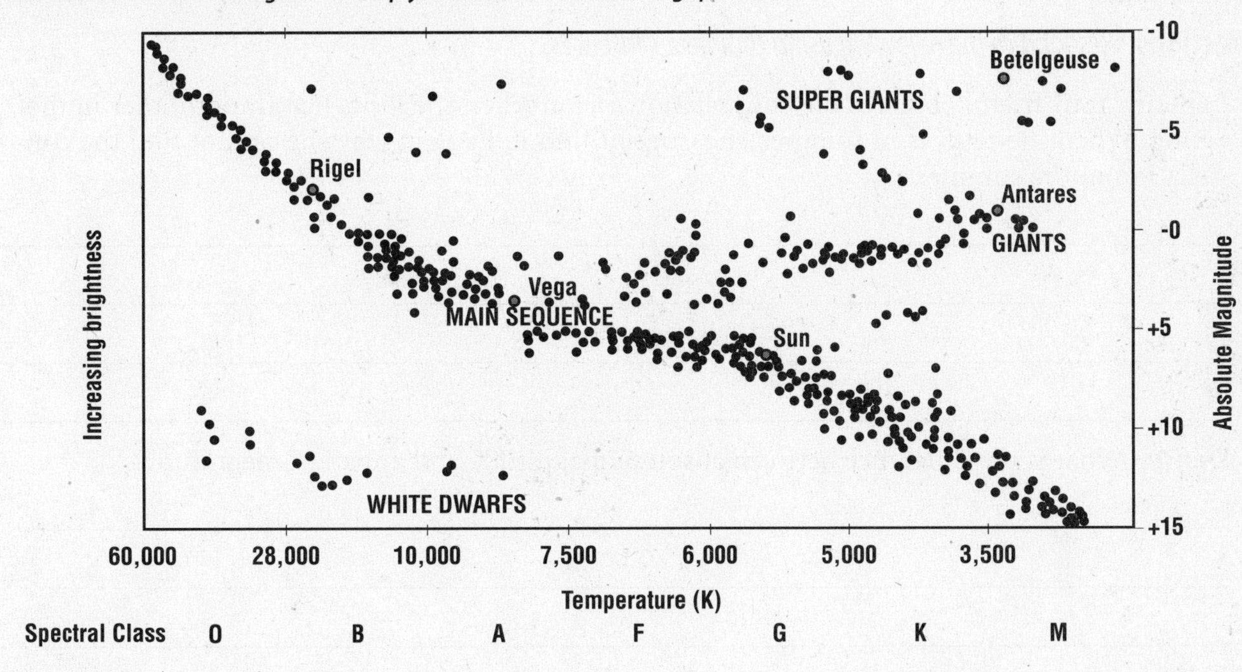

8. Where is the Sun located on the diagram? ______________________

9. Is Vega or the Sun hotter? ______________________

10. Is a white dwarf or a giant brighter? ______________________

11. Does Antares or the Sun have greater absolute magnitude? ______________________

Skill: Sequencing

Directions: *Number each set of terms below to show the correct order, starting at the Sun's inner layer.*

______ 12. radiation zone

______ 13. core

______ 14. convection zone

______ 15. corona

______ 16. photosphere

______ 17. transition zone

______ 18. chromosphere

III. Applying Concepts

Writing Skills

Directions: *Respond to the following using complete sentences.*

1. **Explain** Your friend observes the constellation Orion when she visits her grandmother in the winter. When she returns in summer, she can not find it. Explain why she cannot find the constellation in the summer sky.

2. **Define** What is the difference between absolute magnitude and apparent magnitude?

3. **Locate** Describe the location of the Sun in the Milky Way galaxy.

4. **Explain** How is the movement of the Milky Way galaxy similar to the movement of our solar system?

Name ____ Date ____ Class ____

Stars and Galaxies

I. Testing Concepts

Directions: *Write the letter of the term or phrase that best completes the statement on the blank at the left.*

______ **1.** The positions of the constellations appear to change throughout the year because ______.
a. Earth rotates on its axis
b. Earth revolves around the Sun
c. the constellations revolve around Earth
d. the Sun revolves around the galaxy

______ **2.** Its ______ makes Sirius the brightest star in the night sky.
a. apparent magnitude
b. Uranus's magnitude
c. temperature
d. absolute magnitude

______ **3.** The distances to nearby stars can be measured by using ______.
a. absolute magnitude
b. temperature
c. apparent magnitude
d. parallax

______ **4.** About 90 percent of all stars are ______ stars.
a. nebula **b.** giant **c.** main sequence **d.** white dwarf

______ **5.** The hottest stars in space are ______ in color.
a. yellow **b.** red **c.** blue **d.** green

______ **6.** A main sequence star becomes a ______ after it uses up the hydrogen in its core.
a. nebula **b.** supernova **c.** black hole **d.** giant

______ **7.** The Sun produces energy by fusing hydrogen into ______ in its core.
a. carbon **b.** helium **c.** iron **d.** oxygen

______ **8.** The intense magnetic field associated with Sunspots may cause huge arching columns of gas called ______.
a. solar flares **b.** coronas **c.** photospheres **d.** prominences

______ **9.** Our Sun is all of the following **EXCEPT** ______.
a. part of a binary system
b. a main sequence star
c. a yellow star
d. of average absolute magnitude

______ **10.** A galaxy that has a shape similar to a football is a(n) ______ galaxy.
a. normal spiral **b.** barred spiral **c.** elliptical **d.** irregular

______ **11.** All of the following are true of the Milky Way **EXCEPT** that it ______.
a. is an elliptical galaxy
b. has more than 800 billion stars
c. is a member of the Local Group
d. is about 100,000 light-years across

______ **12.** The Big Bang theory of the formation and expansion of the universe is supported by the observed ______.
a. blue-violet shift in light beyond the Local Group
b. red shift in light beyond the Local Group
c. gravity of matter
d. shorter light wavelengths

Chapter Test B (continued)

______ 13. Although it has a greater ______ than Sirius, Rigel does not look as bright in the night sky.
a. apparent magnitude
b. parallax
c. distance from Earth
d. absolute magnitude

______ 14. A ______ is an object so dense that nothing can escape its gravity field.
a. supernova
b. neutron star
c. black hole
d. supergiant

______ 15. Dark, cooler areas on the Sun's surface are called ______.
a. Sunspots
b. solar flares
c. coronas
d. prominences

______ 16. The Clouds of Magellan are two ______ galaxies that orbit the Milky Way.
a. normal spiral
b. barred spiral
c. irregular
d. elliptical

______ 17. The coolest stars in the sky are ______ in color.
a. yellow
b. red
c. blue
d. green

______ 18. A large group of stars, gas, and dust held together by gravity is a ______.
a. galaxy
b. constellation
c. Local Group
d. elliptical galaxy

II. Understanding Concepts

Skill: Recognizing Cause and Effect

Directions: *Identify the cause and effect given in each sentence by writing* **C** *for cause and* **E** *for effect in the blanks.*

1. ______ a. An object moves away from you.
   ______ b. Its wavelengths get longer and shift to red on a spectrum.
2. ______ a. A supernova is produced.
   ______ b. A star's core collapses and its outer portion explodes.

Skill: Sequencing

3. Sequence the color of the stars according to their temperature. List the hottest color first.

____

____

____

4. Number the following events in the order that they would happen.
   ______ a. High-energy particles emitted by solar flares interact with Earth's atmosphere near the polar regions.
   ______ b. Gases near a sunspot brighten up suddenly and erupt as solar flares.
   ______ c. Earth's atmosphere radiates lights called aurora.

Name _______________ Date _______________ Class _______________

Chapter Test B (continued)

Skill: Interpreting Scientific Illustrations

Directions: *Use the diagram to help you answer the following questions.*

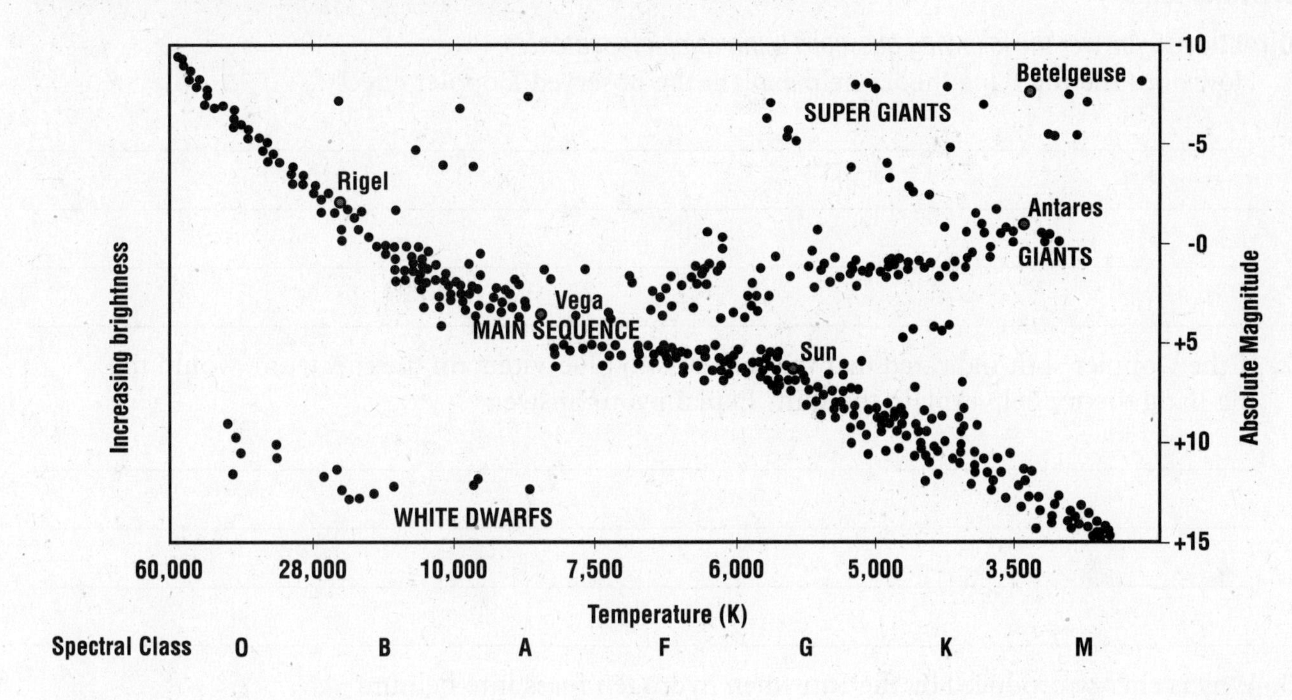

5. Are giants hotter than white dwarfs? _______________

6. Is Antares or Vega hotter than the Sun? _______________

7. What type of star is Betelgeuse? _______________

8. Is the Sun brighter than a white dwarf? _______________

Skill: Observing and Inferring

9. Three stars are 4.3 light-years from Earth. Star A has the least brightness, Star B has the greatest brightness, and Star C has a brightness in between. Which of these stars do you think will have the greatest apparent magnitude? Why?

____

____

____

____

____

III. Applying Concepts

Writing Skills

Directions: *Answer the following questions using complete sentences.*

1. How does the Big Bang theory help explain the observed Doppler effects?

2. If the Doppler shift indicated that the shift was to blue-violet on the spectrum, would the Big Bang theory help explain the shift? Explain your answer.

3. Why is energy produced by the Sun when hydrogen fuses into helium?

4. Why does the position of the constellation Orion appear to change throughout the year, and why can't Orion be seen in the summer sky?

Name ______________________ Date ______________ Class ______________

Stars and Galaxies

I. Testing Concepts

Directions: *Identify each statement as* **true** *or* **false**. *If a statement is false, change the underlined term to make it true.*

______ **1.** A magnascope acts like a prism by breaking light into its component parts.

____

______ **2.** The Sun is located near the core of the Milky Way.

____

______ **3.** Polaris is the closest star to Earth.

____

______ **4.** If a star is moving toward Earth, its wavelengths of light are compressed.

____

______ **5.** Spiral galaxies can be normal or irregular.

____

Directions: *Fill in the blanks to complete the sentences.*

6. Cassiopeia is a(n) ______________________ because it circles Polaris.

7. A(n) ______________________ is the distance that light travels in one year.

8. If you were searching for stars just forming, you would look in a(n) ______________________.

9. When hydrogen fuel is depleted, a star loses its ______________________ status.

10. The cluster to which the Milky Way belongs is called the ______________________.

11. Some scientists think that the world is ______________________ because the galaxies outside the Local Group appear to be moving away from Earth.

12. When scientists study light from galaxies beyond the Local Group, a(n)

______________________ occurs.

13. The ______________________ theory states that the universe began with an explosion about 13.7 billion years ago.

14. There are three categories of galaxies: ______________________, ______________________, and

______________________.

15. The ______________________ theory states that the universe has always been the same as it is now.

Name Date Class

Chapter Test C (continued)

II. Understanding Concepts

Skill: Interpreting Scientific Illustrations

Directions: *Use the diagram to help you answer the following question.*

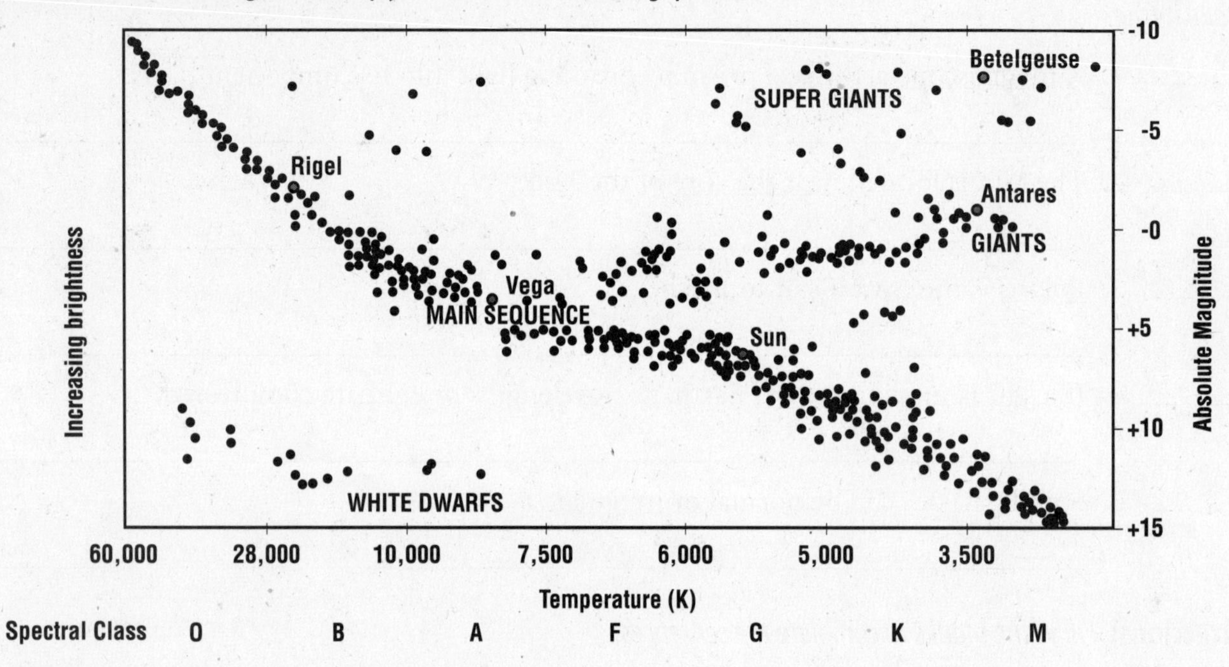

1. **Compare** and **contrast** Vega and the Sun.

____

____

Skill: Concept Mapping

2. Create a concept map to show the relationship between mass and the life cycle of a star.

Skill: Sequencing

Directions: *List the layers of the Sun, using two types of classification. Start with the innermost layer.*

3. ____________________
4. ____________________
5. ____________________
6. ____________________
7. ____________________
8. ____________________
9. ____________________

Chapter Test C (continued)

Skill: Categorizing

Directions: *Place an* **X** *next to the surface features of the Sun and write a brief description of each.*

10. ______ sunspots ____________________

11. ______ auroras ____________________

12. ______ prominences ____________________

13. ______ flares ____________________

14. ______ coronal mass ejections ____________________

15. ______ northern lights ____________________

III. Applying Concepts

Writing Skills

Directions: *Respond to the following using complete sentences.*

1. **Deduce** Would a map of constellations be useful to an astronaut? Explain your answer.

____

____

2. **Infer** A student looks at two constellation maps. He notices that some constellations are the same, but others are totally different. What might account for these differences?

____

____

____

3. **Resolve** Two friends give a report on the star Polaris. Each explains its brightness with a different magnitude, yet both are right. How is this possible?

____

____

____

____

4. **Compare** How is our solar system similar to our galaxy?

____

____

____

Teacher Guide and Answers

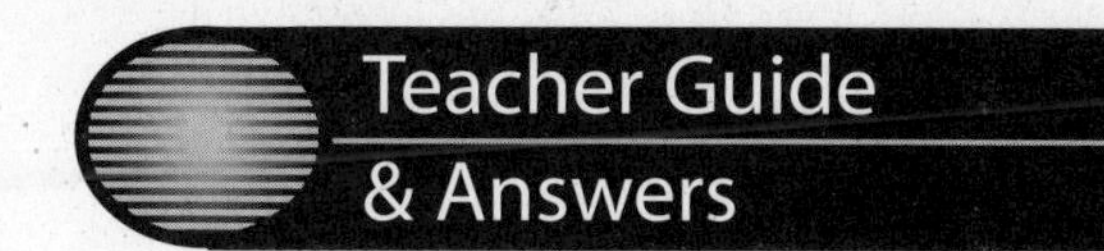

Teacher Guide & Answers

The Nature of Science

Lab A (page 1)

Lab Preview

1. string, a paper clip, and a metal washer
2. a protractor

Conclude and Apply

1. The length of string and the mass were kept constant.
2. length of the string
3. Shorten the length of the string.

Lab B (page 3)

Lab Preview

1. string, a paper clip, and a metal washer
2. a protractor

Conclude and Apply

1. The length of string and the mass were kept constant.
2. length of the string
3. Shorten the length of the string.

Challenge

1. The pendulum will not swing smoothly but will fall awkwardly when the angle of the drop is more than 90 degrees.
2. The force at the pivot point is friction. This friction, along with air resistance, is gradually slowing down the pendulum. These forces will eventually cause the pendulum to stop.
3. Drawings will vary but should include a pendulum drawn from a pivot point. The pendulum should have a weight at the end and be at a less than 90 degree angle. The drawing should also include an arrow pointing left or right to indicate motion and an arrow pointing down to show the force of gravity.

Extension

Student responses will vary, but students should come to their conclusions after conducting multiple trials.

Chapter Test A (page 7)

I. Testing Concepts (page 7)

1. b
2. a
3. d
4. b
5. b
6. b
7. c
8. d
9. c
10. b
11. e
12. a

II. Understanding Concepts (page 8)

1. 3
2. 6
3. 1
4. 5
5. 2
6. 4
7. There is continuous research and improvement in technological instruments.
8. Experiments are repeated many times.
9. A force acts on an object.
10. There is personal bias.
11. dependent variable
12. constant
13. control
14. constant
15. independent variable

III. Applying Concepts (page 9)

1. Possible responses: Satellites and radar are used to predict the weather. Seismographs are used to detect earthquakes. Telescopes are used to study the stars and planets. Ultrasound is used to study ocean depths.
2. A scientist is like a detective because both are on a quest for answers. They gather information, look for possible solutions, analyze the information, and then draw conclusions to solve the "mystery."
3. This is an example of scientific theory, because there was research and data to support his idea. A scientific theory is useful information that developed after testing a hypothesis over a long period of time. Consistent data and results must support the hypothesis for it to become a theory. A law is a statement of fact with no explanation.
4. Earth science topics include rocks, minerals, soil, volcanoes, earthquakes, maps, fossils, mountains, climates, weather, ocean water, and objects in space.
5. For results to be valid or reliable, tests should be repeated many times to see whether the original results can be confirmed. If something in an experiment occurs just once, scientific conclusions cannot be based on it.

Chapter Test B (page 11)

I. Testing Concepts (page 11)

1. d
2. a
3. e
4. h
5. j
6. f

7. l
8. g
9. i
10. b
11. False: Ethics deal with morals and values and *cannot* be measured and tested using the scientific method.
12. True
13. False: You can test *only one variable* in an experiment to get reliable results.
14. False: Earth science is the study of *Earth and space.*
15. False: Bias, or personal opinions, *can* influence results.
16. National Weather Service
17. weather maps
18. 1600's
19. laws
20. scientific methods
21. fraud
22. science

II. Understanding Concepts (page 12)

1. Sample answer: You could place the same amount of water and one thermometer in each beaker and then place each beaker on a hot plate. In one beaker, add salt, then heat both beakers to boiling and compare the temperatures. The independent variable is the salt, and the dependent variable is the boiling point of water.
2. Sample answer: Scientific methods utilize problem-solving methods such as gathering and recording information, hypothesizing, testing, analyzing results, and drawing conclusions from the data. Ethics and belief systems consider what is right and wrong and personal opinions and feelings, and as such cannot be tested by scientific methods.
3. problem
4. hypothesis
5. test
6. analyze
7. conclusions

III. Applying Concepts (page 13)

1. He read accounts of storms from newspapers across the country and noticed that storms generally move from west to east. He concluded that observers could monitor a storm and notify those in its path that is was coming.
2. A system of weather observation sites was set up and weather reports from volunteer weather observers were sent by telegraph to the Smithsonian Institution, where data was collected, and eventually weather maps were drawn.
3. It was the rain gauge and it was used in India.
4. When the burning gases are forced out of the back of the rocket, an equal but opposite force pushes the rocket forward.
5. Sample answer: No, that is not enough data. Any number of things could have caused the illness. Data about the symptoms of the illness, what else the person had eaten recently, the person's condition before eating, what was eaten, whether or not anyone else who ate the same thing became ill, and possibly testing of the food that was eaten would be needed to draw reliable conclusions. Accept all reasonable answers.

IV. Writing Skills (page 14)

1. Answers will vary, but could include the development of better instruments or testing procedures, advances in technology, and new information.
2. No, because it would be impossible to tell which of the variables had caused the observed effects. For accurate results, only one variable can be tested at a time.
3. Sample answer: The placebos serve as a control, or a standard to measure the effects of the real drug against in the experiment.

Chapter Test C (page 15)

I. Testing Concepts (page 15)

1. false—Constants
2. true
3. false—telegraph
4. true
5. true
6. science
7. Possible responses: rocks, minerals, space, volcanoes, weather, fossils
8. comet
9. equal, opposite
10. tree rings
11. ethical, belief system
12. rain gauge
13. discoveries
14. mythology

II. Understanding Concepts (page 16)

1–6. Possible responses: identify a problem; gather information; make a hypothesis; test the hypothesis; analyze the results; draw conclusions
7. there is continuous research and improvement in technological instruments
8. the force of gravity pulls them to Earth
9. a force has acted upon it
10. Thor was throwing his heavy hammer
11. there was a strong earthquake
12. they both search for answers and gather evidence to solve a problem
13. they observed and recorded celestial patterns
14. Possible response: A scientist wants to test the effectiveness of fertilizer in making plants grow taller. She places three seeds of the same kind in three different containers. Each container receives the same amount of light, water, and

soil. One pot receives no fertilizer. Another plant receives 5 grams of fertilizer, and the last plant receives 15 grams of the same fertilizer. The height of the stem is the dependent variable. The type of seeds, light, water, and soil are the constants. The pot with no fertilizer is the control. The amount of fertilizer is the independent variable.

III. Applying Concepts (page 17)

1. Science is the process of observing, studying, and thinking about things in the world to gain knowledge. As scientists observe and study, they make new discoveries that help others. Technology puts these new discoveries to practical uses.
2. Transferable technology is technology that can be applied to new situations that are different from its original purposes. Many types of technology that are now common were originally developed for use in satellites and robotic parts. Radar and sonar that were developed for the military are now being used in the study of space, weather, and medicine.
3. Possible response: Science is limited in what it can explain. For a problem or question to be scientifically studied, there must be variables that can be observed and tested. Problems dealing with ethics cannot be solved using a scientific method. Science is always changing because scientists are continually developing better instruments and testing procedures that allow them to gain an even greater understanding of nature.
4. Answers will vary. Good features of the experiment include the correct use of controls, constants, and independent variables. A possible problem is the lack of confirmation of results by repetition.
5. Placing headrests in cars to prevent whiplash injuries relates to Newton's first law: an object will continue in motion or remain at rest until it is acted upon by an outside force.

Matter

LAB A (page 19)

Lab Preview

1. Students may be measuring objects that have a pointed end or sharp edges.
2. The equation: density = mass/volume.

Analyze Your Data

1. Denser objects feel heavier than less dense objects of the same size. Objects like these are said to have greater heft.
2. Cork and wooden block float in water. Other objects sink.
3. The volume measurement might be increased by the volume occupied by the tool. Increasing the volume would decrease the density found.

Conclude and Apply

1. The cork is less dense than water.
2. Water has a density of 1 g/cm^3.
3. As long as the same sample is used, the density of the clay is not affected by the size of the piece(s).
4. In the case of ships, density and buoyancy are involved. If a clay boat were shaped so it displaced a large enough volume of water, it would float.

LAB B (page 23)

Lab Preview

1. Students may be measuring objects that have a pointed end or sharp edges.
2. The equation: density = mass/volume.

Analyze Your Data

1. Denser objects feel heavier than less dense objects of the same size. Objects like these are said to have greater heft.
2. Cork and wooden block float in water. Other objects sink.
3. The volume measurement might be increased by the volume occupied by the tool. Increasing the volume would decrease the density found.

Conclude and Apply

1. The cork is less dense than water.
2. Water has a density of 1 g/cm^3.
3. As long as the same sample is used, the density of the clay is not affected by the size of the piece(s).
4. In the case of ships, density and buoyancy are involved. If a clay boat were shaped so it displaced a large enough volume of water, it would float.

Challenge

1. Aluminum is a good choice for aircraft because it is less dense, making the aircraft lighter. Titanium is less dense than other metals, making it lighter. Its light weight will help it to travel faster.
2. Ice is less dense than liquid water. Therefore the container of ice water would be less dense.
3. The carbonated drink would be less dense, because gases are less dense than liquids.

Extension

Lab designs will vary, but students should discover that the diet drink is less dense than the sugared drink. Guide students in comparing the amounts of sweetener in each drink. Diet drinks will have less sweetener, while sugared drinks will have more. Students should be able to explain why this causes a difference in the density of the liquids.

Chapter Test A (page 27)

I. Testing Concepts (page 27)

1. b
2. a
3. d
4. a
5. c
6. b
7. c
8. a
9. d
10. f
11. g
12. i
13. h
14. e

II. Understanding Concepts (page 28)

Order may vary:

Compounds	Mixtures
1. contain atoms of more than one type of element	5. contain two or more substances
2. chemically bonded together	6. not chemically combined
3. The properties are different from the properties of the elements that combine to form them.	7. may be heterogeneous or homogeneous
4. may be represented by a chemical formula	8. may be separated

9. Compounds and mixtures are both composed of two or more things.
10. Possible response: Compounds contain atoms of more than one type of element that are chemically bonded together. A mixture is composed of two or more objects that are not chemically combined.
11. protons
12. electron cloud
13. nucleus
14. neutrons

III. Applying Concepts (page 29)

1. Possible response: solid: wood; liquid: water; gas: helium; plasma: lightning
2. Drawings should show two hydrogen molecules combined with one oxygen molecule. The two atoms of hydrogen share outer electrons with the one atom of oxygen.
3. The student made a homogeneous mixture, or solution. The components are mixed equally throughout. You would not be able to see individual components.
4. Possible response: There are ice cubes in a glass, which are water in the solid form. Sunlight (heat) warms the ice cubes, and they melt to form liquid water. The sunlight continues to heat the water causing it to evaporate. The water then becomes water vapor which is a gas.

Chapter Test B (page 31)

I. Testing Concepts (page 31)

1. c
2. c
3. a
4. d
5. c
6. b
7. c
8. a
9. a
10. b
11. d
12. d
13. a
14. c
15. b
16. true
17. false; A compound is a group of substances in which each substance loses its own properties.
18. false; One physical property of a substance is its density.
19. false; A substance that expands to completely fill a container is a gas.
20. true
21. compound
22. compound
23. mixture
24. mixture
25. compound
26. mixture
27. mixture
28. mixture
29. compound
30. compound

II. Understanding Concepts (page 33)

1. 6; 6
2. 1; 1
3. 12; 11
4. 6; 14
5. 18; 17
6. 12; 24
7. 9; 19
8. Atoms a and d are isotopes because they have the same atomic number but different mass numbers.
9. Atoms c, e, and g are ions because they have gained or lost an electron and have electric charges.
10. Atom c is the positively charged ion because it has more protons than electrons.

11. Atom c can combine with atom e because it has a positive charge that is attracted to the negative charge of atom e. or Atom c can combine with atom g.
12. Atoms e and g cannot form a compound because they are both negatively charged ions that do not attract one another.
13. Answers will vary slightly. Topics should indicate that neutrons, protons, and electrons are particles within atoms.
14. elements

III. **Applying Concepts (page 34)**

1. After boiling water for five minutes, there would be less liquid because some of the water molecules would escape into the air as a gas.
2. **a.** Egg whites are liquid at room temperature. The molecules are close to one another but are free to change position with one another. The egg whites take the shape of their container.
   b. Frozen juice bars are solid. Their molecules are very close to one another and in a fixed relationship. The bars retain their shape in the container.

IV. **Writing Skills (page 34)**

3. The wetness is caused by dew. When it is cooler at night than it is during the day, the water molecules in the air cool down to the point where they turn into liquid water. The liquid water molecules are the dew found on the grass and windows.

Chapter Test C (page 35)

I. **Testing Concepts (page 35)**

1. true
2. false—increase
3. true
4. false—appearance
5. false—homogeneous
6. false—negative side
7. d
8. c
9. b
10. e
11. a

II. **Understanding Concepts (page 36)**

1. Diagrams should show a nucleus surrounded by an electron cloud. Protons and neutrons should be labeled in the nucleus. Electrons should be labeled in the electron cloud.
2.

	Number of Protons	Number of Neutrons	Number of Electrons	Atomic Number	Mass Number
Hydrogen-1	1	0	1	1	1
Hydrogen-2	1	1	1	1	2
Hydrogen-3	1	2	1	1	3
Carbon-12	6	6	6	6	12
Carbon-13	6	8	6	6	14

3. Possible response: Kinds of Isotopes
4. No, there are not any ions on the chart, because the electrons are equal to the protons for each isotope.
5. They can form bonds. They will form covalent bonds, because they are not positively or negatively charged.

III. **Applying Concepts (page 37)**

1. The vinegar is more dense than the oil, so the oil floats on the vinegar.
2. It is a good example. If both magnets in a pair have the same type of pole, the two repel each other. If the ends have opposite poles, they attract each other. Ions form similarly; they form electrically neutral compounds when they join together.
3. The water will not overflow because of cohesion. Cohesion is the attraction between water molecules that allows them to form raindrops. The attraction keeps the water from overflowing.
4. The second student is correct. When salt and water join in salt water, they form a mixture that can be separated. If left in a sunny location, the water will evaporate, leaving the salt behind.
5. Possible response: Plasma is composed of ions and electrons. It forms when high temperatures cause some of the electrons normally found in an atom's electron cloud to escape and move outside the electron cloud. Plasma is relatively rare on Earth, because Earth lacks the high temperature needed to create this state of matter. On Earth, plasma is mainly expressed as lightning. However, the Sun and other stars are extremely hot, allowing plasma to form.

Minerals

LAB A (page 39)

Lab Preview

1. eye protection, clothing protection, irritant, sharp object, and disposal

2. Hardness, streak, color, appearance, luster, specific gravity, fracture, and cleavage all can be used to determine mineral identity.

Analyze Your Data

1. Although answers will vary, hardness and streak will likely be the properties cited as most useful. Color is usually the least helpful property.
2. Comparisons among groups will vary but should lead to discussions about different ways to test minerals.

Conclude and Apply

1. Students could choose hardness, cleavage/fracture, reaction to acid, or double refraction.
2. Properties easily field tested include color, luster, crystal shape, and the presence of cleavage and/or fracture.

LAB B (page 41)

Lab Preview

1. eye protection, clothing protection, irritant, sharp object, and disposal
2. Hardness, streak, color, appearance, luster, specific gravity, fracture, and cleavage all can be used to determine mineral identity.

Analyze Your Data

1. Although answers will vary, hardness and streak will likely be the properties cited as most useful. Color is usually the least helpful property.
2. Comparisons among groups will vary but should lead to discussions about different ways to test minerals.

Conclude and Apply

1. Students could choose hardness, cleavage/fracture, reaction to acid, or double refraction.
2. Properties easily field tested include color, luster, crystal shape, and the presence of cleavage and/or fracture.

Challenge

1. Streak is the color of a mineral when it is in powdered form. The color of the rock and the color of the streak may be different. For example, the mineral pyrite is gold in color. However, it leaves a greenish-black or brownish-black streak.
2. They could give more information on the structure and composition of the mineral. Chemical tests could tell what comprises the mineral. The X ray and the optical microscope could provide information about the crystalline structures that form the mineral.
3. Some measures may change. For example, a mineral's color or luster may change as it is exposed to other substances and elements. A mineral's density does not change; it remains constant.

Extension

Answers will vary, but should include the physical properties of hardness, cleavage/fracture, color, specific gravity, luster, streak, and crystal shape.

Chapter Test A (page 45)

I. Testing Concepts (page 45)

1. c
2. b
3. d
4. a
5. b
6. c
7. b
8. e
9. a
10. c
11. d

II. Understanding Concepts (page 46)

1. natural
2. inorganic
3. chemical
4. crystalline
5. no
6. yes
7. yes
8. no
9. yes
10. 2
11. 1
12. 2
13. 3
14. 1

III. Applying Concepts (page 47)

1. Possible response: It could be pyrite, or fool's gold. Both have the same appearance. A streak test would be more accurate. Gold leaves a yellow streak, and pyrite leaves a greenish-black or brownish-black streak.
2. Streak is the color of a mineral in its powdered form. A mineral is rubbed across a piece of unglazed porcelain tile. The color of the powder that results can often be used to help identify the mineral.
3. Possible responses: diamonds, rubies, sapphires, topaz, peridot, or amethyst
4. Possible response: Rubies are prized for their color and cut. They are also used to produce specific types of laser light.
5. A mineral or rock is an ore if it contains a useful substance that can be mined for profit. Aluminum is refined from the ore bauxite. During refining, aluminum oxide powder is separated from unwanted materials. Then the powder is converted to molten aluminum by a process called smelting.

Chapter Test B (page 49)

I. Testing Concepts (page 49)

1. false; solid
2. true
3. true

4. true
5. false; ions
6. true
7. true
8. false; luster
9. false; cleavage
10. false; useful
11. b
12. c
13. d
14. e
15. a
16. b
17. d
18. c
19. c
20. d
21. d
22. c
23. c
24. a
25. a

II. Understanding Concepts (page 50)

1. Minerals are inorganic; have a unique chemical composition; are formed by natural processes; and are all crystalline solids.
2. the type and amount of elements present in the magma
3. A collector would use the Mohs scale of hardness and would use scratch tests against known minerals.
4. Titanium is nontoxic, lightweight, and durable.
5. Coal is not a mineral because it is composed of decayed, once-living matter, and minerals are composed of inorganic matter.
6. Amethyst has an attractive color, due to traces of iron.
7. Advantages—Minerals are useful for construction, energy, and so forth; ores can produce a profit; gem minerals can be used in beautiful art and jewelry. Disadvantages—Some minerals cost more to mine than they are worth; removing waste rock from ore can be expensive; removing waste rock can be harmful to the environment.
8. locating the mineral
9. M, G
10. M, O
11. M, O
12. M
13. M
14. M
15. N

III. Applying Concepts (page 52)

Writing Skills

1. Both contain the useful metal titanium. Titanium can be refined from them profitably.
2. Many ores are found in vein mineral deposits. These deposits form when ions of metals dissolve in fluids and collect in weak parts of rock, such as in cracks and surfaces between layers. To remove the ore, miners also must remove the surrounding waste rock.
3. Sugar is made from plants—minerals are inorganic.
4. Many minerals formed as magma beneath Earth's surface cooled.
5. Some crystals form when magma cools. Some form when liquid evaporates and leaves the mineral material behind. Crystals that form in spacious areas grow regular structures. Grown in small spaces, crystals tend to be irregular in shape.
6. Silicates are minerals that contain silicon and oxygen—the two most abundant elements in Earth's crust—and usually one or more other elements. Silicon and oxygen combine to form the basic parts of most of the minerals in Earth's crust and mantle.

Chapter Test C (page 53)

I. Testing Concepts (page 53)

1. false—six
2. false—dry
3. false—rock material
4. true
5. true
6. synthetic
7. mineral
8. Amethyst
9. laser light
10. Quartz
11. ore
12. smelting
13. Aluminum
14. vein minerals

II. Understanding Concepts (page 54)

1. Minerals dissolve in water. → The water evaporates. → Ions that are left behind form crystals.
2. Magma rises to the surface and cools. → It combines into compounds arranged in orderly, repeating patterns.

3–8. peridot: gem, mineral; hematite: ore, mineral; tanzanite: gem, mineral; bauxite: ore, mineral; amethyst: gem, mineral; sapphire: gem, mineral

9. Graphite has a metallic luster. Fluorite has a nonmetallic, glassy luster.

III. Applying Concepts (page 55)

1. The new sample is probably pyrite, or fool's gold, which has an appearance similar to gold. However, the specific gravity of pyrite is about 5, while the specific gravity of gold is 19. The miner could measure the specific gravity or perform a streak test. Gold will have a yellow streak, while pyrite will have a greenish-black or brownish-black streak.

2. Gems are rare and beautiful, giving them aesthetic value. However, they can also be useful. Gems such as rubies are used to create laser lights. Diamonds are used on drill bits and saw blades, and quartz is used to help watches keep accurate time.
3. Corundum is likely harder than the porcelain tile. Since it is harder than the tile, it can't be scratched to leave a powder residue.
4. All minerals are formed by natural processes, are inorganic, have a definite chemical composition, and are crystal solids. Since coal is formed from plant matter, it is organic, not inorganic.
5. Cleavage and fractures are determined by the arrangement of a mineral's atoms. Because a mineral's atoms form a repetitive pattern, the mineral cannot have a pattern that results in both cleavage and fracture.
6. Weak or fewer bonds within the structures allow them to be broken along smooth, flat cleavage planes.

Rocks

LAB A (page 57)

Lab Preview

1. It warns you to wear goggles to protect your eyes when handling a substance such as hydrochloric acid.
2. Classifying igneous rocks relies on the use of a magnifying lens; classifying sedimentary rocks requires using a magnifying lens and a reaction test.

Conclude and Apply

1. to determine whether calcite was present; carbonates
2. Rocks of both textures form from sedimentary processes. Rocks with a granular, or clastic, texture are made of pieces of other rocks, minerals, and/or shells. Rocks with a nongranular texture are formed by chemical or organic means.

LAB B (page 59)

Lab Preview

1. It warns you to wear goggles to protect your eyes when handling a substance such as hydrochloric acid.
2. Classifying igneous rocks relies on the use of a magnifying lens; classifying sedimentary rocks requires using a magnifying lens and a reaction test.

Conclude and Apply

1. to determine whether calcite was present; carbonates
2. Rocks of both textures form from sedimentary processes. Rocks with a granular, or clastic, texture are made of pieces of other rocks, minerals, and/or shells. Rocks with a nongranular texture are formed by chemical or organic means.

Challenge

1. The rock samples with large grain size are probably intrusive rocks. Intrusive rocks form at depth, and they are surrounded by other rocks. It takes a long time for them to cool. Slowly cooled magma produces individual mineral grains that are large enough to be observed with the unaided eye.
2. Answers will vary. Possible response: Because we are located in a mountainous area, there are probably many igneous rocks that formed as a result of the magma pushing upwards when the mountains were formed.
3. Possible response: Grain size was a useful category, because it helped me to categorize the rock as intrusive or extrusive. Color was least helpful, because one of the granitic rocks was dark in color.

Extension

Charts will vary, but should include headings for metamorphic rocks and sedimentary rocks, with traits listed for each. Students should list texture, color, shape, mineral composition, and foliated/nonfoliated under traits for metamorphic rocks. They should list texture, color, shape, composition, sediment shape, and sediment size under traits for sedimentary rocks.

Chapter Test A (page 63)

I. Testing Concepts (page 63)

1. b
2. a
3. c
4. a
5. b
6. b
7. a
8. c
9. d

II. Understanding Concepts (page 64)

1–3. Order will vary: Sedimentary rocks, Igneous rocks, Metamorphic rocks
4–5. Order will vary: Heat and pressure, Hot fluids
6. magma type
7–12. Order will vary, but students should identify the following pairings:
basaltic: dense and dark
granitic: light-colored and low in density
andesitic: found around the rim of the Pacific Ocean

13. Heat and pressure cause rocks to melt and magma to form.
14. Magma cools, and atoms and compounds in the liquid rearrange to form mineral grains.

III. **Applying Concepts (page 65)**
1. igneous
2. sedimentary
3. metamorphic
4. sedimentary
5. metamorphic
6. igneous
7. A rock is a mixture of minerals and other materials such as rock fragments, volcanic glass, organic matter, or other natural materials.
8. The igneous rock could be formed from molten lava that has cooled. Weathering and erosion cause the rock to be broken into smaller fragments. These fragments might later compact and cement together to form a sedimentary rock.

Chapter Test B (page 67)

I. **Testing Concepts (page 67)**
1. d
2. a
3. b
4. b
5. a
6. b
7. c
8. d
9. c
10. d
11. a
12. d
13. b
14. b
15. d
16. c
17. d

II. **Understanding Concepts (page 68)**
1. true
2. false—igneous rocks are formed from three basic types of lava—basaltic, andesic, and granitic
3. false—foliated rocks have tightly-pressed-together layers (or) nonfoliated rocks have no layers
4. false—sedimentary rock can form from changes in igneous rock; igneous rock can form from changes in sedimentary rock
5. true
6. false—metamorphic rocks can form from igneous and sedimentary rocks
7. D
8. A
9. C
10. B
11. low silica content
12. below
13. Granite has visible crystals; pumice has no visible mineral grains and is full of holes.
14. Lava flows from a volcano.
15. The mineral grains in granite are flattened under pressure.

III. **Applying Concepts (page 70)**
1. sedimentary
2. igneous
3. sedimentary
4. igneous
5. metamorphic
6. metamorphic
7. sedimentary

IV. **Writing Skills (page 70)**
1. Detrital, chemical, and organic rocks are all sedimentary rocks, but they form in different ways. Detrital rocks are made from broken fragments of other rocks. These sediments are compacted and cemented together. Chemical sedimentary rocks form when minerals are precipitated from a solution or are left behind when a solution evaporates. Organic rocks form from the remains of once-living things.
2. It has no beginning; rocks are constantly changing form from one type to another.

Chapter Test C (page 71)

I. **Testing Concepts (page 71)**
1. false—neither destroys nor creates
2. true
3. false—Magma
4. false—less dense
5. false—above
6. magma, igneous
7. Intrusive
8. Extrusive
9. temperature, fluids
10. order will vary: water, carbon dioxide
11. mineral composition
12. layers, bottom
13. Sediments
14. compaction
15. Cementation

II. **Understanding Concepts (page 72)**
1. A. Material sources 1. Igneous rocks 2. Sedimentary rocks 3. Other metamorphic rocks
B. Causes of change 1. Heat and pressure 2. Hot fluids
2. Concept map should show detrital → formed from broken fragments from other rocks; chemical → formed from the deposits of minerals that come out of solution; organic → formed from the remains of once-living things
3. 2
4. 3

5. 1
6. sedimentary rock formation
7. 1
8. 3
9. 2
10. metamorphic rock formation
11. 3
12. 1
13. 2
14. igneous rock formation

III. Applying Concepts (page 73)

1. igneous
2. sedimentary
3. igneous
4. sedimentary
5. igneous
6. metamorphic
7. metamorphic
8. sedimentary
9. Basaltic rock is denser, so the box containing that rock would feel heavier. Once the boxes were open, the darker color of the basaltic rock would provide a further means of identification.
10. Answers will vary. Responses should include the idea that quartz, feldspar, and mica are minerals, not rocks. They combine with other materials to create rocks.
11. Answers will vary. Diagrams should show igneous, sedimentary, and metamorphic rocks along with the processes that form them (weathering and erosion, heat and pressure, melting and cooling). Diagrams should include arrows indicating that the rock cycle is a dynamic process.

Earth's Energy and Mineral Resources

LAB A (page 75)

Lab Preview

1. local gas and electric companies, the library
2. heat, water heater, kitchen appliances, televisions, radios, computers, washer and dryer, etc.

Analyze Your Data

Budgets should list major supplies needed as well as their costs. Students should realize that some energy-efficient designs are prohibitively expensive, but many methods for improving energy efficiency are affordable.

Conclude and Apply

Possible answer: Energy-efficient homes conserve Earth's natural resources and reduce environmental damage, but they are often expensive. Readily available and affordable renewable energy sources are yet to be developed.

LAB B (page 77)

Lab Preview

1. local gas and electric companies, the library
2. heat, water heater, kitchen appliances, televisions, radios, computers, washer and dryer, etc.

Analyze Your Data

Budgets should list major supplies needed as well as their costs. Students should realize that some energy-efficient designs are prohibitively expensive, but many methods for improving energy efficiency are affordable.

Conclude and Apply

Possible answer: Energy-efficient homes conserve Earth's natural resources and reduce environmental damage, but they are often expensive. Readily available and affordable renewable energy sources are yet to be developed.

Challenge

1. Possible answers: Homes lose energy through roofs, ceilings, doors, and windows when they are not insulated or installed properly.
2. Possible answer: The location would determine the type of resource available, such as the amount of wind, access to geothermal sources, or availability of hydropower. The location would also influence the home design. In southern Texas, more energy would be used to cool than heat. A home based in Texas might be designed to have a patio or overhang to reduce solar energy on western windows.
3. Answers will vary.

Extension

Possible recommendations include energy efficient appliances, double-paned windows, insulation, fluorescent lightbulbs, maintaining air conditioning and heater units, and using automated thermostats.

Chapter Test A (page 81)

I. Testing Concepts (page 81)

1. false—natural gas
2. true
3. false—fewer
4. false—Anthracite
5. false—liquid
6. true
7. d
8. e
9. a
10. b

11. c
12. f

II. **Understanding Concepts (page 82)**

1. gas
2. oil
3. roof rock
4. reservoir rock
5. oil, natural gas, and coal
6. coal, natural gas, oil, and nuclear
7. 94 percent
8. Currently, energy from renewable resources is often more expensive to produce. Also, some sources such as geothermal, electric, and hydroelectric are limited to certain areas.
9. D
10. A
11. D
12. D
13. I
14. R
15. I
16. I
17. I
18. R
19. R
20. R

III. **Applying Concepts (page 83)**

1. Possible responses: Hematite and bauxite are metallic mineral resources. Sylvite, halite, corundum, garnet, aggregate, gypsum, granite, and sandstone are nonmetallic mineral resources.
2. Ores are influenced by supply and demand. An ore's value is dependent on how much of it is available, how easily accessible it is, and how many people want it.
3. The mineral must be in demand. Enough of it must be present in the deposit to make it worth removing. It also must be fairly easy to separate the mineral from the material in which it is found.
4. Only a few areas are conducive to creating significant energy supplies.

Chapter Test B (page 85)

I. **Testing Concepts (page 85)**

1. b
2. e
3. c
4. l
5. p
6. q
7. j
8. n
9. a
10. o
11. g
12. d
13. k
14. i
15. h
16. c
17. b
18. a
19. d
20. d
21. b
22. c
23. a
24. c
25. b

II. **Understanding Concepts (page 86)**

1. gas
2. oil
3. roof rock
4. reservoir rock
5. petroleum
6. nuclear
7. other
8. hydroelectric
9. natural gas
10. coal

III. **Applying Concepts (page 87)**

1. 5
2. 2
3. 1
4. 3
5. 4

IV. **Writing Skills (page 88)**

1. Nuclear energy from fission is a nonrenewable energy resource because it uses uranium-235. Also, the waste material from nuclear energy consists of highly radioactive elements that must be carefully disposed of.
2. Water is pumped into rock near magma bodies or through hot, dry rocks. The heat turns the water into steam. The steam is then used to turn turbines that run generators to make electricity.
3. Answers will vary. Answers may include recycling old newspapers and magazines, soft drink cans, and plastic bottles.
4. Answers will vary. Inexhaustible and renewable resources are used less than nonrenewable resources because they are often too expensive (such as distilling biomass), or they generate toxins (such as burning garbage), or our technology is limited (such as solar energy storage).

Chapter Test C (page 89)

I. **Testing Concepts (page 89)**

1. false—have become tilted or folded
2. false—ethanol
3. false—geothermal
4. true
5. false—Oil
6. peat; lignite; bituminous; anthracite
7. land reclamation
8. Methane hydrates
9. Fission
10. smelting
11. energy
12. solar
13. sediment; erosion
14. geothermal

II. **Understanding Concepts (page 90)**

1. Diagrams will vary but should include the roof rock, reservoir rock, gas, and oil.
2. oil

3. nuclear
4. hydroelectric
5. biomass
6. geothermal, wind, solar, and other
7. coal
8. natural gas
9. coal, natural gas, oil, and nuclear
10. 94 percent
11. Currently, energy from renewable resources is often more expensive to produce. Also, some sources such as geothermal, electric, and hydroelectric are limited to certain areas.

12–14. (Order and answers may vary.) Possible response: the Sun; wind; geothermal

15–17. (Order and answers may vary.) Possible response: trees; alcohol; garbage

18. N
19. M
20. N
21. M
22. N
23. N

III. Applying Concepts (page 91)

1. No, it would not be classified as an ore. While it meets two criteria (it is in demand and there is enough there to make it worth removing), it does not meet the third criterion, because it is difficult to separate from the surrounding rock.
2. We currently have the technology to mine and use fossil fuels easily. They are reasonably priced. However, fossil fuel resources are nonrenewable and limited. The mining process can also damage the environment. Nuclear power is more abundant, especially through nuclear fusion, but nuclear fission produces radioactive waste materials.
3. For a resource to be classified as a reserve, the fuel must be able to be extracted economically. Currently, it is difficult to extract methane hydrates from the ocean floor.

Views of Earth

LAB A (page 93)

Lab Preview

1. A topographic map is a map that uses contour lines to show the landscape in three dimensions.
2. It uses contour lines.

Analyze Your Data

1. Students should note that their models approximate the shape of landforms on their maps. One strength is the fact that the sand models actual land features. One weakness is that it is difficult to keep the sand from shifting.
2. If the same scale is not used, the shape of the landform will be distorted. Indicating how the model was exaggerated will help explain distortions in the model.

Conclude and Apply

1. The contour interval is based on how great the change in elevation is on the map.
2. 100 meters; 5 meters

LAB B (page 95)

Lab Preview

1. A topographic map is a map that uses contour lines to show the landscape in three dimensions.
2. It uses contour lines.

Analyze Your Data

1. Students should note that their models approximate the shape of landforms on their maps. One strength is the fact that the sand models actual land features. One weakness is that it is difficult to keep the sand from shifting.
2. If the same scale is not used, the shape of the landform will be distorted. Indicating how the model was exaggerated will help explain distortions in the model.

Conclude and Apply

1. The contour interval is based on how great the change in elevation is on the map.
2. 100 meters; 5 meters

Challenge

1. Possible response: Topographic maps are used to plan the location of roads and buildings. They are used to find natural resources. If they are not accurate, a road or building could be built in a dangerous location. Companies could waste money looking for resources in the wrong location.
2. An aerial photograph and a topographic map both show Earth's surface from a bird's eye view. However, an aerial photograph does not show the elevations of the surface. An aerial photograph could aid in the construction of a topographic map by showing the locations of various landforms and features.
3. Benchmarks need to be placed in permanent locations. A boulder probably will not move or be easily destroyed.

Extension
Models will vary. Students should show an understanding of topographic mapping. The contour lines should be close around hills and basins. The contour lines should never cross, and they should form Vs that point upstream when they cross a stream.

Chapter Test A (page 99)

I. Testing Concepts (page 99)
1. b
2. a
3. d
4. c
5. c
6. c
7. b
8. b
9. e
10. c
11. d
12. a

II. Understanding Concepts (page 100)
1. 60°N
2. 90°W
3. Point B
4. earlier

5–7. order will vary: large, flat area; found in interior regions; thick, fertile soil

8–10. order will vary: flat, raised areas; edges rise steeply; made up of uplifted rocks

11. fault-block
12. folded
13. volcanic
14. upwarped
15. 210 m
16. 20 km

III. Applying Concepts (page 101)
1. Upwarped mountains have high peaks and sharp ridges. Fault-block mountains have majestic peaks and steep slopes. Volcanic mountains are cone-shaped structures.
2. Chicago and Boston are in different time zones. When it is 4:00 in Chicago, it is 5:00 in Boston. The friends forgot to consider the time zones.
3. equator: South America, Africa; prime meridian: Europe, Africa, Antarctica
4. The hiker should choose the trail that has closer contour lines. The closer together the contour lines are, the steeper the elevation.
5. Possible response: A computer can create a three-dimensional model of a landform.
6. The sea level rises and falls. For instance, during the last ice age, the coastal plain was larger than it is now. Much of Earth's water was contained in glaciers.

Chapter Test B (page 103)

I. Testing Concepts (page 103)
1. i
2. a
3. r
4. c
5. k
6. f
7. n
8. s
9. d
10. b
11. h
12. l
13. g
14. j
15. m
16. p
17. q
18. t
19. o
20. e
21. b
22. c
23. a
24. b
25. b
26. d
27. a
28. b
29. c
30. a
31. c
32. c
33. c
34. d

II. Understanding Concepts (page 105)
1. 10 cm
2. 55 m
3. 10 m
4. 150,000 cm = 1.5 km
5. 30° N, 90° W
6. 60° N, 90° E
7. sea level
8. latitude
9. Robinson

III. Applying Concepts (page 106)
1. Both are landforms that are flat. However, plateaus rise steeply from the land around them.
2. 50°
3. 11:00 P.M. on Friday
4. c
5. b
6. d
7. a

IV. Writing Skills (page 106)

1. Remote sensing using computers, radar, sonar, and satellites has made it possible to make a much greater variety of detailed maps of both land and sea features.
2. The Rocky Mountains have high relief, so the contour interval would be large.
3. A Mercator projection map has parallel latitude lines and parallel longitude lines. The map shows the shapes of the continents accurately, but the areas near the poles are very distorted. A Robinson projection map has parallel latitude lines and curved longitude lines. It shows the areas more accurately than the Mercator map.

Chapter Test C (page 107)

I. Testing Concepts (page 107)

1. geologic map
2. Landsat
3. topographic map
4. Conic projection map
5. three-dimensional map
6. scale
7. legend
8. series
9. International Date Line
10. time zones
11. contour line
12. projection
13. false—Himalayas
14. false—fault-block
15. true
16. true

II. Understanding Concepts (page 108)

1. It is a Mercator projection map, because it has lines of longitude that are parallel to each other.
2. Areas near the poles appear bigger than they actually are.
3. They are traveling across several time zones.
4. no
5. 30 degrees
6. Possible response: Plains and plateaus are both large, flat areas. Plains are found mostly in the interior regions of continents. They usually have thick, fertile soil, with thick grass and few trees. Plateaus are found at higher elevations. They also differ from plains in that their edges rise steeply from the land around them.
7.

Mountain Type	Description
folded mountains	form when rock layers are squeezed from opposite sides
upwarped mountains	form when Earth's crust is pushed up by forces inside Earth
fault-block mountains	form when some rock blocks move up, and others move down
volcanic mountains	form when molten material reaches the surface through a weak area of crust

8. 800 km
9. 60 degrees

III. Applying Concepts (page 109)

1. Mercator projection and conic projection maps are both used for navigation. Both maps distort land masses near the poles to appear bigger than they are. The conic projection map also has distortions around the equator. Mercator projection maps are often used on ships, while conic projection maps are often used by car drivers. Conic projection maps are generally used for small areas.
2. A weather map is often a conic map. The driving directions would likely come from a road map, which would be a conic map. A contour map would be useful in choosing a trail with steep elevation; the closer together the contour lines are, the steeper the elevation of the land. Finally, the hiker's car uses a global positioning satellite (GPS) system to send position signals from a satellite back to Earth.
3. The plains are best suited for agriculture. They often have thick, fertile soil. There are also meadows to support livestock. Plateaus are not as well suited, because they have steep sides and rocky areas.

4. Both are imaginary lines that are used to locate positions on Earth. Latitude lines are horizontal and run parallel to the equator. The distance between lines of latitude remains consistent. Longitude lines are vertical lines. The prime meridian is the reference point for longitudinal lines. The lines of longitude get closer together as they reach the poles.
5. Answers will vary, but students should identify the area as a plain, a plateau, or mountainous.

Weathering and Soil

LAB A (page 111)

Lab Preview

1. Answers will vary but could include water, wind, temperature, pressure, acids, etc.
2. They could break down the chalk into smaller and smaller fragments.

Analyze Your Data

1. Acid; answers will vary.
2. The greater the surface area, the faster the weathering because there is more contact with the acid.

Conclude and Apply

1. Material in the chalk reacted with vinegar.
2. Heat increases the rate.
3. Chemical weathering is faster in the tropics and slower in polar regions.

LAB B (page 113)

Lab Preview

1. Answers will vary but could include water, wind, temperature, pressure, acids, etc.
2. They could break down the chalk into smaller and smaller fragments.

Analyze Your Data

1. Acid; answers will vary.
2. The greater the surface area, the faster the weathering because there is more contact with the acid.

Conclude and Apply

1. Material in the chalk reacted with vinegar.
2. Heat increases the rate.
3. Chemical weathering is faster in the tropics and slower in polar regions.

Challenge

1. She should make one sculpture rather than two, because less surface area will be exposed to contact. She should place the sculpture in a garden located in a cool area, as heat speeds up chemical weathering.
2. Order will vary. most effect: chalk in vinegar, broken chalk, heated vinegar
   least effect: chalk in water, whole chalk, room temperature vinegar
3. The small flakes were not a result of chemical weathering. The chalk is a soft surface, and the flakes were rubbed off the chalk when it came into contact with another surface.

Extension

Responses will vary, but should show an understanding of how acid rain is produced and the consequences that increasing the acidity of water can have on the soil, including increased erosion.

Chapter Test A (page 117)

I. Testing Concepts (page 117)

1. d
2. a
3. c
4. a
5. d
6. c
7. false—acid
8. true
9. true
10. false—topsoils
11. false—Terracing

II. Understanding Concepts (page 118)

1. d
2. c
3. a
4. b
5. X
6. [blank]
7. X
8. X
9. [blank]
10. X
11. X
12. mechanical
13. mechanical
14. chemical
15. mechanical
16. chemical
17. chemical
18. Weathering occurs over a short period of time.
19. Minerals containing iron are exposed to water and to the oxygen in air.

III. Applying Concepts (page 119)

1. Farmers can employ several techniques to protect the soil. Many farmers use no-till farming, in which plant stalks are left in the field over the

winter months. This year-round covering helps to protect the soil from water runoff and soil erosion. Another method is contour farming. Plants are placed along the natural contours of the land, slowing the flow of water down the slope and helping prevent the formation of gullies.

2. The cave was likely the result of chemical weathering. Caves form when slightly acidic groundwater dissolves limestone.
3. When forests are removed, soil is exposed and erosion increases. This is especially serious in tropical rain forests, because the soil is almost infertile below the first few centimeters. The soil is useful to farmers for only a few years before the topsoil is gone. Farmers then clear new land, repeating the process and increasing the damage to the soil.
4. Chemical weathering is more rapid in warm, wet climates, such as tropical rain forests. The lack of moisture in deserts slows down chemical weathering.
5. Most soils have three horizons. The A horizon is the top layer of soil. The A horizon is generally dark and fertile. The dark color is caused by the humus, which provides nutrients for plant growth. The B horizon is below the A horizon. Less organic matter is added to this horizon, so it is lighter in color than the A horizon and contains less humus. The C horizon consists of partially weathered rock and is the bottom horizon in the soil profile. It is often the thickest soil horizon. It does not contain much organic matter.

Chapter Test B (page 121)

I. Testing Concepts (page 121)

1. d
2. a
3. d
4. b
5. b
6. c
7. a
8. a
9. b
10. c
11. d
12. c
13. b
14. b
15. a
16. d
17. c
18. b
19. a
20. c

II. Understanding Concepts (page 122)

1. c
2. b
3. a
4. a
5. b
6. c
7. effect
8. cause; Plants grow into cracks in the rocks, causing wedges to form and the rocks to break apart.
9. effect
10. cause; Because cattle eat all the grass on the land, wind and water are able to carry away the topsoil.
11. cause
12. effect; Because the area has a rainy climate and a lot of plants, the soil is rich with humus.
13. rock weathers; plants begin to grow; animals such as insects and worms appear; plants and animals die and decay; humus forms; humus and weathered rock mix and form soil
14. contour farming—planting along the natural contours of the land; terracing—building flat areas of land on sides of slopes on which plants can be grown

III. Applying Concepts (page 124)

1. oxidation
2. Chemical weathering
3. Leaching
4. mechanical weathering
5. soil
6. ice wedging
7. Humus
8. soil profile
9. contour farming
10. no-till farming
11. shelter belts

IV. Writing Skills (page 124)

12. Weathering helps break rocks down into smaller pieces called sediments. Sediments gradually change into soil. Plants need soil to grow in, and we need plants for food and other resources. Weathering turns rock into soil.

Chapter Test C (page 125)

I. Testing Concepts (page 125)

1. false—topsoil
2. true
3. false—water
4. false—runoff, erosion
5. false—slows, reduces
6. true
7. Soil
8. humus, nutrients
9. litter, organic
10. water, A, B

11. horizons
12. profile
13. rocks, vegetation

II. **Understanding Concepts (page 126)**

1. I. Soil conservation
   - A. Manage crops
     1. Shelter belts of trees
     2. No-till farming
   - B. Reduce erosion on slopes
     1. Contour farming
     2. Terracing
   - C. Reduce erosion of exposed soil
     1. Spraying water in construction areas
     2. Reclaiming land after mining
2. 2
3. 1
4. mechanical
5. 1
6. 2
7. chemical
8. 2
9. 1
10. mechanical
11. Diagrams will vary but should include the following elements: horizon A is dark and fertile; horizon B is lighter than horizon A and contains materials moved down from level A through leaching; horizon C is often the thickest level. It does not contain much organic matter, and it is coarser than the horizons above.

III. **Applying Concepts (page 127)**

1. On steep slopes, soils often are poorly developed because material moves downhill before it can be weathered much. In bottomlands, sediment and water are plentiful. Bottomland soils are often thick, dark, and full of organic material.
2. Possible answer: Burning down trees to create farmland is harmful to Earth, especially to the soil. When forests are removed, soil is exposed and erosion increases. This is serious in tropical rain forests, because the soil is almost infertile below the first few centimeters. The soil is useful to farmers for only a few years before the topsoil is gone. Farmers then clear new land, repeating the process and increasing the damage to the soil.
3. Possible answer: Climate influences the soil types. Deserts are dry. The soil contains little organic material and has a thin layer of topsoil. The soil in a tropical rain forest is moister and has a thin layer of topsoil. Climate also affects the rate of chemical weathering. Chemical weathering is more rapid in warm, wet areas such as tropical rain forests. Lack of moisture in deserts slows down chemical weathering.
4. Possible answer: The groundwater will be more acidic than the pure water. As water seeps through soil, it reacts with carbon dioxide in the air below the surface to form carbonic acid, causing the groundwater to be slightly acidic.
5. The city in the Northeast experiences ice wedging, during which water enters cracks in rocks and freezes. Because the water expands when it turns to ice, pressure builds up in the cracks. This pressure can extend the cracks and break apart the rock. The ice melts, allowing more water to enter the crack, where it freezes and breaks the rock even more. This ice wedging can cause potholes to form in roads. The city in the Southwest would not get cold enough to have much pothole damage from ice wedging.

Erosional Forces

Lab A (page 129)

Lab Preview

1. To protect eyes from blowing sand.
2. Yes. The more powerful the wind, the more material it can move around.

Analyze Your Data

1. Results could vary slightly with variations in experimental design and procedure.
2. The greater the wind speed, the larger the sediments it moved.

Conclude and Apply

1. When energy of motion increases, erosion increases. The greater the wind speed, the greater the amount of erosion.
2. Moist sediments are not easily eroded.

Lab B (page 133)

Lab Preview

1. To protect eyes from blowing sand.
2. Yes. The more powerful the wind, the more material it can move around.

Analyze Your Data

1. Results could vary slightly with variations in experimental design and procedure.
2. The greater the wind speed, the larger the sediments it moved.

Conclude and Apply

1. When energy of motion increases, erosion increases. The greater the wind speed, the greater the amount of erosion.
2. Moist sediments are not easily eroded.

Challenge

1. If the dryer were closer or at a different angle, it would cause the wind to hit with more or less force.
2. Because the dry sand was easier to pick up than the wet sand, the desert would be more susceptible to wind erosion than the beach.
3. The construction company could leave as much of the vegetation as possible. Where they do remove vegetation, they could add some gravel or keep the soil moist to help reduce the soil erosion.

Extension

Students should understand that creating a windbreak blocks the wind and decreases the amount of sand erosion by trapping the sand on the beach.

Chapter Test A (page 137)

I. Testing Concepts (page 137)

1. b
2. d
3. a
4. c
5. e
6. b
7. c
8. a
9. d
10. a
11. b
12. d

II. Understanding Concepts (page 138)

1. rockfall
2. rock slide
3. slump
4. creep
5. mudflow
6. In a rockfall, the rock tumbles freely through the air. In a rock slide, the rock slides down the slope.
7. During slump, the mass movement occurs on a curved surface. During creep, the mass movement occurs along a downhill slope.
8. They all involve the movement of sediment, and they all are a result of the force of gravity.
9. 3
10. 1
11. 2
12. 5
13. 4

III. Applying Concepts (page 139)

Writing Skills

1. Order of first two may vary: scouring, plucking; till; outwash
2. Till is a mixture of different-sized pieces of sediment that is deposited when a glacier retreats. Outwash is material deposited by meltwater from a glacier. Both are sediments formed as a result of glacier action.
3. A dune is a mound of sediment blown by the wind. The wind sweeps around or over an obstacle, such as the scrub brush. Sediment is dropped when the air's energy decreases. Sediment starts to build up behind the obstacle. The sediment itself then becomes an obstacle, trapping even more of the material. If the wind blows long enough, the mound will become a dune.
4. Gravity is always an agent of erosion. When you build homes on steep slopes, you must constantly battle naturally occurring erosion. Removing the vegetation that once existed on the slope causes additional problems and speeds up the erosion process. Also, some steep slopes are prone to slumps because of weak sediment layers underneath.

Chapter Test B (page 141)

I. Testing Concepts (page 141)

1. a, b, g
2. a, e, f
3. a, h, i
4. a, d, e h
5. b
6. i
7. k
8. e
9. g
10. a
11. d
12. j
13. h
14. f
15. c
16. water
17. Star
18. 10
19. windbreaks
20. Grooves
21. *Abrasion* is similar to sandblasting.
22. Much farmland of the midwestern United States is on fertile soil that developed from *loess* deposits.
23. Agents of erosion *deposit* sediments when they lose their energy of motion.
24. *Cirques* are bowl-shaped basins resulting from glacial erosion in the sides of a mountain.
25. *Planting vegetation* is one of the best ways to reduce erosion.

II. Understanding Concepts (page 142)

1. 3, 1, 4, 2
2. 4, 1, 5, 3, 2
3. slump
4. creep

5. rock slides
6. mudflows
7. Slump takes place on slopes when loose materials or rock layers slip downward as one large mass. Creep takes place on hills where sediments move very slowly downslope.
8. I. Glacial Erosion
   A. Scouring
   B. Plucking
   II. Glacial Deposition
   A. Till
      1. Moraine deposits
   B. Outwash deposits
      1. Eskers

III. Applying Concepts (page 144)

Writing Skills

1. The prevailing winds in this area are from the west and northwest, causing sand to build up on the beaches on the eastern and southeastern shores. These winds tend to blow the sand on the western shore into the lake before the sand reaches an obstacle.
2. The plot in the country could suffer more wind erosion. The major city's buildings would help protect the city plot from wind erosion. The country plot is also more likely to suffer from water erosion. The city plot would be protected from heavy runoff by curbs.
3. Because the roots of wheat are not strong or deep, they would not hold the soil as well as prairie grass. As a result, erosion of the soil might occur when it rains. To stop the erosion, the farmer could leave some of the prairie grass and plant trees as windbreaks around the field. If the field is on a slope, the farmer might build walls or install a drainage system.

Chapter Test C (page 145)

I. Testing Concepts (page 145)

1. wear away, move
2. drop, lose
3. gravity, down slope
4. cirques
5. arête
6. horn
7. (Order may vary.) continental, valley
8. retreat
9. windbreaks
10. grass(es)
11. Plucking occurs when boulders, gravel, and sand are picked up and added to the bottom and sides of a glacier.
12. When a glacier melts and retreats, it leaves behind sediment. Till, moraine, and outwash are kinds of sediment deposits left behind.
13. Wind erodes Earth's surface by deflation and abrasion.
14. Over time, windblown deposits develop into landforms such as dunes and accumulations of loess.

II. Understanding Concepts (page 146)

1. Concept maps will vary, but should include the following: rockfalls (blocks of rock break loose from a steep slope and tumble through the air), rock slides (layers of rock slip downslope suddenly), slump (a mass of material slips down along a curved surface), creep (sediments slowly shift their positions downhill), and mudflow (thick mixture of sediment and water flowing down a slope).
2. A curved scar is left where the slumped materials originally rested. Creep is generally slower and leaves behind curved trees and bent posts.
3. A rockfall would have a group of rocks, while a rock slide would have an entire layer of rock.
4. When glaciers melt, striations, or grooves, can be found on the rocks beneath. I could infer that a glacier had once traveled over these rocks.
5. Valleys that have been eroded by glaciers have different shapes from those eroded by streams. Valleys eroded by streams are normally V-shaped, while glacially eroded valleys are U-shaped.

III. Applying Concepts (page 147)

1. Possible response:
   (Order of I & II below may vary.)
   I. Glacial Erosion
   (Order of A & B below may vary.)
   A. scouring
   B. plucking
   II. Glacial Deposition
   (Order of A & B below may vary.)
   A. till
      1. moraine deposits
   B. outwash
      1. eskers
2. Possible response: Erosion is a concern. One of the best ways to reduce erosion is to plant vegetation. The roots will bind the soil together, reducing the risk of mass movement. Walls of concrete or boulders can also help reduce erosion by holding the soil in place. Water, which can cause a mudslide, is another issue. Plants help absorb water. Drainage pipes can also be inserted into the slope, preventing water from building up and making the slope more stable.
3. Possible response: Deflation and abrasion are both forms of wind erosion. Deflation occurs when wind blows across loose sediment, removing small pieces. Abrasion occurs when windblown sediment strikes rock and the surface gets scraped and worn away. Beaches and deserts have fewer plants to hold the sediments in place. When wind blows over

them, they can be eroded rapidly. The grasslands and prairies have many plants that hold the soil in place, so there is little soil erosion caused by wind.

4. A sand dune is forming. Sand dunes form when wind sweeps around or over an obstacle. Sediment starts to build up behind the obstacle, trapping even more sediment. The scrub brush is acting as an obstacle to trap the sand, creating a sand dune. If they removed the scrub brush, there would be no obstacle to collect the sand.
5. The walls can act as obstacles for the sand. They would eventually form a sand dune, which would keep the beach from eroding.

Water Erosion and Deposition

LAB A (page 149)

Lab Preview

1. Water could make the floor slippery, creating a safety problem.
2. to allow gravity to make the water flow

Conclude and Apply

1. Constants: amount of sand, elevation of the slope, the amount of time water ran on the slope; variables: water speed, amount of water that ran on the slope, amount of sand eroded by water.
2. the fastest water speed
3. the fastest water speed
4. The faster the water moves, the greater the erosion that occurs.
5. The steeper the slope, the faster the water flows and the more it erodes.
6. When water flows through streams and rivers, it erodes soil and carries it to other areas. These processes change the shape of the land.

LAB B (page 151)

Lab Preview

1. Water could make the floor slippery, creating a safety problem.
2. to allow gravity to make the water flow

Conclude and Apply

1. Constants: amount of sand, elevation of the slope, the amount of time water ran on the slope; variables: water speed, amount of water that ran on the slope, amount of sand eroded by water.
2. the fastest water speed
3. the fastest water speed
4. The faster the water moves, the greater the erosion that occurs.
5. The steeper the slope, the faster the water flows and the more it erodes.
6. When water flows through streams and rivers, it erodes soil and carries it to other areas. These processes change the shape of the land.

Challenge

1. The water would have run off into the existing channels.
2. The water would pool instead of running into streams, because gravity would pull it straight down.
3. You would decrease the slope. The water would flow more slowly down the hill, allowing more time for the water to be absorbed by the sand.

Extension

Responses will vary, but may include creating artificial gullies to collect and divert the water, reducing the steepness of the slope by creating terraces or ledges, and planting vegetation such as grass and trees.

Chapter Test A (page 155)

I. Testing Concepts (page 155)

1. carbonic acid
2. rainwater
3. absorbed
4. cracks
5. cave
6. b
7. c
8. e
9. a
10. d
11. c
12. e
13. b
14. a
15. d

II. Understanding Concepts (page 156)

1. old stream
2. young stream
3. mature stream
4. 3
5. 1
6. 2
7. The groundwater system has connecting pores.
8. The soil has few pore spaces and is not well connected.
9. Water reaches a layer of impermeable rock.
10. Rocky Shorelines: cliffs, rocks
    Sandy Beaches: smooth, beaches, gently sloping;
    both: wind erosion, water erosion

III. Applying Concepts (page 157)

1. delta
2. alluvial fan
3. spring
4. geyser

5. There are several factors that influence runoff. The amount of rain and the length of time are two factors. More rainfall over a shorter time period creates more runoff. Gravity influences runoff by pulling water downhill. The steepness of a slope also influences runoff; a steeper slope causes the water to run faster, which means more runoff. Vegetation slows runoff.
6. Rill erosion begins when a small stream forms during a heavy rain. As this stream flows down the same path, it creates a channel on the slope where the water eroded the soil. If water frequently flows in the same channel, rill erosion may change over time into gully erosion. During gully erosion, a rill channel becomes broader and deeper.
7. Possible response: Waves break rocks and seashells down to sand-sized particles. The constant wave motion bumps sand grains together. This bumping not only breaks particles into smaller pieces, but also smoothes their jagged corners, making them more rounded.
8. If there is a drought, the amount of water in the water table will decrease. This will make less water available to wells. If the drought is severe, the water could dry up.

Chapter Test B (page 159)

I. Testing Concepts (page 159)

1. t
2. o
3. b
4. w
5. e
6. j
7. g
8. d
9. v
10. f
11. a
12. r
13. u
14. c
15. k
16. m
17. l
18. q
19. n
20. h
21. s
22. p
23. i
24. true
25. false; An aquifer is a layer of permeable rock containing water. (or) A cave is an underground opening caused by acids dissolving rock.
26. true
27. true
28. false; Waves shape shorelines by eroding and redepositing sediments
29. d
30. b
31. b
32. b
33. b

II. Understanding Concepts (page 161)

1. 3
2. 1
3. 2
4. b
5. a
6. c
7. c
8. a
9. b

III. Applying Concepts (page 162)

Writing Skills

1. Heavy rains or melting snow can cause a river to flood. Dams are built to control the flow of water downstream, and levees are built along the sides of a river. The purpose of both is to prevent flooding.
2. Answers will vary. A community's groundwater source may be over used, insufficient, or polluted.
3. Answers will vary. Like all seashore features, barrier islands are short-term landforms. They are easily damaged by storms and human activities such as construction.
4. Answers will vary. As water runs off the land, it may carry pollutants with it to the streams it enters.
5. Pounding waves break-up rocks and carry away sediment at rocky shorelines. Some of this sediment is carried by longshore currents to other points where the waves tend to be less violent. There these sediments are deposited and combined with finely broken-up minerals and pieces of shell, they form sandy beaches.

Chapter Test C (page 163)

I. Testing Concepts (page 163)

1. false—rocky shores
2. false—length of time it falls
3. true
4. true
5. false—permeable rock
6. Rill erosion
7. channel
8. gully erosion
9. Sheet erosion
10. stream erosion
11. stalagmite
12. calcium carbonate
13. artesian well

14. suspended
15. bed

II. **Understanding Concepts (page 164)**

1. Answers will vary but should include rainwater → soaks into ground → reaches impermeable rock → fills up pores
2. old stream
3. young stream
4. mature stream
5. rocky shorelines
6. sandy beaches
7. erode
8. waves; sand

III. **Applying Concepts (page 165)**

1. water forming a triangular shape as it empties into a lake or ocean
2. water emptying from a mountain valley into an open plain
3. water flowing out of the ground and collecting in pools
4. water shooting high in the air
5. Beaches are deposits of sediment that are parallel to the shore. Each beach is made up of different materials, depending on its location and the types of rocks and shells that form the deposit. For example, black sands are made of basalt; green sands may have the mineral olivine; and white sands may be made of coral and shell fragments.
6. Groundwater keeps going deeper until it reaches a layer of impermeable rock. When this happens, the water stops moving, and the water begins filling up the pores in the rocks. The area where all of the pores in the rock are filled is the zone of saturation. The upper surface of this zone is the water table. If the rock never hit impermeable rock, it would continue to be absorbed deeper and deeper, and there would not be a water table to supply water to plants and animals.
7. It may have come from groundwater. Water mixes with carbon dioxide to form a weak acid called carbonic acid. Some of this carbon dioxide is absorbed from the air by rainwater. Most carbon dioxide is absorbed by groundwater as it moves through soil.

Plate Tectonics

LAB A (page 167)

Analyze Your Data

1. Predictions will likely match the locations of plate boundaries.
2. Answers will depend on data collected. Most occur along plate boundaries. Hot spot eruptions may not coincide with plate boundaries.

Conclude and Apply

1. by collecting more data points
2. Yes; it would provide more data, which would help to more closely pinpoint these areas.
3. Earthquakes occurred near convergent and transform boundaries. Volcanoes occurred near divergent boundaries and subduction zones.
4. Convergent ocean-ocean and ocean-continental boundaries where one plate is subducted under the other produce magma that rises and forms volcanoes. Volcanoes also form along divergent boundaries where magma rises through cracks in the crust, either at mid-ocean ridges or on land in rift valleys.

LAB B (page 169)

Analyze Your Data

1. Predictions will likely match the locations of plate boundaries.
2. Answers will depend on data collected. Most occur along plate boundaries. Hot spot eruptions may not coincide with plate boundaries.

Conclude and Apply

1. by collecting more data points
2. Yes; it would provide more data, which would help to more closely pinpoint these areas.
3. Earthquakes occurred near convergent and transform boundaries. Volcanoes occurred near divergent boundaries and subduction zones.
4. Convergent ocean-ocean and ocean-continental boundaries where one plate is subducted under the other produce magma that rises and forms volcanoes. Volcanoes also form along divergent boundaries where magma rises through cracks in the crust, either at mid-ocean ridges or on land in rift valleys.

Challenge

1. Earthquakes are common at convergent boundaries, where two plates collide. However, volcanoes do not form at convergent boundaries because there is no or little subduction. Transform boundaries are also common sites of earthquakes. When one plate slides past another, an earthquake occurs.
2. Mountains are often formed from compression forces when plates collide. Rift valleys and mid-ocean ridges form where Earth's crust separates.
3. As continental plates collide, the forces that are generated cause massive folding and faulting of rock layers into mountain ranges. The type of faulting produced is generally reverse faulting. Along a reverse fault, the rock layers above the

fault surface move up relative to the rock layers below, creating the conditions for formation of mountains and volcanoes.

Extension
Student models will vary, but should show rocks on either side of the fault moving past each other without much upward or downward movement.

Chapter Test A (page 173)

I. Testing Concepts (page 173)

1. true
2. false—youngest rocks
3. false—created
4. true
5. false—parallel
6. Alfred Wegner
7. Pangaea
8. Harry Hess
9. mid-ocean ridges
10. plates
11. plasticlike
12. lithosphere
13. convection current

II. Understanding Concepts (page 174)

1. divergent
2. convergent
3. transform
4. Fault-block mountains form.
5. A mid-ocean ridge forms.
6. Mountains form.
7. Chains of volcanic islands form.
8. An earthquake occurs.

III. Applying Concepts (page 175)

1. 2
2. 4
3. 1
4. 3
5. 5
6. According to the hypothesis of continental drift, continents were originally part of one large landmass called Pangaea. They have moved slowly to their current locations.
7. **a.** Fossil remains of animals such as *Mesosaurus* have been found on more than one continent (South America and Africa). Since this animal could not swim between continents, it supports the theory that the continents were once joined together.
   b. Fossils of plants such as *Glossopteris* have been found on multiple continents (Africa, Australia, India, South America, and Antarctica). Because the seeds could not travel so far, this supports the theory that the continents were once joined together.
   c. Glacial deposits have been found in Australia and Africa. Because there are no glaciers on these continents now, this supports the theory that they were once connected to colder continents.
   d. Similar rock structures have been found in locations where they were possibly joined. For instance, parts of the Appalachian Mountains are similar to those in Greenland and Western Europe.

Chapter Test B (page 177)

I. Testing Concepts (page 177)

1. b
2. d
3. d
4. d
5. c
6. d
7. a
8. c
9. b
10. a
11. c
12. c
13. a
14. c
15. c
16. b
17. b
18. d
19. b
20. plate tectonics
21. seafloor spreading
22. Convection currents
23. asthenosphere
24. plates
25. continental drift
26. lithosphere
27. Pangaea

II. Understanding Concepts (page 179)

1. Convergent plates move together. Divergent plates move apart.
2. Warmer material rises.
3. The edges of some continents looked as though they would fit together like a puzzle.
4. lithosphere
5. All were formed at convergent boundaries.
6. The Andes were formed at the convergent boundary of an oceanic plate and a continental plate. The islands of Japan were formed where two oceanic plates collided. The Himalayas formed where two continental plates collided.
7. Hot, less-dense material below Earth's crust is forced upward at the mid-ocean ridges. Then it turns and flows sideways, carrying the seafloor away from the ridge in both directions.

III. Applying Concepts (page 180)

1. The plates that collide to form the Himalayas crumple, but no subductions take place. Volcanoes occur above subduction zones.

2. When the continents were connected, they were covered with ice near Earth's south pole.
3. It's possible for ocean fish to swim all over the world, so they could have reached all continents.

IV. Writing Skills (page 180)

1. The *Glomar Challenger* had a drilling rig that allowed scientists to obtain rock samples from the seafloor. They discovered that the youngest rocks are located at the mid-ocean ridges. The rocks became increasingly older in samples obtained farther from the ridges, adding to the evidence for seafloor spreading.
2. As new crust is added in one place, it disappears below the surface in another. The disappearance of crust can occur when seafloor cools, becomes denser, and sinks. This occurs when two plates meet at a convergent boundary.

Chapter Test C (page 181)

I. Testing Concepts (page 181)

1. Alfred Wegner
2. Pangaea
3. seafloor spreading
4. mid-ocean ridge
5. magnetic reversal
6. magnetometer
7. plasticlike
8. crust; upper mantle
9. asthenosphere
10. subduction zone
11. convection currents
12. faults
13. separates
14. island arcs
15. Satellite Laser Ranging System

II. Understanding Concepts (page 182)

1. Concept maps should include the following: divergent boundaries: formed when two plates are moving apart; convergent boundaries: formed when two plates are moving together; transform boundaries: formed when two plates are sliding past each other.
2. Fault-block mountains form.
3. A mid-ocean ridge forms.
4. Mountains form.
5. Chains of volcanic islands form.
6. An earthquake occurs.
7. Possible answer: 1. Hot, less dense material below Earth's crust rises toward the surface at the mid-ocean ridge. 2. The material flows sideways, carrying the seafloor away from the ridge. 3. As the seafloor spreads apart, magma is forced upward and flows from the cracks. 4. It cools, contracts, and becomes denser. 5. The denser, colder seafloor sinks, helping to form the ridge.

III. Applying Concepts (page 183)

1. The evidence that Wegner presented was not enough to convince many people. He was unable to explain exactly how the continents drifted apart. He proposed that the continents plowed through the ocean floor, driven by the spin of Earth. Many strongly disagreed, yet Wegner could not offer another explanation.
2. 1. Fossil remains of animals such as *Mesosaurus* have been found on more than one continent (South America and Africa). Since this animal could not swim between continents, it supports the theory that the continents were once joined together. 2. Fossils of plants such as *Glossopteris* have been found on multiple continents (Africa, Australia, India, South America, and Antarctica). Because the seeds could not travel so far, this supports the theory that the continents were once joined together. 3. Glacial deposits have been found in Australia and Africa. Because there are no glaciers in these continents now, this supports the theory that they were once connected to colder continents. 4. Similar rock structures have been found in locations where they were possibly joined. For instance, parts of the Appalachian Mountains are similar to those in Greenland and Western Europe.
3. Diagrams should show convection currents in circular motion, causing dense materials to sink and lighter materials to rise to the surface.

Earthquakes

LAB A (page 185)

Lab Preview

1. The depth of earthquakes and the distance of their epicenters form the coast of a continent.
2. earthquake G

Conclude and Apply

1. Earthquake foci become deeper as epicenters are plotted toward the east.
2. Below this depth, the rock in the subducting slab can no longer behave rigidly. It becomes too hot.
3. One plate is subducting beneath a second plate. The subducting plate is moving east relative to the overriding plate.
4. The earthquakes are occurring because of subduction. Earthquakes occur in the comparatively cool and rigid sinking plate.
5. They are occurring along the western side of a continent.

6. Drawings should show an oceanic plate subducting beneath a continental plate. The western plate (oceanic plate) should have an arrow pointing east. The eastern plate (continental plate) should have an arrow pointing west.
7. The west coast of South America or the northwest coast of the North America; subducting slabs sink into the mantle with relative easterly motion at both of these locations.

LAB B (page 187)

Lab Preview

1. The depth of earthquakes and the distance of their epicenters form the coast of a continent.
2. earthquake G

Conclude and Apply

1. Earthquake foci become deeper as epicenters are plotted toward the east.
2. Below this depth, the rock in the subducting slab can no longer behave rigidly. It becomes too hot.
3. One plate is subducting beneath a second plate. The subducting plate is moving east relative to the overriding plate.
4. The earthquakes are occurring because of subduction. Earthquakes occur in the comparatively cool and rigid sinking plate.
5. They are occurring along the western side of a continent.
6. Drawings should show an oceanic plate subducting beneath a continental plate. The western plate (oceanic plate) should have an arrow pointing east. The eastern plate (continental plate) should have an arrow pointing west.
7. the west coast of South America or the northwest coast of North America; subducting slabs sink into the mantle with relative easterly motion at both of these locations.

Challenge

1. Most stress is at boundaries or edges, where rock is more likely to move and cause quakes than in central areas.
2. The closer an earthquake is to the surface, the higher the Richter score usually is.
3. I would expect to locate plate boundaries.

Extension

Student rankings will vary, but should indicate that the areas at greatest risk for earthquakes include the California coast, southern California, southern Illinois, southeastern Missouri, coastal South Carolina, the western edge of New York, and portions of Montana, Idaho, and Utah.

Chapter Test A (page 191)

I. Testing Concepts (page 191)

1. c
2. d
3. a
4. a
5. b
6. a
7. d
8. e
9. c
10. f
11. a
12. d
13. b

II. Understanding Concepts (page 192)

1. normal faults, reverse faults, strike-slip faults
2. 0 min 40 s
3. 1 min 20 s
4. 0 min 40 s
5. 2 min 40 s
6. 4 min 45 s
7. 2 min 5 s
8. primary
9. secondary

III. Applying Concepts (page 193)

1. As rocks move past each other along a fault, their rough surfaces catch, temporarily halting movement along the fault. However, forces keep driving the rocks to move. This builds up stress at the points where the rocks are stuck. The stress causes the rocks to bend and change shape. When they are stressed beyond their elastic limit, they can break, move along the fault, and return to their original shapes. This causes an earthquake.
2. The layers are crust, upper mantle, lower mantle, outer core, and inner core.
3. You are more likely to experience a damaging earthquake in California. It is located along a fault boundary.
4. To reduce the danger of injuries from falling objects, move heavy objects from high shelves. Learn how to turn off the gas, water, and electricity in your home. Make sure that water heaters and other gas appliances are held securely in place. Prepare an emergency kit.
5. Tension is the force that pulls rocks apart, and compression is the force that squeezes rocks together. Shear is the force that causes rocks on either side of a fault to slide past each other.
6. This is a sign of a tsunami. He should head for higher ground immediately.

Chapter Test B (page 195)

I. Testing Concepts (page 195)

1. elastic limit
2. come together
3. Secondary waves
4. epicenter
5. seismic waves
6. Richter Scale
7. lower

8. strike-slip
9. surface
10. epicenter
11. magnitude
12. Secondary waves
13. liquid
14. surface waves
15. first
16. earthquake
17. Moho
18. shadow zone
19. lithosphere
20. farther away
21. Primary waves
22. tension
23. move apart
24. Compression
25. reverse

II. Understanding Concepts (page 196)

1. 35 km
2. 2,200 km
3. 1,990 km
4. the solid inner core
5. the liquid outer core
6. solid mantle; 2,135
7. 2
8. 3
9. 1

Answer graph:

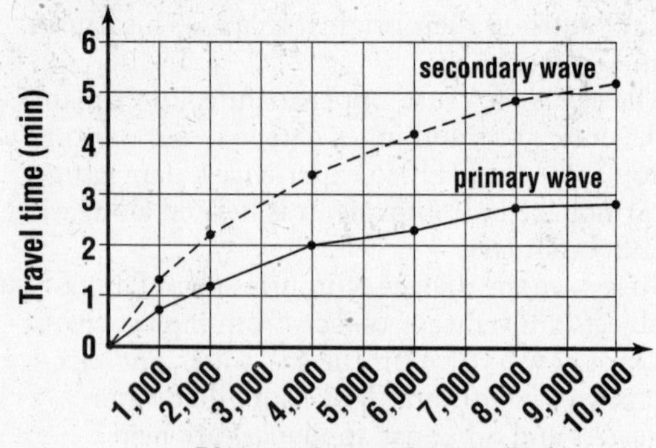

10. **a.** about 1 minute **b.** about 2 minutes
11. The difference in travel time increases as distances from the epicenter increase.

III. Applying Concepts (page 198)

1. e
2. a
3. b
4. d
5. c

IV. Writing Skills (page 198)

1. Seismologists at no fewer than three seismograph stations use the records of arrival times of primary and secondary waves to determine the distance to an epicenter. They draw circles around each station on a map. The radii of the circles they draw are equal to the distances from the stations to the epicenter. The point where all three circles intersect on the map is the epicenter of the earthquake.
2. Securing the appliances would keep them from moving a great deal during an earthquake. There would be less chance that the pipeline would jar loose and cause a gas leak or the appliance would break, which could lead to a fire or an explosion.
3. By studying seismic information, scientists noted that the paths and speeds of seismic waves change as they travel through different densities. By plotting these changes, scientists were able to develop a model of the layers of the interior of Earth.

Chapter Test C (page 199)

I. Testing Concepts (page 199)

1. false; height
2. false; intensity
3. true
4. true
5. true
6. focus
7. epicenter
8. liquefaction
9. tsunami
10. primary wave
11. secondary wave
12. Surface waves
13. asthenosphere
14. lithosphere
15. shadow zone

II. Understanding Concepts (page 200)

1. Concept maps should show the following: Normal faults form when rocks undergo tension; reverse faults form by compression forces; strike-slip faults form when rocks move past each other without much upward or downward movement.
2. 55 s; 2 min 25 s
3. The gap between the two lines would grow.
4. Surface waves are the slowest, so the gap would be even larger.
5. Seismographs register the waves and record the time that each wave arrived. A rolling drum vibrates, while a pendulum remains at rest. The stationary pen traces a record of the vibrations on the moving drums of paper.

III. Applying Concepts (page 202)

1. The second friend is correct. Earthquakes can occur anywhere on Earth where energy builds up in rocks. However, they are more likely on fault boundaries. California is located on a fault boundary, so it is more likely than other states in the U.S. to experience earthquakes.

2. The Richter magnitude scale is used to describe the strength of an earthquake and is based on the height of the lines on the seismogram. The Mercalli intensity scale describes the intensity of an earthquake using the amount of structural and geological damage in a specific location.
3. It could be built with seismic-safe structures to stand up to the vibrations, such as flexible circular moorings placed under the building to absorb the vibrations or steel rods to reinforce the walls. The builders could make shelves low to the ground. They could secure heavy items such as shelving and water heaters. They could also place sensors on utilities, so that they automatically turn off when vibrations are detected.

Volcanoes

LAB A (page 203)

Lab Preview

1. Students may create explosive model volcanoes.
2. Students may suggest that doing more than one trial will help verify their experimental process.

Analyze Your Data

1. Answers will vary, but students should note the shape and the materials used to make and fill the volcano.
2. Students should describe the process for quickly removing material from the interior and the collapse of the cone.
3. Students should describe a collapsed volcano.
4. Students should report any other observations.
5. Students should report additional recorded data.

Conclude and Apply

1. Observations should support hypotheses. Possible answer: Yes; quickly emptying the magma chamber produces a caldera.
2. In a real volcano, the eruption removes material quickly from the volcano's interior, causing the top to collapse. In the experiment, removing material from the interior of the model volcano causes the model to collapse in on itself.

LAB B (page 205)

Lab Preview

1. Students may create explosive model volcanoes.
2. Students may suggest that doing more than one trial will help verify their experimental process.

Analyze Your Data

1. Answers will vary, but students should note the shape and the materials used to make and fill the volcano.
2. Students should describe the process for quickly removing material from the interior and the collapse of the cone.
3. Students should describe a collapsed volcano.
4. Students should report any other observations.
5. Students should report additional recorded data.

Conclude and Apply

1. Observations should support hypotheses. Possible answer: Yes; quickly emptying the magma chamber produces a caldera.
2. In a real volcano, the eruption removes material quickly from the volcano's interior, causing the top to collapse. In the experiment, removing material from the interior of the model volcano causes the model to collapse in on itself.

Challenge

1. Possible answer: The conditions that caused the initial volcano to form are still present below the surface. There is a possibility of the presence of magma, which could be pushed to the surface again.
2. Yes. Possible answer: The forces of erosion could result in the formation of a caldera.
3. Possible answer: Calderas form in all types of volcanoes. Because all of the volcanoes have a magma chamber and can have large explosions, a lack of structure and support creates the possibility for magma to escape in all three cases.

Extension

Students may recreate the lab, creating a smaller and larger vent. Depending on the size of the vent, students may discover that a smaller vent does not create a caldera.

Chapter Test A (page 209)

I. Testing Concepts (page 209)

1. d
2. e
3. b
4. a
5. c
6. a
7. b
8. c
9. b
10. d
11. a

II. Understanding Concepts (page 210)

1. composite volcano; loose layers of tephra
2. cinder cone volcano; loose layers of tephra
3. shield volcano; flat layers of silica-poor lava

4. I. What controls eruptions?
   A. Trapped Gases
      (Order may vary.)
      1. Carbon dioxide
      2. Water vapor
   B. Composition of Magma
      1. Silica poor
         a. Basaltic magma
      2. Silica rich
         a. Granitic magma
      3. Medium silica
         a. Andesitic composition
5. sunken shape; the top of a volcano collapsing after an eruption.
6. tall, eroded shape; the softer cone eroding around the solid igneous core.

III. Applying Concepts (page 211)

1. Most volcanoes give enough warning for people to escape from an eruption. However, property is often damaged. Volcanic ash, if inhaled, can cause respiratory problems. Eruptions may also cause giant waves, which can endanger people and property.
2. Batholiths are the largest intrusive igneous rock bodies. They form when magma bodies that are being forced upward from inside Earth cool slowly and solidify before reaching the surface. A dike is formed from magma that is forced into a crack that cuts across rock layers and hardens. A sill forms when magma is forced into a crack parallel to rock layers and hardens.
3. At divergent plate boundaries, Earth's plates are moving apart, forming long, deep cracks. Lava flows through these rifts and is cooled quickly by seawater. As more lava flows and hardens, it builds up on the seafloor, forming a volcano.
   A convergent plate boundary forms where Earth's plates move together. This occurs as one plate slides below another. Volcanoes that form on convergent plate boundaries tend to erupt more violently than other volcanoes do. Magma forms when the plate sliding below another plate gets deep enough and hot enough to melt partially. The magma is forced upward to the surface, forming a volcano.
4. The type of magma determines what kind of eruption will occur. Basaltic lava is low in silica, and it is fluid. Its liquid state enables it to pour from volcanic vents and run down the sides of mountains. Granitic magma is silica-rich and thick. Gas gets trapped inside, causing pressure to build up. The gases expand rapidly, often carrying pieces of lava and causing explosive eruptions to occur.

Chapter Test B (page 213)

I. Testing Concepts (page 213)

1. b
2. a
3. b
4. a
5. b
6. d
7. c
8. a
9. c
10. c
11. false; Volcanic material comes in many different sizes, from ash to large rocks called blocks and bombs.
12. false; Magma is forced upward because it is less dense than the surrounding rock.
13. true
14. false; A volcanic neck forms when a volcano's cone erodes.
15. true
16. false; Most igneous activity takes place underground because most magma never reaches the surface.
17. false; People are still killed by volcanic eruptions.
18. false; A cinder cone volcano is caused by an explosive eruption. (or) A shield volcano is formed by a quiet eruption.
19. false; Volcanoes are related to the movement of Earth's plates; they frequently occur at plate boundaries.

II. Understanding Concepts (page 215)

1. **a.** 2
   b. 1
   c. 3
2. **a.** 3
   b. 2
   c. 1
3. composite volcano; alternating layers of lava and tephra
4. cinder cone volcano; loose layers of tephra
5. shield volcano; flat layers of silica-poor lava
6. Magma is squeezed into a generally vertical crack in rock below the surface.
7. Hardened magma forms a dike.
8. Silica-poor magma is very fluid and contains little silica; gases trapped in it can escape easily, so it produces quiet volcanic eruptions. Silica-rich magma is very thick and contains a lot of silica and water vapor; gases trapped in it are released under high pressure, so it produces explosive volcanic eruptions

III. Applying Concepts (page 216)

1. volcanic neck
2. composite
3. batholith
4. shield
5. caldera
6. cinder cone

IV. Writing Skills (page 216)

1. The movement that occurs at Earth's plate boundaries creates volcanoes in two ways. Either the plates separate and form rifts, from which magma flows and cools on the seafloor, or the plates collide and one plate is forced under the other plate. Magma then forms and moves to Earth's surface. Volcanoes form over hot spots because magma melts through these weak spots in Earth's crust.
2. Both contain gases. If the pressure is reduced gradually, the gases escape easily and there is a quiet eruption. But if the pressure stays high, once released the gases escape in an explosive eruption.

Chapter Test C (page 217)

I. Testing Concepts (page 217)

1. true
2. true
3. false; convergent
4. false; moving
5. false; scoria
6. pyroclastic flow
7. divergent
8. hot spots
9. crater
10. vent
11. acid rain
12. lung disease

II. Understanding Concepts (page 218)

1.

Types of Volcanoes	
Volcano	**Formation**
Composite	alternating layers of lava and tephra
Cinder cone	loose layers of tephra
Shield	flat layers of silica-poor lava

2. I. What controls eruptions?
    A. Trapped Gases
        1. Carbon dioxide
        2. Water vapor
    B. Composition of Magma
        1. Silica-poor
            a. Basaltic magma
        2. Silica-rich
            a. Granitic magma
        3. Medium silica
            a. Andestic composition
3. sunken shape; a dormant volcano
4. tall, eroded shape; a dormant volcano

III. Applying Concepts (page 219)

1. X
2. blank
3. X
4. X
5. blank
6. A batholith forms when magma bodies that are being forced upward from inside Earth cool slowly and solidify before reaching the surface. A sill forms when magma is forced into a crack parallel to rock layers and hardens. A dike forms when magma is forced into a crack that cuts across rock layers and hardens.
7. Concept maps will vary but should include pahoehoe, which is fluid and forms a rope-like structure; aa, which is stiff and slow moving; and pillow, which forms pillow-shaped lumps on the ocean floor.
8. Living near a volcano can be dangerous. Even a volcano that has not erupted for some time can potentially erupt. While people generally have time to evacuate, property can be destroyed by lava flow. The volcanic ash can cause respiratory problems. The gases can result in acid rain, which is harmful to groundwater.
9. There must be a source of magma and a vent to release the magma. Volcanoes often form at plate boundaries where plates are moving together or apart. They are also found at hot spots.

Clues to Earth's Past

LAB A (page 221)

Lab Preview

1. fossilized tracks and other evidence of the activities of organisms
2. Answers will vary, but students should show an understanding of how trace fossils are formed.

Analyze Your Data

1. Answers will be individualized and based on students' opinions of their research. Look for depth and quality of research performed.
2. Answers will vary depending on what materials students used. Clay would show three-dimensional fossils, whereas paper or fabric would be only two-dimensional.

Conclude and Apply

1. The models may be easier to interpret because they will not have any extraneous features and were not subject to weather or other factors that could damage them.

2. Answers will vary. Look for identification of behaviors like mating rituals or communication that wouldn't necessarily leave any marks on sediments for later fossilization.

LAB B (page 223)

Lab Preview

1. fossilized tracks and other evidence of the activities of organisms
2. Answers will vary, but students should have an understanding of how trace fossils are formed.

Analyze Your Data

1. Answers will be individualized and based on students' opinions of their research. Look for depth and quality of research performed.
2. Answers will vary depending on what materials students used. Clay would show three-dimensional fossils, whereas paper or fabric would be only two-dimensional.

Conclude and Apply

1. The models may be easier to interpret because they will not have any extraneous features and were not subject to weather or other factors that could damage them.
2. Answers will vary. Look for identification of behaviors like mating rituals or communication that wouldn't necessarily leave any marks on sediments for later fossilization.

Challenge

1. The rock could provide information about the climate and date of the fossil.
2. Yes; trace fossils are fossilized tracks and other evidence of an organism's activity.
3. They are not parts of the original organism.

Extension

Possible question topics include feeding patterns, locomotion, habitat, shelter, travel patterns, and solitary or herd behavior.

Chapter Test A (page 227)

I. Testing Concepts (page 227)

1. c
2. a
3. b
4. d
5. b
6. a
7. c
8. b
9. a
10. c
11. d

II. Understanding Concepts (page 228)

1. limestone
2. A
3. a fault
4. before
5. igneous intrusive feature
6. permineralized remains
7. carbon film
8. coal
9. mold
10. cast
11. original remains
12. trace fossils
13. angular unconformity
14. disconformity
15. nonconformity

III. Applying Concepts (page 229)

1. 10 g; 70 g
2. At each half-life, half of the parent material decays.
3. At each half-life, the half of the parent isotopes that are decayed transfer to a daughter isotope.
4. As the parent isotope decays, the daughter isotope grows.
5. By measuring the ratio of the parent isotope to the daughter product, one can determine the absolute age of rock. Living organisms less than 75,000 years old can be dated using carbon-14.
6. Whether or not a dead organism becomes a fossil depends on how well it is protected from scavengers and agents of physical destruction. Organisms also have a better chance of becoming a fossil if they have hard parts.
7. One way is to use fossil evidence. If the same types of fossils are found in limestone layers in both places, it is likely that the limestone at each location is the same age, and therefore one continuous deposit.

Chapter Test B (page 231)

I. Testing Concepts (page 231)

1. a
2. i
3. n
4. l
5. h
6. e
7. d
8. b
9. m
10. k
11. f
12. g
13. c
14. j
15. true
16. false; a permineralized bone is composed of a mineral, such as quartz, that has replaced the calcium
17. false; the hard parts of an organism are most likely to become fossils
18. true
19. true

20. false; only fossils up to 75,000 years old can be dated by carbon-14

II. **Understanding Concepts (page 232)**

1. hard parts

2–5 can be in any order.

2. permineralized
3. cast
4. trace fossils
5. index fossils
6. Relative dating compares layers of rocks; ages are stated relative to other layers. Absolute dating involves half-lives and can tell in which geologic period a rock was formed.
7. E, D, F, C, B, A
8. between B and A
9. 1—40g, 40g
   2—20g, 60g
   3—10g, 70g

III. **Applying Concepts (page 233)**

Writing Skills

1. The layers had to be there before the fault could form if the fault ran through the horizontal layers. The relative age of the rocks is older than the relative age of the fault.
2. Footprints may indicate how it walked; the rock type it is found in will indicate water or land; some traces may show how it rested or ate.
3. Correlating rock layers means matching exposed layers of rock in places that are apart from each other. You try to identify layers of rock in both places, matching the sequence of the layers of rock and any fossils in them. If the rock layers correlate, it means they are from the same rock formation and rock between the two locations has eroded.
4. Not all rocks contain fossils. Dead organic matter is usually destroyed by scavengers or bacteria. Only when the organism was quickly covered could it be preserved. Hard parts of organisms were less apt to be consumed or eroded by weather.
5. Half-life is the time it takes for half of the atoms in a radioactive isotope to decay. A geologist can measure the parent and daughter materials and, using the half-life of the parent material, calculate the length of time that has elapsed since the rock or fossil formed.

Chapter Test C (page 235)

I. **Testing Concepts (page 235)**

1. imprints
2. in comparison
3. absolute age
4. Radiometric dating
5. half-life
6. radioactive decay
7. true
8. false—bad
9. false—brief
10. false—youngest
11. false—unconformities
12. false—Carbon-14
13. true
14. true

II. **Understanding Concepts (page 236)**

1. E, D, F, C, B, A
2. A fault occurred between levels B and A, causing the sediment layers to separate and shift. An igneous intrusion occurred between levels C and D, causing an interruption in the rock layers through levels D and E.
3. Yes; because the fault caused a shift in the shale layer, causing it to appear in levels B and C, it is possible for the same index fossil to appear in both layers.
4. permineralized remains
5. carbon film
6. coal
7. mold
8. cast
9. original remains
10. trace fossils
11. angular unconformity
12. disconformity
13. nonconformity

III. **Applying Concepts (page 237)**

1. 40 g/40 g; 20 g/60 g; 10 g/70 g
2. The half-life of an isotope is the time it takes for half of the atoms in the isotope to decay. As the atoms in the parent material decay, they are transferred to the daughter product.
3. After many half-lives, such a small amount of the parent isotope would remain that it might not be measurable.
4. In beta decay, a neutron breaks down into a proton and an electron. In alpha decay, the isotope gives off two protons and two neutrons.
5. By measuring the ratio of the parent isotope to the daughter product, one can determine the absolute age of rock. Living organisms less than 75,000 years old can be dated using carbon-14.
6. The armored animal is most likely to form a fossil for two reasons. Animals with hard parts are more likely to become preserved, because scavengers are less likely to get at these hard parts, and they decay more slowly than soft parts. Also, the tar will bury the body quickly before scavengers or decaying organisms can attack the body.
7. It is possible that at one time these two rock structures were continuous. One way to confirm this is to use fossil evidence. If the same types of fossils are found in the limestone layer in both places, it is likely that the limestone at each location is the same age, and therefore one continuous deposit.

Geologic Time

LAB A (page 239)

Analyze Your Data
Answers will be subjective and based on students' individual research.

Conclude and Apply
Answers will be individualized and often based on the student's opinion of his or her research. Look for depth and quality of research performed.

LAB B (page 241)

Analyze Your Data
Answers will be subjective and based on students' individual research.

Conclude and Apply
Answers will be individualized and often based on the student's opinion of his or her research. Look for depth and quality of research performed.

Challenge
1. Answers will be based on students' individual research and will vary.
2. Answers will be based on students' individual research and will vary.
3. Answers will be based on students' individual research and will vary.

Extension
Answers will vary, but should show the chronological progression of the fossil record for the location.

Chapter Test A (page 245)

I. Testing Concepts (page 245)
1. d
2. b
3. a
4. c
5. c
6. c
7. d
8. b
9. c
10. a

II. Understanding Concepts (page 246)
1. 2
2. 4
3. 3
4. 1
5. Precambrian Time; Phanerozoic Eon; Paleozoic Era; Mesozoic Era; Cenozoic Era
6. Cyanobacteria produced oxygen, which helped change Earth's atmosphere.
7. Ancient fish had lungs as well as gills.
8. Some amphibians were able to survive farther away from water.
9. Some trilobites had eyes in the front of their heads.

III. Applying Concepts (page 247)
1. Possible response: By the end of the Paleozoic Era, sea levels had dropped, and the continents had come together to form one giant landmass, the supercontinent Pangaea. Because trilobites lived in the oceans, their environment was changed or destroyed.
2. During the Paleozoic Era, the ocean separating North America from Europe and Africa closed, and the African Plate collided with the North American Plate. This resulted in mountain-building. At the end of the Paleozoic Era, more than 90 percent of marine species and 70 percent of land species died off. These changes may have been due to changes in the climate and a lowering of the sea level.
3. Many Precambrian rocks have been so deeply buried that they have been changed by heat and pressure, and many fossils cannot withstand these conditions. In addition, most Precambrian organisms did not have hard parts, lessening their chances of being preserved as fossils.
4. During the Mesozoic Era, dinosaurs were the dominant land animals. Birds, mammals, and flowering plants appeared. During the Cenozoic Era, mammals became the dominant animals, with many new life-forms, including humans, appearing after the dinosaurs disappeared.
5. In natural selection, organisms best suited to their environments survive and produce the most offspring.
6. Dinosaur bones do not show ring structures like modern reptiles. Instead, they look more like mammal and bird bones, leading scientists to believe that dinosaurs may have been warm-blooded.

Chapter Test B (page 249)

I. Testing Concepts (page 249)
1. c
2. a
3. d
4. d
5. c
6. a
7. a
8. a
9. a
10. a
11. c
12. b
13. b
14. b
15. d
16. d
17. d
18. a

II. Understanding Concepts (page 250)
1. Plate tectonics changes Earth's environments. Species adapt to the changes or become extinct.
2. The breaking up of Pangaea changed climates and habitats. One type of organism that adapted was the reptile.

3. Competition with other species for food and overhunting might have led to the extinction of other mammals.
4. Their seeds are protected and enclosed in a fruit, allowing them to develop in varied environments.
5. evolution of cyanobacteria
6. disappearance of Ediacaran fauna
7. dinosaurs as dominant life-form
8. development of birds
9. appearance of humans
10. a. Quarternary; Holocene, Pleistocene; humans appear
    b. Tertiary; Pliocene, Miocene, Oligocene, Eocene, Paleocene; mammals abundant, angiosperms are dominant, dinosaurs were extinct

III. Applying Concepts (page 252)

1. As plates moved, continents collided with and separated from one another. This resulted in mountain building and the draining of seas, which caused changing environments. This process continues today. Thus species need to adapt to different environments.
2. Little is known because rocks from the Precambrian time have been buried deeply and changed by heat and pressure. They have been eroded more than more recent rocks. These changes have affected the fossil record as well. In addition, early invertebrates were soft-bodied and not easily preserved as fossils.
3. The reptile evolved an egg with a membrane that protected it from drying out. This enabled it to lay eggs in dry environments, rather than having to return to water to reproduce.
4. Mass extinctions of many land and sea animals occurred. These extinctions might have been caused when all the continental plates came together to form Pangaea, and the climate changed as a result.
5. Until Earth was shielded from ultraviolet rays, most organisms couldn't survive when exposed to the Sun.
6. Trilobites are marine animals. They were widespread during the Paleozoic era because seas covered much of Earth's surface then. Species of trilobites existed for short periods of time.
7. Precambrian life had primarily soft parts; during the Paleozoic era, animals with hard parts evolved.
8. They had common ancestors.
9. Animal life in the Mesozoic era included marine life, amphibians, and reptiles. Dinosaurs were dominant by the Jurassic period. By the early Cenozoic era, dinosaurs and many other life-forms were extinct. Birds and mammals had evolved.

Chapter Test C (page 253)

I. Testing Concepts (page 253)

1. false—geologic time scale
2. true
3. false—environment
4. false—Trilobites
5. false—Pangaea
6. true
7. false—extinction
8. false—mice and shrews
9. true
10. true
11. false—Amphibians

II. Understanding Concepts (page 254)

1. eon
2. era
3. period
4. epoch
5. vertebrates
6. dinosaurs
7. humans
8. trilobites
9. Phanerozoic Eon
   I. Paleozoic Era
      A. Trilobites live in oceans.
      B. First land plants appear.
   II. Mesozoic Era
      A. Dinosaurs roam Earth.
      B. Gymnosperms are abundant.
   III. Cenozoic Era
      A. Mammals are common.
      B. Angiosperms are abundant.
10. They produced oxygen, which helped change Earth's atmosphere.
11. Ancient fish had lungs as well as gills.
12. They were able to survive farther away from water.
13. They had eyes in the front of their heads.

III. Applying Concepts (page 255)

1. During the Mesozoic Era, Pangaea separated into two large landmasses: Laurasia and Gondwanaland. Laurasia, the northern mass, moved further north. This caused changes in the climate and vegetation. Species needed to adapt to survive these changing conditions.
2. Possible response: There are several possible reasons. First, the mammals were better suited to the changed environment. The mammals also no longer had to compete with the dinosaurs for food and resources.
3. This is very unlikely. Scientists have identified trilobites as an index fossil of the Paleozoic Era, which means that they existed only in that period.

4. Amphibian eggs were originally soft and needed to be in water to keep from drying out. Eventually, those eggs that were harder and had a membrane to keep them from drying out were the ones that survived and hatched. As those amphibians laid eggs, they passed on the trait for the hard, membrane-covered shell to their offspring. Eventually, the eggs were hard enough to survive outside of and farther away from water.
5. Angiosperm seeds are enclosed and protected. This enables them to live in a diverse range of climates and environments.
6. Cyanobacteria are thought to be one of the earliest forms of life on Earth. They contained chlorophyll and used photosynthesis. This is important because during photosynthesis, they produced oxygen, which helped change Earth's atmosphere. Following the appearance of cyanobacteria, oxygen became a major atmospheric gas.

Atmosphere

LAB A (page 257)

Lab Note: Review with students the proper safety precautions to take when working with electrical equipment. Emphasize that students should not touch the lamp as it can burn the skin when hot. Water and wet hands should be kept away from electrical cords and outlets. If the light must be moved while it is hot, wear heat-insulated gloves.

Lab Preview

1. Be careful when handling objects that can cause burns, such as an overhead light.
2. soil and water

Analyze Your Data

1. Graphs should show that energy absorption and release by soil is faster.
2. soil
3. Air above the land heated faster.

Conclude and Apply

1. Answers will vary depending on results.
2. soil
3. When the light was first turned off, the temperature above the soil was higher. After several minutes, the temperature above the water was higher. Soil absorbs and releases heat more quickly than water.

LAB B (page 261)

Lab Note: Review with students the proper safety precautions to take when working with electrical equipment. Emphasize that students should not touch the lamp as it can burn the skin when hot. Water and wet hands should be kept away from electrical cords and outlets. If the light must be moved while it is hot, wear heat-insulated gloves.

Lab Preview

1. Be careful when handling objects that can cause burns, such as an overhead light.
2. soil and water

Analyze Your Data

1. Graphs should show that energy absorption and release by soil is faster.
2. soil
3. Air above the land heated faster.

Conclude and Apply

1. Answers will vary depending on results.
2. soil
3. When the light was first turned off, the temperature above the soil was higher. After several minutes, the temperature above the water was higher. Soil absorbs and releases heat more quickly than water.

Challenge

1. During the evening, the ocean keeps its warm temperature, which helps to keep the area warm. However, in the desert, the sand loses its warmth quickly, helping to make the area cool.
2. Possible answer: Because water heats more slowly and cools more slowly, the addition of water to the soil would slow the heating and cooling rate slightly.
3. The water heats all summer. As the fall comes, the water is slower to cool than the surrounding ground. The warmth from the lake water helps to keep the area warmer than similar areas without a large body of water. The water has a moderating effect on the temperature.

Extension

Lab designs will vary, but should lead students to conclude that soil solarization increases the soil temperature.

Chapter Test A (page 265)

I. Testing Concepts (page 265)

1. atmosphere
2. troposphere
3. ionosphere
4. ozone layer
5. ultraviolet radiation
6. chlorofluorocarbons
7. water
8. jet streams
9. sea breeze
10. d
11. c

12. b
13. a

II. **Understanding Concepts (page 266)**
1. nitrogen
2. water vapor
3. oxygen
4. 8 degrees
5. 3 degrees
6. sand
7. 7 degrees
8. 1 degree
9. sand
10. radiation and convection
11. troposphere
12. stratosphere
13. mesosphere
14. thermosphere
15. exosphere

III. **Applying Concepts (page 267)**
1. Because of Earth's curved surface, the Sun's rays strike the equator more directly than areas toward the north or south poles.
2. As Earth's gravity pulls the gases toward the surface, the weight of these gases presses down on the air below. As a result, the molecules nearer Earth's surface are closer together. The dense air exerts more force than the less dense air near the top of the atmosphere.
3. Radiation from the Sun can be reflected into space, absorbed by the atmosphere, or absorbed by land and water on Earth's surface.
4. Water moves between the hydrosphere and the atmosphere through a continual process of evaporation and condensation. Condensation causes clouds. When the rain falls to Earth, it evaporates and repeats the cycle.
5. The Coriolis effect describes how the rotation of Earth causes moving air and water to appear to turn to the right north of the equator and to the left south of the equator.

Chapter Test B (page 269)

I. **Testing Concepts (page 269)**
1. b
2. a
3. d
4. c
5. c
6. a
7. d
8. c
9. a
10. c
11. b
12. c
13. c
14. d
15. a
16. b
17. b
18. a
19. d
20. c
21. c
22. a
23. b
24. a
25. c
26. c
27. e
28. b
29. a
30. d

II. **Understanding Concepts (page 271)**
1. sand
2. sand
3. The differences in the heating and cooling of land and water affect the movement of cool and warm air in the area.
4. Land warms more easily than water. During the day, the cooler, denser air from over water flows over the land and forces up the warm air; this is a sea breeze. Land cools more quickly than water. At night, the air above land cools, sinks, and moves out over water, forcing up the warmer air over the water. This is a land breeze.
5. oxygen
6. 0 to 4%
7. nearly four–fifths or more than three-fourths
8. 3
9. 1
10. 2

III. **Applying Concepts (page 272)**

Writing Skills
1. It's a layer in the stratosphere that absorbs most of the ultraviolet radiation from the Sun. Holes in the ozone layer expose us to too much UV radiation, which causes skin cancer and other health problems.
2. Smog is a form of pollution that can harm plants and damage our lungs.
3. Air pressure is greatest at sea level because there are more air molecules pushing down from above.
4. Because of Earth's rotation and the air's location in the southern hemisphere, the northbound air would appear to be turning to the west as Earth turns east.
5. The radiation can be reflected or escape back into space, be absorbed by the atmosphere, or be absorbed by land and water surfaces.

Chapter Test C (page 273)

I. **Testing Concepts (page 273)**
1. false—doldrums
2. false—tropical

3. true
4. true
5. false—Land breezes
6. temperature
7. electrically charged particles
8. ultraviolet radiation
9. chlorofluorocarbon
10. hydrosphere
11. condensation
12. Antarctica

II. Understanding Concepts (page 274)

1. nitrogen
2. trace gases, liquid elements such as water, and solid elements such as dust
3. "Major Gases in the Atmosphere"
4. The air above the sand is heated more rapidly than the air above the water.
5. The air above the sand is cooled more rapidly than the air above the water.
6. Land warms more easily than water. During the day, the cooler, denser air from over water flows over the land and forces up the warm air; this is a sea breeze. Land cools more quickly than water. At night, the air above land cools, sinks, and moves out over the water, forcing up the warmer air over the water. This is a land breeze.
7. Heat is transferred through radiation waves and convection flow.
8. troposphere
9. stratosphere
10. mesosphere
11. thermosphere
12. exosphere

III. Applying Concepts (page 275)

1. Concept maps should show the following: On Earth, radiation from the Sun can be reflected into space, absorbed by the atmosphere, or absorbed by land and water. Once it is absorbed, heat can be transferred by radiation, conduction, or convection.
2. Illustrations should demonstrate the following: Because of Earth's curved surface, the Sun's rays strike the equator more directly than areas toward the north or south poles.
3. The higher up you travel, the less weight pulls down on air molecules and the less dense the air is. This means there is less air pressure. Since the air molecules are less dense, there is less oxygen for people to breathe. The plane cabin is pressurized to increase the amount of air molecules.
4. Water moves between the hydrosphere and the atmosphere through a continual process of evaporation and condensation. Condensation causes clouds. When rain falls to Earth, it evaporates and repeats the cycle. Classification of world climates is commonly based on annual and monthly averages of temperature and precipitation.
5. The rotation of Earth causes moving air and water to appear to turn to the right north of the equator and to the left south of the equator.

Weather

LAB A (page 277)

Lab Preview

1. a British navy admiral who in 1805 invented a method for estimating wind speeds based on their effect on sails
2. by measuring the distances they travel in the wind

Analyze Your Data

1–3. Answers will vary.

Conclude and Apply

1. aid in weather forecasts, warn of severe weather, warn air traffic of dangerous winds, and decide on locations for using wind power to generate electricity
2. Answers will vary, but students should discuss how their instruments or measuring systems would measure and compare increases in wind speed or wind gusts.

LAB B (page 279)

Lab Preview

1. a British navy admiral who in 1805 invented a method for estimating wind speeds based on their effect on sails
2. by measuring the distances they travel in the wind

Analyze Your Data

1–3. Answers will vary.

Conclude and Apply

1. aid in weather forecasts, warn of severe weather, warn air traffic of dangerous winds, and decide on locations for using wind power to generate electricity
2. Answers will vary, but students should discuss how their instruments or measuring systems would measure and compare increases in wind speed or wind gusts.

Challenge

1. Answers will vary.
2. The scale measures approximate wind speed. It does not measure wind direction.
3. Possible response: In aviation, you need to know the wind speed and the wind direction.

Extension

Student models will vary. Students can create an approximation of a vertical-axis wind collector that can measure revolutions per minute. Students can poke two straws through a small paper cup, creating an X. At the end of each straw another small paper cup can be placed on its side, allowing wind to collect inside the cup. This can then be placed on top of a stick in the ground so that it can spin freely.

Chapter Test A (page 283)

I. Testing Concepts (page 283)

1. b
2. a
3. d
4. c
5. a
6. b
7. d
8. c
9. d
10. a
11. c
12. a

II. Understanding Concepts (page 284)

1. a
2. c
3. b
4. c
5. a
6. b
7. 147
8. –13
9. 18
10. 19

III. Applying Concepts (page 285)

1. A tornado is a violently rotating column of air in contact with the ground. In severe thunderstorms, wind at different heights blows in different directions and at different speeds. This difference in wind speed creates a rotating column parallel to the ground. A thunderstorm's updraft can tilt the rotating column upward into the thunderstorm, creating a funnel cloud. If the funnel comes into contact with the ground, it is called a tornado.
2. Fronts are the boundaries between two air masses of different densities, moisture content, or temperatures. Cloudiness, precipitation, and storms sometimes occur at frontal boundaries.
3. A storm warning means that severe weather conditions already exist. You should take immediate action. During a thunderstorm or tornado warning, take shelter in the basement or middle of the house away from windows. During a hurricane or flood warning, leave your home and move farther inland. During a blizzard, stay indoors.
4. Low-pressure systems at Earth's surface are regions of rising air. Clouds form when air is lifted and cools. Areas of low pressure usually have cloudy weather. Sinking motion in high-pressure air masses makes it difficult for air to rise and clouds to form. High pressure usually means good weather.
5. Meteorologists take measurements of temperature, air pressure, winds, humidity, and precipitation. Computers, weather satellites, Doppler radar, and instruments attached to balloons are used to gather data.
6. The Sun provides almost all of Earth's energy. Heat from the Sun is absorbed by Earth's surface, which then heats the air above it. Differences in Earth's surface temperature lead to uneven heating of Earth's atmosphere. Heat is eventually redistributed by air and water currents. Weather is the result of heat and Earth's air and water.

Chapter Test B (page 287)

I. Testing Concepts (page 287)

1. c
2. a
3. b
4. c
5. c
6. b
7. a
8. c
9. b
10. d
11. c
12. a
13. c
14. d
15. d
16. a
17. c
18. c
19. a
20. b
21. b
22. d
23. d
24. b
25. d

II. Understanding Concepts (page 289)

1. altostratus (2), cirrocumulus (3), cirrus (4), stratocumulus (1)
2. Ames only
3. falling; minus sign in front of 13 indicates pressure change
4. 18° C
5. 19° C
6. yes
7. A cold front forms when a cold air mass pushes under a warm air mass. The cold air pushes the warm air up rapidly, and a narrow band of

violent storms forms along the front, including thunderstorms. A warm front develops when a less-dense, warm air mass slides over a departing cold air mass. High cirrus clouds may form and produce precipitation.

8. Both are forms of precipitation, but sleet forms when rain passes through a layer of freezing air near the ground and freezes into ice pellets. Hail forms when drops of water freeze in layers around a small nucleus of ice. Hailstones grow larger as they are tossed up and down by rising and falling convection currents.
9. A cloud forms.

III. **Applying Concepts (page 290)**

Writing Skills

1. Some of the most severe thunderstorms produce tornadoes. Thunderstorms occur when the warm, moist air moves upward rapidly, cools, and condenses. In severe thunderstorms, winds at different heights blow in different directions and at different speeds. This difference in wind direction and speed is called wind shear. A strong updraft will tilt the wind shear and produce rotation inside the thunderstorm.
2. When the amount of humidity in the air begins to reach full saturation, the air feels damp and sticky; sweat cannot evaporate off our skin, making it difficult to cool off.
3. Meteorologists measure temperature, air pressure, winds, humidity, and precipitation at specific locations by using weather satellites, Doppler radar, computers, and instruments attached to weather balloons. They use this information to make weather maps, which are used to make weather forecasts.
4. As temperatures drop during the night, air near the ground cools to its dew point. The water vapor in the air condenses and forms water droplets on the grass.
5. A stationary front may remain in the same place for several days. Light wind and precipitation across the entire frontal region occur. As a result, it is possible for meteorologists to make more precise predictions about temperature, precipitation, and the like.

Chapter Test C (page 291)

I. **Testing Concepts (page 291)**

1. false—four; rain, snow, sleet, and hail
2. false—anticyclones
3. false—A stationary front
4. false—stratus
5. true
6. true

II. **Understanding Concepts (page 291)**

1. isotherm; isobar
2. tornado; hurricane; typhoon; cyclone
3. humidity; relative humidity; dew point
4. layered clouds, high in the sky
5. thick, puffy clouds with a high water content
6. layered clouds in the middle of the sky
7. thick, puffy clouds in the middle of the sky
8. layered clouds with a high water content
9. thick, puffy clouds in the lower sky
10. The barometric pressure is 147, and there has been a pressure change of 13. The temperature is 18, and the dew point is 19. Given the dew point and temperature, it is likely that the station is experiencing precipitation. Since it is below 32 degrees, the precipitation is probably in the form of snow.
11. cold front
12. warm front
13. occluded front
14. stationary front

III. **Applying Concepts (page 293)**

1. Rain, hail, sleet, and snow are all forms of precipitation. Air temperature determines which type of precipitation will form. Drops of water falling at temperatures above freezing fall as rain. Snow forms when the air temperature is so cold that water vapor changes directly to a solid. Sleet forms when raindrops pass through a layer of freezing air near Earth's surface, forming ice pellets. Hail forms in thunderstorms when water freezes in layers around a small nucleus of ice. Hailstones grow larger as they are tossed up and down by rising and falling air.
2. The Sun provides almost all of Earth's energy. It evaporates water to power the water cycle. It heats the air and ground, creating uneven heating of Earth's atmosphere. This uneven heating redistributes the air and water currents. The weather is the result of heat and Earth's air and water. Without the Sun's rays, there would be no changes to the weather.
3. Low-pressure systems are regions of rising air. Clouds form when air is lifted and cooled. Areas of low-pressure systems can have cloudy weather. It may be bad news, but you would need more information to determine if these clouds will produce rain.
4. A severe weather watch means that weather conditions are favorable for a severe storm. During a watch, monitor weather reports to check for changes in status. A severe weather warning means that severe weather conditions already exist. You should take immediate action. If there's a thunderstorm or tornado warning, you should take shelter in a basement or the middle of the house. For a hurricane or flood warning, you should evacuate or take shelter in a safe area. For a blizzard, you should stay inside.
5. The friend is wrong. A tornado can develop from a severe thunderstorm. In a severe thunderstorm,

winds at different heights blow in different directions and at different speeds. This creates a rotating column parallel to the ground. The thunderstorm's updraft can tilt the rotating column upward into the thunderstorm, creating a funnel cloud. If the funnel cloud comes into contact with the ground, a tornado is produced.

Climate

LAB A (page 295)

Lab Preview

1. Ask teacher to dispose of the glass.
2. Streets, parking lots, and buildings absorb solar radiation; pollution traps the warmed air, resulting in the heat-island effect.

Conclude and Apply

1. To see what the climate was like when not influenced by the building; when test sites were compared to the control, climatic effects caused by the building could be determined.
2. Answers will be subjective and based on the student's individual research.
3. Possible answers: shaded areas, walls blocking wind or rainfall. Students may infer that a large city would have similar microclimates because of the effects of the buildings.

LAB B (page 297)

Lab Preview

1. Ask teacher to dispose of the glass.
2. Streets, parking lots, and buildings absorb solar radiation; pollution traps the warmed air, resulting in the heat-island effect.

Conclude and Apply

1. To see what the climate was like when not influenced by the building; when test sites were compared to the control, climatic effects caused by the building could be determined.
2. Answers will be subjective and based on the student's individual research.
3. Possible answers: shaded areas, walls blocking wind or rainfall. Students may infer that a large city would have similar microclimates because of the effects of the buildings.

Challenge

1. Each would be a microclimate. The temperatures would probably be higher in the industrial park because of the buildings and asphalt. The buildings might also block the wind.
2. Understanding the variations in sunlight/shading, wind, and temperature in a microclimate will help gardeners to select the proper plants. For example, a gardener will plant a shade-loving plant next to a building that blocks the sunlight.
3. slope of the ground exposes the soil differently, type of vegetation/ground covering, and bodies of water

Extension

Student responses will vary, but should demonstrate an understanding of the variance in temperature, relative humidity, and precipitation in different areas around the school.

Chapter Test A (page 301)

I. Testing Concepts (page 301)

1. c
2. b
3. a
4. c
5. d
6. b
7. a
8. d
9. b
10. a
11. c
12. a

II. Understanding Concepts (page 302)

1. buildings
2. Answers will vary, but students should mention some form of energy conservation.
3. Answers will vary.
4. A city is located next to a large body of water. A city is located next to a large body of water, causing it to be warmer in winter.
5. In the tropics, the Sun shines almost directly over the area. In the tropics, the Sun shines almost directly over the area, causing the temperatures to be almost always hot.
6. Warm ocean currents from the equator flow toward higher latitudes. Warm ocean currents from the equator flow toward higher latitudes, warming the land areas they pass.
7. Earth's atmosphere is thinner at higher altitudes. Earth's atmosphere is thinner at higher altitudes, so there are fewer molecules to heat.
8. Air rises, cools, and drops moisture on the windward side of a mountain range. Air rises, cools, and drops moisture on the windward side of a mountain, leaving little precipitation for the leeward side.
9. Air pollution traps heat from sidewalks, roads, and buildings. Air pollution traps heat from sidewalks, roads, and buildings, making cities hotter than rural areas.

III. Applying Concepts (page 303)

1. He had six major groups: tropical, mild, dry, continental, polar, and high elevation. He subdivided each of the major groups into smaller groups.
2. Possible response: Bears undergo a period of greatly reduced activity in winter called hibernation. Lungfish use estivation to survive intense heat by burrowing into the mud and covering themselves in a leathery mixture of mud and mucus.
3. Seasons are short periods of climate change caused by changes in the amount of solar radiation an area receives. Because Earth is tilted, different areas of Earth receive changing amounts of solar radiation throughout the year.
4. El Niño can affect weather patterns. It can alter the position and strength of one of the jet streams. This changes the atmospheric pressure off California and wind and precipitation patterns around the world, and can cause drought in Australia and Africa. El Niño also affects monsoon rains in Indonesia and causes storms in California.
5. Possible response: Climatic change has many varied causes. Catastrophic events, short- or long-term changes in solar output, changes in Earth's movements in space, and the movement of Earth's plates can work separately or together to alter Earth's climate.
6. The greenhouse effect is a natural heating process that occurs when certain gases in Earth's atmosphere trap heat. Radiation from the Sun strikes Earth's surface and causes it to warm. Some of this heat then is radiated back toward space. Some gases in the atmosphere, known as greenhouse gases, absorb a portion of this heat and then radiate heat back toward Earth. This keeps Earth warmer than it would be otherwise.

Chapter Test B (page 305)

I. Testing Concepts (page 305)

1. c
2. a
3. b
4. d
5. b
6. b
7. d
8. c
9. a
10. b
11. a
12. b
13. c
14. d
15. a
16. d
17. a
18. b
19. c
20. b

II. Understanding Concepts (page 307)

1. c
2. These are two distinct things. The greenhouse effect is a natural heating process caused by gases in the atmosphere trapping heat. Global warming refers to the increase in average global surface temperatures, perhaps as a result of various human activities that increase certain atmospheric gases. Some of those gases, such as carbon dioxide, are the same ones responsible for the greenhouse effect.
3. Answers will vary. Examples might include: (1) reducing use of private automobiles by carpooling, substituting public transportation, or biking; (2) establishing tighter controls on industrial emissions and finding ways to recycle carbon dioxide wastes; (3) reducing the temperature to which buildings are heated and/or reducing the number of hours that they are heated
4. When moisture-laden wind comes off the ocean and runs into mountains, the winds rise, cool, and lose their moisture as rain. The fact that the strip of land is so narrow means that the rain falls in a small area. That might be why there is a rain forest in this area.
5. As one moves toward higher latitudes, sunlight strikes Earth from an angle closer to the horizon. The same amount of heat from solar radiation is therefore spread over a larger area of Earth's surface, meaning that it cannot raise that area's temperature as much.
6. The water's temperature does not rise or fall as rapidly as the temperature of the surrounding land. This results in a moderating influence on the temperatures of land that border the body of water: they are warmer in the winter and at night, and cooler in the summer and during the day, as compared to inland areas. Bodies of water also affect the amount of precipitation.
7. These animals avoid moving around during the heat of the day, and when there is little water available to drink, they get the moisture they need from the food they eat.
8. Trees take in carbon dioxide. When trees are cut down, more carbon dioxide remains in the atmosphere. Carbon dioxide is one of the greenhouse gases that contributes to global warming.
9. In the tropics, because water is more plentiful, there is no extreme cold, and an organism can adapt to temperature that does not vary greatly throughout the year.

III. Applying Concepts (page 308)

1. Burning fossil fuels, which releases carbon dioxide into the atmosphere, is one cause. Deforestation may be another because trees absorb

carbon dioxide naturally. When trees are removed, carbon dioxide remains in the atmosphere. When trees are burned, carbon dioxide is released into the atmosphere.

2. On one hand, the city's climate will be similar because it has the same lattitude and the same relationship to bodies of water and mountain ranges. On the other hand, it will be different for various reasons. More solar radiation is absorbed in the city than in the country because of streets, parking lots, and buildings, causing heat to build up. Industrial and automobile pollutants in the air tend to trap this heat. Also, skyscrapers affect wind and precipitation patterns.

Chapter Test C (page 309)

I. Testing Concepts (page 309)

1. true
2. true
3. true
4. false—downwind
5. false—sunspots
6. low angle
7. tropics
8. (Wladimir) Köppen
9. (Order will vary.) thick waxy stems; needles
10. (Order will vary.) temperature; hours of daylight
11. weaken; reverse
12. (Order will vary.) water vapor; carbon dioxide; methane
13. thick atmosphere
14. carbon dioxide

II. Understanding Concepts (page 310)

1. Possible answer: Each contributes approximately one third of the emissions.
2. natural sources of carbon dioxide, such as plants and volcanoes
3. Possible answer: "Human Sources of Carbon Dioxide in the U.S."
4. Possible answer: It will be warmer than inland cities during the winter.
5. Possible answer: The tropics have temperatures that are almost always hot.
6. Possible answer: They warm the land areas that they pass.
7. Possible answer: The mountain air has fewer molecules to heat.
8. Possible answer: The windward side of a mountain receives more precipitation than the leeward side.
9. Possible answer: Temperatures in cities are hotter than in rural areas.
10. Possible answer: The energy is spread over a larger area, so the zones never get warm.
11. Possible answer: Coastal areas often have wetter climates than places farther inland.

III. Applying Concepts (page 311)

1. Estivation and hibernation both describe periods of inactivity by animals. Hibernation occurs during winter months, while estivation occurs during the summer months.
2. Both behavioral and structural adaptations help organisms to survive in particular climates. A structural adaptation is a body structure, such as thick fur on polar bears or waxy skin on a cactus. A behavioral adaptation is a behavior, such as bees clustering together to keep warm or snakes hiding under rocks in the heat of the day, that helps an organism survive in the climate.
3. It won't be significantly cooler in December. Because of fairly constant solar radiation near the equator, the tropics do not have much seasonal temperature change. However, they do experience dry and rainy seasons.
4. This could possibly be the effect of El Niño. You could confirm this by studying the trade winds and water temperatures. During normal years, strong trade winds blow east to west along the equator, pushing warm surface water toward the western Pacific Ocean. Cold water is then forced up from the deep regions along the coast of South America. During El Niño years, these winds weaken and sometimes reverse. The change in the winds allows warm, tropical water in the upper layers of the Pacific to flow back eastward to South America. Cold water is no longer forced up from the ocean below.

Ocean Motion

LAB A (page 313)

Lab Preview

1. You should safely dispose of food items in any experiment.
2. to measure the extent to which the potato sinks

Analyze Your Data

1. As the salinity of the water increased, the potato became more buoyant.
2. If the salinity is lowered, denser objects will not float as well. The density of the object affects whether or not it will float. For example, a bobber will float in freshwater or salt water.

Conclude and Apply

1. Answers will vary.
2. Students might indicate that the ship will sink if it travels into freshwater.

LAB B (page 315)

Lab Preview

1. You should safely dispose of food items in any experiment.
2. to measure the extent to which the potato sinks

Analyze Your Data

1. As the salinity of the water increased, the potato became more buoyant.
2. If the salinity is lowered, denser objects will not float as well. The density of the object affects whether or not it will float. For example, a bobber will float in freshwater or salt water.

Conclude and Apply

1. Answers will vary.
2. Students might indicate that the ship will sink if it travels into freshwater.

Challenge

1. Possible response: The density of water increases as the temperature increases. The potato would have floated at lower salinity levels in boiling water.
2. The temperature of the water could have been different. Also, they may have used a larger container with more water. More water would require more salt to reach the same level of salinity.
3. The salt water weighs more, because it has the weight of the salt and the weight of the water.

Extension

Lab designs will vary, but should allow students to conclude that density influences buoyancy, while size does not.

Chapter Test A (page 319)

I. Testing Concepts (page 319)

1. c
2. b
3. a
4. e
5. f
6. d
7. a
8. c
9. d
10. b
11. c
12. a

II. Understanding Concepts (page 320)

1. B
2. D
3. A
4. C
5. density current
6. Gulf Stream
7. surface current
8. upwelling
9. 2
10. 1
11. 3
12. 2
13. 3
14. 1

III. Applying Concepts (page 321)

1. Scientists hypothesize that about 4 billion years ago, water vapor began to be stored in Earth's early atmosphere. Over millions of years, it cooled enough to condense into storm clouds. Torrential rains began to fall. Oceans were formed as storm water filled low areas on Earth called basins.
2. Oxygen enters the ocean in two ways: directly from the atmosphere and from organisms that photosynthesize. Carbon dioxide enters the ocean from the atmosphere and from organisms when they respire.
3. The ship sailing to the United States is going against the Gulf Stream, which can delay its travels west.
4. The California Current that flows along the West Coast of the United States is a cold surface current. The current begins near the poles where water is colder.
5. A density current forms when a mass of ocean water becomes denser than the surrounding water. Gravity causes denser ocean water to sink beneath less dense ocean water. This deep, dense water then slowly spreads to the rest of the ocean. The density of ocean water increases if salinity increases. It also increases when temperature decreases.
6. Water molecules in a wave move around in circles. Only the energy moves forward while the water molecules remain in about the same place. Below a depth equal to about half the wavelength, water movement stops.

Chapter Test B (page 323)

I. Testing Concepts (page 323)

1. b
2. a
3. d
4. d
5. b
6. c
7. d
8. a
9. a
10. b
11. b
12. b
13. d
14. a
15. d
16. true
17. gravity

18. spring
19. true
20. true
21. slowly
22. true
23. turn to the right
24. true
25. true
26. B
27. D
28. A
29. C

II. Understanding Concepts (page 325)

1. The Gulf Stream is a surface current. Ships ride the Gulf Stream current from North America to England.
2. Both are affected by the Sun and the Moon. During spring tides, high tides are higher and low tides are lower. During neap tides, high tides are lower and low tides are higher.

III. Applying Concepts (page 325)

1. c
2. a
3. h
4. f
5. e
6. i
7. b
8. d
9. g
10. j

IV. Writing Skills (page 326)

1. When the wind blows, it transfers energy to the water. If the wind speed is great enough, the water begins to pile up, forming a wave.
2. The cold deep water contains a lot of nutrients. Fish come to areas of upwelling to eat.
3. The explanation may include facts such as: High tides can cut off high land separated from the mainland by a stretch of low beach. Tides affect fish feeding areas. Low tides can strand boats.
4. Sailing to England, ships would get added speed from sailing with the Gulf Stream.
5. It flows to the Atlantic Ocean, where it forms the Mediterranean Intermediate Water.

Chapter Test C (page 327)

I. Testing Concepts (page 327)

1. basins
2. (Order will vary.) gases; salts
3. right
4. amplitude
5. amplitude; energy
6. decreases; increases
7. the Moon and the Sun
8. ocean floor
9. Drift bottles
10. steady state
11. few hundred meters
12. energy
13. High tide refers to an apparent rise in sea level. Low tide refers to the apparent drop in sea level.
14. During spring tides, high tides are higher and low tides are lower than normal. During neap tides, high tides are lower and low tides are higher than normal.

II. Understanding Concepts (page 328)

1. wave height
2. trough
3. crest
4. wavelength
5. density current
6. upwelling
7. surface currents
8. North Atlantic Deep Water
9. California Current
10. Gulf Stream
11. Mediterranean Intermediate Water
12. Possible response: 1. Seawater is piped into a glass-roofed building. 2. The sun heats and evaporates the water. 3. The water vapor is collected, and the salt is left behind.

III. Applying Concepts (page 329)

1. Ocean water consists primarily of dissolved gases and salts. You would want to check to see if the ocean was growing more or less salty. The proportion and amount of dissolved salts in seawater has remained nearly constant for hundreds of millions of years. The proportion of salts would tell if the composition of the oceans is in balance.
2. The current on the West Coast of the United States begins near the pole where water is colder. It flows through the California Current, bringing the colder water with it. The East Coast current originates near the equator, where the water is warmer. Warm surface currents distribute heat from equatorial regions.
3. Density currents would be stronger near the poles for two reasons. The temperature is lower near the poles. The density of water increases as temperature decreases. Because of this lower temperature, there is also more ice formation. As ice forms, ocean water freezes, and the salt is left behind in the unfrozen water. This extra salt increases the salinity, and therefore the density of the ocean water.
4. In the deep ocean, the water molecules in a wave move around in circles. Only the energy moves forward while the water molecules remain in about the same place. A wave changes shape in the shallow area near shore. The friction with the ocean bottom slows water at the bottom of the wave. As the wave slows, its crest

and trough come closer together. The wave height increases. The top of the wave, not slowed by friction, moves faster than the bottom. Eventually the top of the wave outruns the bottom and it collapses. The collapse of the wave propels the buoy forward.

5. They should factor in the speed of the wind, the distance over which the wind blows, and the length of time the wind blows.

Oceanography

LAB A (page 331)

Analyze Your Data

1. They can be used for food and as a raw material for products and medicines. For example, seaweeds are a source of iodine; algin from kelp is used in making ice cream, pudding, and paint; diatomaceous earth is used to make toothpaste and car polish; horseshoe crab blood is used to detect dangerous bacteria in fluids used on human patients.
2. Answers depend on products chosen. Possible answers: using synthetic sponges instead of sponges, using plastic or glass instead of pearls.

Conclude and Apply

1. Activities that pollute the oceans kill organisms.
2. Answers will vary depending on the product chosen. Alternative products may be more expensive.
3. Answers will vary.
4. Marine organisms are a good source of foods, medicines, and oxygen. Polluting the oceans may endanger these organisms.

LAB B (page 333)

Analyze Your Data

1. They can be used for food and as a raw material for products and medicines. For example, seaweeds are a source of iodine; algin from kelp is used in making ice cream, pudding, and paint; diatomaceous earth is used to make toothpaste and car polish; horseshoe crab blood is used to detect dangerous bacteria in fluids used on human patients.
2. Answers depend on products chosen. Possible answers: using synthetic sponges instead of sponges, using plastic or glass instead of pearls.

Conclude and Apply

1. Activities that pollute the oceans kill organisms.
2. Answers will vary depending on the product chosen. Alternative products may be more expensive.
3. Answers will vary.
4. Marine organisms are a good source of foods, medicines, and oxygen. Polluting the oceans may endanger these organisms.

Challenge

1. Most were from the continental shelf, because it is the most shallow and easiest to harvest.
2. Possible answer: More products will be mined in the future, as we better understand what is available and technology makes it easier to get at resources deeper in the ocean.
3. Both have issues of overharvesting, causing extinction of organisms and depletion of natural resources. Also, the surrounding ecosystem can be destroyed if resources are not harvested or mined with conservation in mind.

Extension

Student responses will vary depending on the organisms selected, but should demonstrate an understanding of the relationships between organisms.

Chapter Test A (page 337)

I. Testing Concepts (page 337)

1. d
2. a
3. b
4. c
5. true
6. false—is sinking beneath
7. true
8. false—continental shelf
9. false—Tide pools
10. true
11. true

II. Understanding Concepts (page 338)

1. continental shelf
2. continental slope
3. abyssal plain
4. ocean trench
5. mid-ocean ridge
6. nekton
7. plankton
8. benthos
9. benthos
10. plankton
11. nekton
12. 3
13. 2
14. 1
15. 5
16. 4
17. 6

III. Applying Concepts (page 339)

1. A mid-ocean ridge is an area where new ocean floor is formed. Crustal plates are moving constantly. When ocean plates separate, hot magma from Earth's interior forms new ocean crust. New ocean floor forms along mid-ocean ridges as lava erupts through cracks in Earth's crust. When the lava hits the water, it cools quickly into solid rock, forming new seafloor.
2. Many mineral deposits such as petroleum, natural gas, and limestone can be found on the continental shelf. Other mineral deposits, such as manganese nodules, silver, and iron, can be found in deep water.
3. Sewage, industrial wastes, oil, solid waste, and sediment are the main types of pollution entering ocean water.
4. Several things can be done to prevent ocean pollution. You can dispose of waste properly and volunteer for beach cleanups. You can recycle materials such as newspaper, glass, and plastics and dispose of chemicals, oil, and paint properly.
5. On the ocean floor, subduction zones are marked by deep ocean trenches.
6. In the deep ocean, sediment derived mostly from land settles constantly on the ocean floor. These deposits fill in valleys and create the flat seafloor of an abyssal plain.
7. The continental shelf is a gradual sloping at the end of a continent that extends into the ocean. The continental slope is where the ocean floor drops more steeply.

Chapter Test B (page 341)

I. Testing Concepts (page 341)

1. continental slope
2. pollutant
3. placer deposits
4. producers
5. plankton
6. abyssal plains
7. Benthos
8. silt

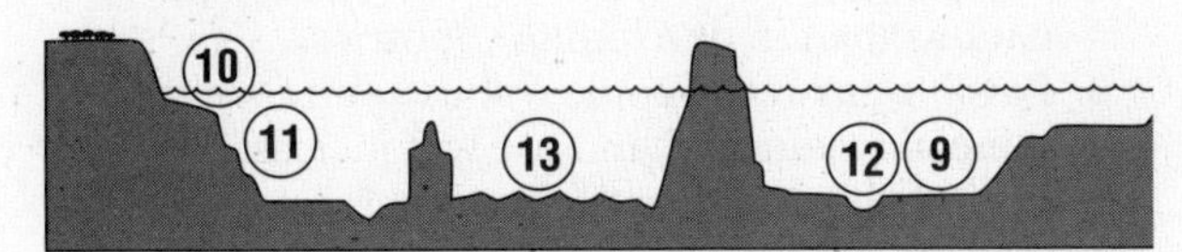

14. d
15. b
16. c
17. b
18. b
19. d
20. d
21. b

II. Understanding Concepts (page 342)

1. light
2. Answers include type of water, volume of water, number of plants, and type of plants.
3. one; one
4. another variable
5. You could measure the growth of the plants.
6. Nothing—you would not know if the plant's changes resulted from food or light differences.
7. 4
8. 3
9. 2
10. 1
11. a, d, h, j
12. c, d, f, h, i
13. b, d, e, g, h

III. Applying Concepts (page 344)

Writing Skills

1. Radiant energy from the Sun penetrates seawater and is trapped by chlorophyll-containing organisms that use the Sun's energy to make food. The food made by these chlorophyll-containing organisms is the bottom of food chains in the ocean. Animals eat these food producers for energy to sustain their lives. Other animals feed on the animals that eat the producers.
2. If one link in a food chain dies out, all the organisms in the chain that consume it also might disappear unless the link is replaced.
3. The ocean floor has mountains, valleys, and plains like Earth's surface does. Trenches in the ocean are much deeper and longer than valleys on Earth's surface. The ocean floor also has mid-ocean ridges that form new crust.
4. In photosynthesis, ocean organisms create food using light energy, carbon dioxide, and water. In chemosynthesis, bacteria produce food by breaking down compounds that contain elements such as sulfur, or nitrogen.
5. Oceans provide water, energy in the form of sunlight, energy in the form of other food, and water in which to reproduce easily.
6. Pollution can be dumped directly, lost during storms or shipwrecks, enter from air through rain, and be carried by rivers that empty into the ocean.
7. Sewage can act as fertilizer, causing algae to grow. When the algae dies, bacteria use up much of the oxygen that fish need. The result can be a fish kill.

Chapter Test C (page 345)

I. Testing Concepts (page 345)

1. abyssal plains
2. Sea mounts
3. mid-ocean ridge

4. Pacific
5. Placer deposits
6. continental shelf
7. food chains
8. buoyancy
9. sunlight
10. fertilizer
11. Estuaries
12. upper intertidal zone
13. mid-intertidal zone
14. light-generating
15. zooplankton

II. Understanding Concepts (page 346)

1. continental shelf
2. continental slope
3. abyssal plain
4. ocean trench
5. mid-ocean ridge
6. Possible response:

Types of Marine Life		
	Description	Examples
plankton	float in the upper layers of water	microscopic algae jellyfish
nekton	actively swim rather than drift in the currents; control their own buoyancy	herring, whales
benthos	plants and animals that live on or in the seafloor	crabs, snails, sea urchins, flounder

7. Possible answer: 1. Fertilizer and other waste materials run off from land and ships. 2. The fertilizers cause the algae to reproduce rapidly, causing a toxic bloom. 3. The algae die. 4. Bacteria decompose algae, depleting water and oxygen. 5. Fish die due to lack of oxygen. 6. People can become sick from contaminated fish and water.

III. Applying Concepts (page 347)

1. Continental shelves are at the edge of a continent. They are gradually sloped. The continental slope is next to the continental shelf and drops off more steeply.
2. The continental shelf has many resources, including petroleum, natural gas, limestone, phosphorite, sand, and gravel. The deep ocean has minerals such as sulfur and metals like iron, copper, zinc, and silver. It is expensive to mine materials in deep water, so few minerals are extracted.
3. During photosynthesis, carbon dioxide and water are changed to sugar and oxygen in the presence of sunlight. Chemosynthesis involves using sulfur or nitrogen compounds as an energy source, instead of light from the Sun, to produce food.
4. At beaches, the shorelines are sandy areas. Burrowing animals such as crabs and clams make homes in sandy beaches. In rocky shore areas, the shorelines are rocky. Sea anemones, sea stars, and octopuses live in the shore area. An estuary is an area where the mouth of a river opens into an ocean. Estuaries are often inhabited by newly hatched fish, shrimp, and crabs. Coral reefs are found in clear, warm water that receives lots of sunlight. The reef is home to coral as well as to sea stars, sponges, fish, and turtles.
5. Cleaning up the beaches is a great start to solving the pollution problem. However, it will not stop future pollution. It also addresses only one form of pollution. There are also sewage, chemical, oil, and sediment pollutants.

Our Impact on Land

LAB A (page 349)

Lab Preview

1. to illustrate population growth over 10 years
2. 1 million new people

Analyze Your Data

1. Students' graphs should show a steady increase in population over the 10 years.
2. Use 6.1 billion for the year 2000 as the starting point. (71,000,000/year × 50 years) + 6,100,000,000 = 9,650,000,000 people in 50 years.
3. (4,500,000/year × 10 years) + 6,100,000,000 = 6,145,000,000

Conclude and Apply

1. 78,000,000/year × 10 years = 780,000,000 in 10 years. Based on 2000 population of 6.1 billion, Earth's population in ten years will be 780,000,000 + 6,100,000,000 = 6,880,000,000 people.
2. Both show population growth. However, population growth is much slower in industrialized nations than in developing countries.
3. Possible answers: People will use more fuel and mineral resources. Land use will increase, resulting in habitat destruction and increased soil erosion. Air and water pollution may increase.

LAB B (page 351)

Lab Preview

1. to illustrate population growth over 10 years
2. 1 million new people

Analyze Your Data

1. Students' graphs should show a steady increase in population over the 10 years.

2. Use 6.1 billion for the year 2000 as the starting point. (71,000,000/year × 50 years) + 6,100,000,000 = 9,650,000,000 people in 50 years.
3. (4,500,000/year × 10 years) + 6,100,000,000 = 6,145,000,000

Conclude and Apply

1. 78,000,000/year × 10 years = 780,000,000 in 10 years. Based on 2000 population of 6.1 billion, Earth's population in ten years will be 780,000,000 + 6,100,000,000 = 6,880,000,000 people.
2. Both show population growth. However, population growth is much slower in industrialized nations than in developing countries.
3. Possible answers: People will use more fuel and mineral resources. Land use will increase, resulting in habitat destruction and increased soil erosion. Air and water pollution may increase.

Challenge

1. As one population increases, it leaves fewer resources for other populations. As humans take up more land and resources, they leave less for plants and other animals.
2. Possible response: Humans might have reached the carrying capacity of Earth. When there are not enough resources, the population levels off or decreases.
3. Possible response: The developing countries are experiencing the improved nutrition and access to health care that industrialized nations experienced earlier in the century. This is leading to longer lives.

Extension

Graphs will vary, depending on the area. Check that graphs accurately represent the data.

Chapter Test A (page 355)

I. Testing Concepts (page 355)

1. d
2. b
3. a
4. c
5. b
6. a
7. c

II. Understanding Concepts (page 355)

1. recycling
2. reusing
3. reusing
4. reducing
5. reusing
6. recycling
7. metal absorbed
8. composting
9. metal recovered
10. burning
11. ash disposal
12. 3.0 billion
13. 6.05 billion
14. It has increased.
15. The population in 2010 will be larger than 2000.
16. It represents an omitted time span.

III. Applying Concepts (page 357)

1. More trash is created.
2. Trees are cut down, and oil is used to transport them.
3. Pesticides used to grow plants can get into the water supply.
4. Refining oil to make this product can produce air pollutants.
5. Earth is changed when fossil fuels are mined.
6. Answers will vary, but should include four of the following: agriculture, feeding livestock, development, harvesting resources, and landfills.
7. Hazardous wastes such as paint and chemicals that are thrown in the trash are taken to landfills. There they can remain unchanged for hundreds of years. These should be taken to special hazardous waste collection sites.
8. Paper makes up about 40 percent of the mass of trash. Recycling paper uses 58 percent less water and generates 74 percent less air pollution than producing new paper from trees.

Chapter Test B (page 359)

I. Testing Concepts (page 359)

1. false, 200,000
2. false, paving over land prevents water from soaking into soil
3. true
4. true
5. true
6. false, a container law requires a refundable deposit on most beverage containers
7. false, although sanitary landfills are lined, some hazardous substances may still leak into the soil
8. true
9. true
10. false, the term composting means piling up grass clippings and leaves so they can decompose
11. d
12. b
13. a
14. c
15. a
16. d
17. c
18. c
19. d
20. b

II. Understanding Concepts (page 361)

1. I. **A.** 1 or 4
2. **B.** 1 or 4
3. II. **A.** 5 or 6
4. **B.** 5 or 6

5. III. A. 3 or 2
6. B. 3 or 2
7. 3.0 billion
8. 150 years
9. 400 million
10. about 500,000 years ago

III. Applying Concepts (page 362)

1. An American consumer uses electricity that is usually generated by burning fossil fuels, uses water that needs cleaning, and eats foods that take the land, pesticides, and herbicides to grow. He or she buys overpackaged materials that generate waste.
2. It would save 26 million trees; keeping 26 million trees alive would save habitats.
3. Covering the garbage with soil prevents it from blowing away and reduces odor. Linings reduce the chance that pollutants will leak into the soil and underground water.
4. Citizens can practice conservation by reducing their use of materials, reusing and recycling materials and composting.
5. Answers will vary. If effective recycling is occurring without legislation, most people would agree that it can continue that way. Those who think recycling is needed will want government action if other means have not been effective.

Chapter Test C (page 363)

I. Testing Concepts (page 363)

1. true
2. true
3. false—liquid wastes
4. false—increases
5. true
6. stream discharge
7. enzymes
8. composting
9. (Order will vary.) no-till farming, planting tree rows, planting cover crops
10. centimeters
11. Carrying capacity

II. Understanding Concepts (page 364)

1. The graph begins at 7000 B.C. Then there is a gap indicated by the zigzag line. The graph resumes with A.D. 1100 and continues at 100-year intervals.
2. Population growth was slow until recent years. Then, in modern time, population growth increased rapidly.
3. Health care and nutrition are improving, allowing people to live longer. More people are reaching childbirth age and having more children.
4. Responses will vary. Maps should show that metals are absorbed by the plant. The plant matter is then composted or burned. If the plant is composted, the metal is recovered. If the plant is burned, the ash must be disposed of safely.

III. Applying Concepts (page 365)

1. Possible response: More trash is created.
2. Possible response: Trees are cut down, and oil is used to transport the them.
3. Possible response: Pesticides used to grow plants can get into the water supply.
4. Possible response: Refining oil for plastic can produce air pollutants.
5. Possible response: Earth is damaged when fossil fuels are mined.
6. Possible response: turning off the lights to save electricity
7. Possible response: taking aluminum cans to a recycling center
8. Possible response: composting
9. Possible answers include recycling (products), reusing (products, composting), and reducing consumption of water, electricity, and fossil fuels.
10. Responses will vary. Possible advantages: Most landfills are lined with cement, clay, or a plastic liner to prevent leakage of liquid materials. They are covered with layers of soil to reduce the odor of decaying materials. Possible disadvantages: They are unattractive. Materials that were improperly stored could result in leakage or runoff of pollutants, endangering soil quality, wildlife, and people.
11. Possible responses include reducing the risk of flooding, increasing the underground water supply, beautifying the environment, and providing space for recreation and other outdoor activities.

Our Impact on Water and Air

LAB A (page 367)

Lab Preview

1. The hot plate and the pan or pot will become hot enough that a thermal mitt will be necessary to protect your hand as you work with the hot items.
2. The plastic lids are for the collection of particulate matter in the air.

Analyze Your Data

1. Possible materials: dust particles, soot, paint chips, plant seeds, pieces of leaves and twigs, small insects

2. Answers will vary depending on actual number of particles collected.
3. Controls: plastic lids with gelatin before placement in the environment. Variables: direction of wind, proximity to factories, trees, and other particulate sources.
4. Graphs will vary depending on materials collected.

Conclude and Apply

1. Answers will vary and will be based on the students' individual research.
2. The size of the particles will depend on their source.
3. Some locations, such as truck stops or construction sites, were closer to sources of particulates.

LAB B (page 369)

Lab Preview

1. The hot plate and the pan or pot will become hot enough that a thermal mitt will be necessary to protect your hand as you work with the hot items.
2. The plastic lids are for the collection of particulate matter in the air.

Analyze Your Data

1. Possible materials: dust particles, soot, paint chips, plant seeds, pieces of leaves and twigs, small insects.
2. Answers will vary depending on actual number of particles collected.
3. Controls: plastic lids with gelatin before placement in the environment. Variables: direction of wind, proximity to factories, trees, and other particulate sources.
4. Graphs will vary depending on materials collected.

Conclude and Apply

1. Answers will vary and will be based on the students' individual research.
2. The size of the particles will depend on their source.
3. Some locations, such as truck stops or construction sites, were closer to sources of particulates.

Challenge

1. No; possible explanation: some of the particulate is so small that it cannot be observed with the human eye.
2. Possible response: They might place filters on air vents to keep particulate matter out of the air. They could wear masks to limit exposure outside.
3. Possible responses: underneath an air vent, near a window or door

Extension

Student designs will vary. Successful filters will keep out larger particles while still allowing air to flow.

Chapter Test A (page 373)

I. Testing Concepts (page 373)

1. c
2. a
3. b
4. d
5. b
6. d
7. c
8. a
9. sewage
10. photochemical smog
11. carbon monoxide
12. scrubbers
13. Particulate matter

II. Understanding Concepts (page 374)

1. Fertilizer runs off into the water. → Algae grow and multiply. → Algae decompose and use up oxygen. → Without enough oxygen, fish may die.
2. X
3. X
4. blank
5. X
6. X
7. X
8. X
9. X
10. 2
11. 5
12. 1
13. 6
14. 3
15. 4
16. Oil and gasoline run off roads into streams and rivers when it rains.
17. At gas stations, old gasoline tanks were made of steel.
18. A factory releases hot water into a stream.

III. Applying Concepts (page 375)

1. Possible responses include turning off water while brushing your teeth, repairing leaky faucets, taking shorter baths, washing your car less often, watering your lawn less often, and turning off the water while you are washing the dishes.
2. Ozone can irritate and burn your nose and throat. Compounds found in smog can cause your eyes to water and sting. Particulates can disrupt normal breathing. Acid rain can increase the number of lung infections. Carbon monoxide reduces the amount of oxygen in the blood. This can cause chest pains.
3. Possible response: You can reduce air pollution by walking, riding a bike, or using public

transportation instead of your own car. You can also set the thermostat in your house lower in the winter and higher in the summer to save energy made by burning fuels.

4. Smog is the hazy, yellowish-brown blanket of polluted air that is sometimes found over cities. Pollutants in the air react to the presence of sunlight to produce other substances. One of the substances is ozone. Ozone near Earth's surface is a major component of smog. Smog can damage sensitive tissues, like plants or your lungs. You should limit your outside activities when possible.
5. Possible responses include the Clean Water Act of 1987 and the Safe Drinking Water Act of 1996. The Clean Water Act of 1987 made additional money available for sewage treatment and set goals for reducing point source and nonpoint source pollution. The Safe Drinking Water Act of 1996 strengthens health standards for drinking water. It also protects the rivers, lakes, and streams that are sources of drinking water.

Chapter Test B (page 377)

I. Testing Concepts (page 377)

1. b
2. d
3. b
4. a
5. c
6. c
7. c
8. b
9. d
10. c
11. d
12. b
13. a
14. c
15. d
16. b
17. a
18. d
19. c
20. c
21. d
22. a
23. b

II. Understanding Concepts (page 379)

1. coal
2. gasoline
3. nitrogen
4. oxygen
5. sunlight
6. ozone
7. ozone-depleting chemicals
8. acid rain
9. airborne toxins
10. urban air pollution

III. Applying Concepts (page 380)

Writing Skills

1. Hazardous wastes pass through the soil and reach the groundwater below. Groundwater is the largest source of drinking water in the United States.
2. Photochemical smog forms with the aid of light. Sometimes cool, dense air is trapped near the ground, which prevents air circulation. Mountains affect smog development by restricting air movements. Natural sources add pollutants to the air.
3. Soil and groundwater become more acidic. Increased acidity damages, tress, and buildings. It also kills fish when streams, rivers, and lakes become more acidic.
4. Point source pollution is easier to control. Since it comes from a specific location, it may be treated before release.

Chapter Test C (page 381)

I. Testing Concepts (page 381)

1. Water Pollution Control Act
2. (Order will vary.) how much water needs to be treated; water pollution
3. sewage
4. temperature inversion
5. 5.6
6. particulates
7. Sulfur dioxide; scrubber
8. catalytic converters

II. Understanding Concepts (page 381)

1. Point source pollution enters water from a specific location such as a drainpipe. Nonpoint source pollution enters a body from a large area such as a lawn or construction site.
2. Pesticides are substances used to kill pests to keep insects and weeds from destroying crops and lawns. Fertilizers are chemicals that help plants grow.
3. Acids are substances with a pH lower than 7. Bases are substances with a pH above 7.
4. These compounds can cause cancer.
5. The tank could rust and leak, damaging the water supply.
6. The sediments released are poisonous and can run off into rivers and lakes.
7. 1. Metal screens remove large solids. 2. The sewage flows into the primary settling tank. 3. The wastewater is pumped from the primary tank to a bed of gravel. 4. The sewage flows to a secondary settling tank. 5. Bacteria are killed by adding chlorine, ultraviolet rays, or ozone. 6. The water flows to a trickling bed and sand filter before it is discharged.
8. Possible answer: Fertilizer applied to lawns or farms runs off. → Algae grow and multiply. → Algae die and decay, using up oxygen. → Without enough oxygen, fish may die.
9. Possible responses: type: ozone-depleting chemicals, goal: immediately cease production in 1996; type: acid rain, goal: reduce sulfur dioxide emissions by 2000; type: airborne toxins, goal: limit emissions of 200 compounds that cause cancer/birth defects; type: urban air pollution, goal: nitrogen oxide emissions reduced in new cars by 60 percent of 1990 levels.

III. **Applying Concepts (page 383)**

1. Possible response: They may be seeing water pollution from sediment. The sediment may be running off from the construction sites and cleared woods. The residents should be concerned. The sediment makes the water cloudy and blocks sunlight that underwater plants need to make food. Sediment also covers the eggs of organisms that live in water, preventing them from receiving the oxygen they need to develop.
2. The temperature of the water should be tested. The power plant may be releasing heated water. This water can pollute because it contains less oxygen than cool water does. In addition, organisms that live in water are sensitive to changes in temperature. A sudden release of heated water can kill a large number of fish in a short amount of time.
3. Certain natural conditions contribute to smoggy air. Some cities do not have serious smog problems because their pollutants often are dispersed by winds. In other areas, landforms add to smog development by preventing the smog from being carried away by winds. The atmosphere can also influence smog formation. If warm air traps cool air near the ground, it can cause pollutants to accumulate near Earth's surface.
4. Air pollution does not stay put. It crosses city, state, and country borders. This makes it difficult to control. Even if one state or country reduces its air pollution levels, pollutants can blow across borders. When states and nations cooperate, pollution problems can be reduced.
5. Possible response: Much of air pollution, such as car emissions, CFCs, and industrial emissions is the result of human action. However, natural events, such as fires and volcano eruptions, also contribute to air pollution.

Exploring Space

LAB A (page 385)

Analyze Your Data

1. Students can use an atlas to locate cities at approximately the same longitude as your hometown.
2. Answers will vary depending on readings.
3. Answers will vary on cities chosen.
4. Earth's circumference at the equator is 40,079 km.

Conclude and Apply

1. Values should be close.
2. Possible answers: making errors in calculations, choosing a city not on your longitude, misreading the astrolabe. Students might suggest being more careful in repeating calculations several times.

LAB B (page 389)

Analyze Your Data

1. Students can use an atlas to locate cities at approximately the same longitude as your hometown.
2. Answers will vary depending on readings.
3. Answers will vary on cities chosen.
4. Earth's circumference at the equator is 40,079 km.

Conclude and Apply

1. Values should be close.
2. Possible answers: making errors in calculations, choosing a city not on your longitude, misreading the astrolabe. Students might suggest being more careful in repeating calculations several times.

Challenge

1. 4.2 years; All you need to know is the number of light-years away a star is. That number will be the number of years the star's light has been in transit.
2. The North Star is simply the star that happens to be directly overhead when you are standing at the North Pole. Since Earth spins on a north-south axis, that star will not appear to move in the sky. Stars in the east and west will always appear to be in motion.
3. We could tell it was there if it gave off other wavelengths of electromagnetic energy.

Extension

You can go to the equator, at which point the North Star will be on the horizon. South of the equator the North Star will no longer be visible.

Chapter Test A (page 393)

I. **Testing Concepts (page 393)**

1. Earth
2. space shuttle
3. space station
4. Moon
5. space probe
6. a
7. a
8. c
9. c
10. b
11. a
12. false—observatories
13. true
14. true
15. false—rockets
16. false—satellite
17. true

II. **Understanding Concepts (page 394)**

1. Answers should note that the Hubble Space Telescope is outside the atmosphere, which absorbs and distorts some of the energy that comes from space. However, the cost and difficulty of lifting a telescope into orbit, as well as

repairing it, is much greater than using a land-based telescope.

2. Answers should note that a space probe can come much closer to and take much more detailed readings of other planets than a telescope on Earth can. However, it is difficult and costly to get space probes to other planets, and the amount of time they are able to operate is often limited.
3. b
4. c
5. a
6. d
7. f
8. e

III. **Applying Concepts (page 395)**

1. The International Space Station will be a permanent laboratory designed for long-term research projects. A space shuttle is a reusable spacecraft that transports astronauts, satellites, and other materials to and from space.
2. the Sun, Saturn, Earth, the Moon, a space station, an astronaut

Chapter Test B (page 397)

I. **Testing Concepts (page 397)**

1. natural
2. refracting
3. reflecting
4. *Cassini*
5. electromagnetic spectrum
6. Project Mercury
7. space probes
8. space station
9. Optical
10. artificial
11. Project Apollo
12. Project Gemini
13. optical
14. reflecting
15. satellites
16. space shuttle
17. Radio
18. space station
19. space shuttle
20. Earth
21. space shuttle
22. space station
23. Moon
24. space probe

II. **Understanding Concepts (page 398)**

1. **a.** 3
   b. 5
   c. 4
   d. 2
   e. 7
   f. 1
   g. 6
2. true
3. Soviet, or Russian
4. Project Mercury
5. The entry would be included under reusable spacecraft.

III. **Applying Concepts (page 399)**

1. No. You need an optical telescope to study visible light. Visible light is not detected by radio telescopes. Radio telescopes study radio waves that penetrate Earth's atmosphere.
2. Orbital space stations are useful because they can remain in space for long periods of time. Therefore, scientists in space can perform long-term experiments.
3. Both are optical telescopes that magnify images of objects in space. Both can be used to view only visible light waves, and the images picked up by both may be distorted by Earth's atmosphere. Reflecting telescopes use concave mirrors to focus light from the objects viewed. Refracting telescopes use convex lenses to focus light.
4. They were part of the U.S. "race to the Moon" with the former Soviet Union. Project Mercury was the first leg in the race, providing data and basic experience for piloted space flight. Project Gemini took up the baton next. It practiced techniques for linking up two spacecraft in orbit. Project Apollo finished the race, actually putting astronauts on the Moon.
5. Students' opinions may vary. Many are likely to favor continuation of the program because it has provided such benefits as launching satellites as well as space probes. Because the shuttle can be reused, the cost of the program is not as great as it would be if the shuttles could not be reused. Other students may say the money could be better used for other government programs.
6. Answers will vary and may include recent developments in the news. They also should note several items in the text, such as the International Space Station and explorations of the Moon, Mars, and Saturn by space probe.
7. Solid-propellant rockets are generally simpler, but can't be shut down after they are ignited. Liquid-propellant rockets can be shut down after they are ignited, and can be restarted.

Chapter Test C (page 401)

I. **Testing Concepts (page 401)**

1. spectrum
2. 300,000 km/sec—the only speed it can go
3. visible light
4. refracting
5. reflecting
6. adaptive optics
7. Earth
8. space shuttle
9. space station

10. Moon
11. space probe

II. Understanding Concepts (page 402)

1. While optical telescopes allow us to examine distant objects, it is true that the information reaching us from those objects is coming in the form of light. Other types of telescope are used to study energy at other wavelengths.
2. While the term "light" is reserved for visible wavelengths of electromagnetic energy, it is true that the only difference between light and radio waves is wavelength.
3. Both optical and radio telescopes use electromagnetic energy to examine distant objects. Optical telescopes only gather information through the frequencies that constitute visible light, however, while radio telescopes examine much lower frequencies. Each gives useful information.

III. Applying Concepts (page 403)

1. In a way, this is true. When we look out into space we are looking back in time. The farther a telescope allows us to look, the more ancient the objects we can see.
2. Answers should note that the Hubble is already outside Earth's atmosphere, which distorts and absorbs energy coming from distant objects. Moving it farther away would not increase its ability to gather energy in that sense. However, NASA has proposed placing a telescope on the Moon for other reasons.

The Sun-Earth-Moon System

LAB A (page 405)

Lab Preview

1. The lab suggests that eye protection should be worn, as it is important to always protect your eyes when performing an experiment in the laboratory. Hand protection is indicated because the light source used in the activity will become hot. Care should be taken when using the protractor in this activity to avoid injury. Beware of possible electrical hazard.
2. The angle with the greatest surface area exposed to direct light will be the hottest.

Conclude and Apply

1. Students should mention that they varied the angle at which light struck the thermometer. The independent variable was the angle of the light. The dependent variable was the increase in the temperature of the sheet of paper.
2. Graphs should have time on the y-axis and temperature on the x-axis.
3. Temperature increased more as the angle of the light approached 90°F.
4. White paper would produce similar results, but the temperature would not rise as high as with black paper.
5. During our summer, the Sun's rays strike the northern hemisphere at the highest angles, causing higher temperatures. During our winter, the Sun's rays strike the northern hemisphere at lower angles, causing lower temperatures.

LAB B (page 409)

Lab Preview

1. The lab suggests that eye protection should be worn, as it is important to always protect your eyes when performing an experiment in the laboratory. Hand protection is indicated because the light source used in the activity will become hot. Care should be taken when using the protractor in this activity to avoid injury. Beware of possible electrical hazard.
2. The angle with the greatest surface area exposed to direct light will be the hottest.

Conclude and Apply

1. Students should mention that they varied the angle at which light struck the thermometer. The independent variable was the angle of the light. The dependent variable was the increase in the temperature of the sheet of paper.
2. Graphs should have time on the y-axis and temperature on the x-axis.
3. Temperature increased more as the angle of the light approached 90°F.
4. White paper would produce similar results, but the temperature would not rise as high as with black paper.
5. During our summer, the Sun's rays strike the northern hemisphere at the highest angles, causing higher temperatures. During our winter, the Sun's rays strike the northern hemisphere at lower angles, causing lower temperatures.

Challenge

1. All of the graphs showed that the temperature increased as the angle of the light approached 90°. The slope of the lines changed as different people chose different angles; some of the intervals were closer together and others were further apart.
2. The model shows the influence of angle of the Sun on the heating of Earth's surface. However, because the temperature was gathered from a flat surface, it does not show the influence of Earth's curved surface.
3. Possible response: Yes, other planets are probably tilted, so they would have temperature variations. However, I would expect the angle of the tilt to be

different, so the amount of temperature variation would be different.

Extension

Students need to select a spherical object and devise a method to hold the sphere at the angles they chose to investigate. Students should discover that the temperature is higher in the middle and cooler at the top and bottom.

Chapter Test A (page 413)

I. Testing Concepts (page 413)

1. a
2. b
3. c
4. d
5. d
6. a
7. b
8. c
9. d
10. b
11. a
12. c

II. Understanding Concepts (page 414)

1. new moon
2. waxing crescent
3. first quarter
4. waxing gibbous
5. full moon
6. waning gibbous
7. third quarter
8. waning crescent
9. Earth; the Sun; the Moon
10. The Moon; Earth; the Sun
11. *Luna 3*
12. *Surveyor 1*
13. Apollo 8
14. Neil Armstrong is the first human to walk on the Moon.
15. Crew deploys first lunar roving vehicle.
16. The last crewed Moon mission launches.

III. Applying Concepts (page 415)

1. The tilt of Earth's axis and its revolution cause the seasons.
2. A Mars-sized object collided with Earth. The blast ejected material from both objects into space. A ring of gas and debris formed around Earth. Particles in the ring joined together to form the Moon.
3. The Moon seems to shine because its surface reflects sunlight.
4. Just as half of Earth experiences day as the other half experiences night, half of the Moon is lighted while the other half is dark. As the Moon revolves around Earth, you see different portions of its lighted size, which causes the Moon's appearance to change.
5. The solstice is the day when the Sun reaches its greatest distance north or south of the equator. In the northern hemisphere, summer solstice is in June and winter solstice is in December. Summer solstice is about the longest period of daylight of the year. After summer solstice, the number of daylight hours becomes less and less until winter solstice, about the shortest period of daylight of the year. Then, the hours of daylight start to increase again.
6. Earth's magnetic field protects you from harmful solar radiation by trapping many charged particles from the Sun. It is also used for navigation.

Chapter Test B (page 417)

I. Testing Concepts (page 417)

1. f
2. k
3. m
4. q
5. c
6. j
7. p
8. e
9. b
10. a
11. i
12. l
13. o
14. d
15. h
16. n
17. g
18. r
19. T
20. F; day
21. F; rotation on its axis
22. T
23. T
24. T
25. F; longer
26. T
27. F; magnetic
28. T
29. T
30. F; closest
31. ellipse
32. equinox
33. sunshine
34. north or south of
35. Earth

II. Understanding Concepts (page 419)

1. b
2. a
3. b
4. a
5. 5.98×10^{24} kg/5.52 g/cm^3 = 1.07×10^{27} cm^3

III. Applying Concepts (page 420)

1. When the Moon moves directly between the Sun and Earth, the Moon blocks sunlight from hitting part of Earth, casting a shadow. This is a solar eclipse.
2. The Sun's light is reflected by the Moon. As the Moon revolves around Earth, an increasing, then decreasing, part of its surface is visible, causing the Moon's appearance to change. On Earth, we see the different phases of the Moon.
3. The maria indicate that in the past the Moon has experienced lava flows that filled up basins. The basins were formed by meteorites, asteroids, and comets striking the Moon's surface. These impacts also may have formed cracks, which allowed lava from the Moon's interior to reach its surface.

4. There is no liquid water on the Moon. These ice deposits could be melted to provide water for explorers.

Chapter Test C (page 421)

I. Testing Concepts (page 421)

1. umbra
2. penumbra
3. iron-rich
4. under impact basins
5. red
6. 29.5; 27.3
7. Earth's revolution
8. reflects sunlight

II. Understanding Concepts (page 421)

1. Earth rotates on its axis and revolves around the Sun.
2. An impact basin is a depression left behind by an object striking the Moon. A mare is a flat, dark region within this crater.
3. Solstices are days when the Sun reaches its farthest points north or south of the equator, while equinoxes are the points when the Sun is directly over the equator.
4. During waning phases, the illuminated portion of the Moon grows smaller, while during waxing phases, it grows larger.
5. new moon
6. waxing crescent
7. first quarter
8. waxing gibbous
9. full moon
10. waning gibbous
11. third quarter
12. waning crescent
13. Earth passing directly between the Sun and the Moon causes a lunar eclipse.
14. The Moon passing between Earth and the Sun causes a solar eclipse.
15. Possible response:

III. Applying Concepts (page 423)

1. If this were true, then all of Earth would experience seasons at the same time. Earth is exposed to almost the same amount of Sun all year, but the amount of solar energy any one place on Earth receives varies greatly during the year. Seasons are the result of the tilt of Earth's axis and its revolution. The number of daylight hours is greater for the hemisphere, or half, of Earth that is tilted toward the Sun. Earth's tilt also causes the Sun's radiation to strike the hemispheres at different angles. Sunlight strikes the hemisphere tilted toward the Sun at a higher angle than it strikes the hemisphere that is tilted away. Thus, it receives more total solar radiation.
2. According to impact theory, a Mars-sized object collided with Earth. Vaporized materials ejected by the collision began orbiting Earth and quickly consolidated into the Moon. Because the materials that formed the Moon came from Earth and the colliding object, the Moon should have similar but not identical properties to Earth.
3. The finding, by *Clementine* and the *Lunar Prospector*, that frozen water was present in deep craters at both lunar poles would be of interest. This is an important discovery for colonization, as water would be critical for survival and would take up a lot of space and energy to transport. It would also help to develop possible locations for the colony, as you would want to be close to the water source.
4. A compass would not be useful in finding its exact location. The compass points to Earth's magnetic pole, which does not align with its rotational axis. The axis is inclined at an angle of 11.5 degrees to the rotational axis. If you followed a compass needle, you would end up at the magnetic pole rather than the rotational north pole.

History of Moon Exploration		
Luna 3	October 7, 1959	Russian space probe returns first pictures of the Moon's far side.
Surveyor 1	June 2, 1966	The first of seven U.S. missions makes a perfect soft landing on the Moon.
Apollo 8	December 24, 1968	The first manned mission orbits the Moon.
Apollo 11	July 20, 1969	Neil Armstrong is the first human to walk on the Moon.
Apollo 15	July 30, 1971	Crew deploys first lunar roving vehicle.
Apollo 17	December 11, 1972	The last crewed Moon mission launches.

The Solar System

LAB A (page 425)

Lab Preview

1. to be careful when working with sharp objects, protect the eyes
2. No. Mercury is so much smaller than the Sun and the outer planets that the model would be unreasonably large.

Planetary Distances

Students complete the chart using their own scale. Following shows numbers for distance scale 1 AU = 10 cm.

Planet	distance to sun (km)	Distance to Sun (AU)	Scale Distance	Scale Distance (1AU = 2 m)
1. Mercury	5.97×10^7	0.39	3.9 cm	78.00 cm
2. Venus	1.08×10^8	0.72	7.2 cm	1.44 m
3. Earth	1.50×10^8	1.00	10.0 cm	2.00 m
4. Mars	2.28×10^8	1.52	15.2 cm	3.04 m
5. Jupiter	7.78×10^8	5.20	52.0 cm	10.4 m
6. Saturn	1.43×10^9	9.54	95.4 cm	19.08 m
7. Uranus	2.87×10^9	19.19	191.0 cm	38.38 m
8. Neptune	4.50×10^9	30.07	300.7 cm	60.14 m

Analyze Your Data

1. by multiplying the AU distance of planets by the scale selected
2. Answers will be subjective and based on the individual student's choices.
3. about 79 m
4. Possible answers: For a scale of 1 AU = 10 cm, Proxima Centauri would be about 27 km away from the model Sun.

Conclude and Apply

1. Distances between the inner planets are smaller than distances between the outer planets.
2. Venus is closest; Mars is second closest.

LAB B (page 427)

Lab Preview

1. to be careful when working with sharp objects, protect the eyes
2. No. Mercury is so much smaller than the Sun and the outer planets that the model would be unreasonably large.

Planetary Distances

Students complete the chart using their own scale. Following shows numbers for distance scale 1 AU = 10 cm.

Planet	distance to sun (km)	Distance to Sun (AU)	Scale Distance	Scale Distance (1AU = 2 m)
1. Mercury	5.97×10^7	0.39	3.9 cm	78.00 cm
2. Venus	1.08×10^8	0.72	7.2 cm	1.44 m
3. Earth	1.50×10^8	1.00	10.0 cm	2.00 m
4. Mars	2.28×10^8	1.52	15.2 cm	3.04 m
5. Jupiter	7.78×10^8	5.20	52.0 cm	10.4 m
6. Saturn	1.43×10^9	9.54	95.4 cm	19.08 m
7. Uranus	2.87×10^9	19.19	191.0 cm	38.38 m
8. Neptune	4.50×10^9	30.07	300.7 cm	60.14 m

Analyze Your Data

1. by multiplying the AU distance of planets by the scale selected
2. Answers will be subjective and based on the individual student's choices.
3. about 79 m
4. Possible answers: For a scale of 1 AU = 10 cm, Proxima Centauri would be about 27 km away from the model Sun.

Conclude and Apply

1. Distances between the inner planets are smaller than distances between the outer planets.
2. Venus is closest; Mars is second closest.

Challenge

1. Possible response: As you continue away from the Sun, the distance from one neighboring planet to the next increases.
2. Mars is the most likely planet because it is close and has a hospitable environment. We have also already sent several probes and landers to gather useful information.
3. You would need to know the location of Earth and Mars in their orbits. You would want to minimize the distance between the two planets to save on fuel and make the trip shorter.

Extension

Student models will vary, but should demonstrate an understanding of the varying sizes of the planets in relationship to one another.

Chapter Test A (page 431)

I. Testing Concepts (page 431)
1. a
2. d
3. b
4. c
5. false—comets
6. false—a comet
7. true
8. false—solar system
9. false—contracted
10. true
11. false—faster
12. true
13. false—Nicholas Copernicus

II. Understanding Concepts (page 432)
1. 4
2. 2
3. 1
4. 3
5. a
6. c
7. d
8. b
9. b
10. d
11. a
12. c
13. Sun-centered; Nicholas Copernicus
14. Earth-centered; early Greek astronomers
15. (Order will vary.) size; mass
16. greenhouse effect
17. Venus; Earth
18. Earth

III. Applying Concepts (page 434)
1. The Sun's gravity holds the planets and other objects in the solar system in their orbits. Because it contains 99.86 of the mass of the solar system, the Sun's gravity is immense.
2. As a comet approaches the Sun, it changes. Ices of water, methane, and ammonia vaporize because of the heat from the Sun, releasing dust and bits of rock. The gases and dust form a bright cloud, called a coma, around the nucleus. The solar wind pushes on the gases and dust in the coma, causing the particles to form separate tails that point away from the Sun.

Chapter Test B (page 435)

I. Testing Concepts (page 435)
1. c
2. c
3. b
4. a
5. b
6. d
7. d
8. b
9. a
10. c
11. d
12. d
13. c
14. c
15. b
16. d
17. a
18. c
19. b
20. b
21. c
22. b
23. d
24. c
25. a

II. Understanding Concepts (page 436)
1. Jupiter
2. faint dust rings, Io's volcanoes
3. Neptune
4. Great Dark Spot, moons, several rings
5. Saturn
6. Titan has a thick atmosphere. The clouds block the surface from sight.
7. Solar energy is trapped by gases in the planets' atmospheres, raising their surface temperatures.
8. Scientists hypothesize that about 4.6 billion years ago, a nearby star may have exploded causing a nebula—cloud of gas, dust, and ice—to begin contracting. As the nebula contracted, it fragmented. Each fragment contracted further, rotating faster and faster, and increasing in temperature. Eventually the temperature in one fragment's core reached ten million degrees Celsius—nuclear fusion began, and a star was born. A cluster of stars likely formed from fragments of original cloud. The star that became our Sun separated out and formed its own solar system.
9. Figure 2 shows the Earth-centered model of the solar system; all other solar system bodies, including the Sun, are orbiting Earth.

III. Applying Concepts (page 438)
1. Pluto is much smaller than the other outer planets and does not have a gaseous atmosphere as they have. Pluto is made of material like that of the inner planets, but is not near them. Asteroids are pieces of rock similar to the material that later formed the planets. The *Hubble Space Telescope* found data supporting the presence of a belt of ice comets near Neptune's orbit. Pluto might belong to this.
2. Comets and asteroids are probably composed of material that formed early in the history of the solar system. Scientists study the structure and composition of these space objects to better understand what the solar system may have been like long ago.

3. When the Sun formed from a nebula of gas, ice, and dust, not all of the particles were drawn into the core that became the Sun. The remaining particles collided and stuck together. The objects closest to the Sun became solid and rocky because lighter elements vaporized in the heat. These objects became the inner planets. Except for Pluto, which is made of rock and ice, the outer planets are made mostly of lighter elements such as hydrogen, helium, methane, and ammonia.
4. Shooting stars are meteoroids that enter Earth's atmosphere and burn up. "Meteor showers" occur when the Earth passes through a loose group of particles from the old orbit of a comet.
5. The Sun contains 99.86 percent of the mass of the entire solar system. Because of its gravitational pull, the Sun is the central object around which the objects of the solar system revolve.

Chapter Test C (page 439)

I. Testing Concepts (page 439)

1. Oort cloud
2. Jupiter
3. Nicholas Copernicus
4. Venus
5. nebula
6. elliptical
7. faster
8. nuclear fusion
9. Viking
10. *Pathfinder*
11. magnetic field
12. Mars
13. Loose pieces of comet debris, along with other sources, form meteoroids. When meteoroids burn up in the atmosphere they are called meteors. When a meteoroid strikes Earth's surface, it is called a meteorite.

II. Understanding Concepts (page 440)

1. Possible response:

Order from Sun

Name	Description	
1	Mercury	smallest planet; no atmosphere; many craters and cliffs; big range in temperature; no moons
2	Venus	similar to Earth in size and mass; thick atmosphere; yellowish color; has craters, cracks, and volcanoes; greenhouse effect causes high surface temperatures; no moons
3	Earth	atmosphere protects life; temperatures allow water to exist in all three states; life is known to exist; one large moon
4	Mars	reddish-yellow; frozen polar ice caps; channels, volcanoes, and valleys; thin atmosphere; large temperature ranges; dust storms; two small moons
5	Jupiter	largest planet; faint rings; continuous storms, the largest is the Great Red Spot; has 4 large moons and 57 smaller moons
6	Saturn	second-largest planet; thick atmosphere; complex ring system; has at least 31 moons
7	Uranus	large, gaseous planet; thin, dark rings; axis of rotation is nearly parallel to plane of orbit; has at least 21 moons
8	Neptune	large, gaseous planet with rings; sometimes farther than Pluto; bluish-green color; dark-colored storms; at least 11 moons

2. Figure 1 represents a Sun-centered model of the solar system. It shows the Moon revolving around Earth and Earth and another planet revolving around the Sun. Figure 2 illustrates an Earth-centered model of the solar system. The Moon, planet, and Sun are all thought to revolve around Earth.
3. Possible response: Similarities: similar size and mass; atmosphere that creates a greenhouse effect; craters and volcanoes. Venus: thicker atmosphere, which leads to higher surface temperatures; droplets of sulfuric acid in the atmosphere give it a yellowish color; no moons. Earth: atmosphere protects life; surface temperature that allows water to exist in all three states; one large moon.

III. Applying Concepts (page 441)

1. Because the Sun contains 99.86 percent of the mass of the solar system, its gravity is immense. The Sun's gravity holds the planets and other objects in the solar system in their orbits. If its mass was considerably less, it might not have enough gravitational pull to hold some of the larger and farther out planets in their orbits.
2. A comet is composed of dust and rock particles mixed with frozen water, methane, and ammonia. As a comet approaches the Sun, it changes. Ices vaporize because of the heat from the Sun, releasing dust and bits of rock. The gases and released dust form a bright cloud, called a coma, around the nucleus. The solar wind pushes on the gases and dust in the coma, causing the particles to form separate tails that point away from the Sun. The presence of a coma and tail would indicate it was closer to the Sun. After many trips around the Sun, most of the ice in a comet's nucleus has vaporized, leaving dust and rock.
3. When Earth passes through the loose group of particles within the old orbit of a comet, particles of rock and dust enter the atmosphere. Most are burned up by the atmosphere. Some meteorites do collide with Earth's surface. Some asteroids do have orbits that cross Earth's orbit, but it is unlikely that an asteroid will hit Earth in the near future.

Stars and Galaxies

LAB A (page 443)

Lab Preview

1. to protect eyes from the meterstick
2. apparent shift in the position of an object when viewed from two different positions

Analyze Your Data

1. The position of the pencil seemed to shift, but this motion was only apparent.
2. the closest distance used
3. the farthest distance

Conclude and Apply

1. As distance from the observer increased, the pencil's apparent shift decreased. As the distance from the observer decreased, the pencil's apparent shift increased.
2. Astronomers use parallax angles or shifts in the apparent position of astronomical objects to determine distances to the objects.

LAB B (page 445)

Lab Preview

1. to protect eyes from the meterstick
2. apparent shift in the position of an object when viewed from two different positions

Analyze Your Data

1. The position of the pencil seemed to shift, but this motion was only apparent.
2. the closest distance used
3. the farthest distance

Conclude and Apply

1. As distance from the observer increased, the pencil's apparent shift decreased. As the distance from the observer decreased, the pencil's apparent shift increased.
2. Astronomers use parallax angles or shifts in the apparent position of astronomical objects to determine distances to the objects.

Challenge

1. No; parallax is most helpful for measuring distance for objects that are close.
2. In this lab, the observer remained in one spot. When astronomers figure parallax, they observe the same star when Earth is at two different points in its orbit around the Sun.
3. Parallax can be used to measure the distance to nearby stars by measuring against background stars, which do not appear to move.

Extension

Student responses will vary depending on the constellation chosen. Students should identify the stars within the constellation and their distance in light-years from Earth.

Chapter Test A (page 449)

I. Testing Concepts (page 449)

1. a
2. d
3. b
4. c
5. b
6. a
7. d
8. a
9. c
10. b
11. c
12. a
13. d
14. b

II. Understanding Concepts (page 450)
1. nebula
2. red supergiant
3. supernova

4–5. (Order may vary.) neutron star; black hole

6. red giant
7. white dwarf
8. on the main sequence
9. Vega
10. giant
11. the Sun
12. 2
13. 1
14. 3
15. 4
16. 1
17. 3
18. 2

III. Applying Concepts (page 452)
1. As Earth orbits the Sun, different constellations come into view, while others disappear. Orion, which is visible in the winter in the northern hemisphere, cannot be seen there in the summer because the daytime side of Earth is facing it.
2. Both refer to the brightness of a star. Absolute magnitude is a measure of the amount of light it gives off. Apparent magnitude is a measure of the amount of light received on Earth.
3. The Milky Way galaxy is a spiral galaxy. The Sun is located near the outer edge of the Milky Way on one of the spiral arms.
4. In our solar system, the planets are held in place by the gravitational pull of the Sun. The planets orbit around the Sun. In the Milky Way galaxy, stars are held in place by a black hole at the center. The stars orbit around the black hole at the core.

Chapter Test B (page 453)

I. Testing Concepts (page 453)
1. b
2. a
3. d
4. c
5. c
6. d
7. b
8. d
9. a
10. c
11. a
12. b
13. d
14. c
15. a
16. c
17. b
18. a

II. Understanding Concepts (page 454)
1. C; E
2. E; C
3. blue, yellow, red
4. 2; 1; 3
5. no
6. Vega
7. a supergiant
8. yes
9. All three stars are the same distance from Earth. As a result, real brightness would be equal to apparent brightness, so Star B would have the greatest apparent magnitude.

III. Applying Concepts (page 456)
1. The Big Bang theory suggests that the universe was formed and is expanding as a result of a large explosion. The Doppler shift to red indicates that galaxies outside the Local Group are moving away from the Local Group. The shift indicates that the universe is indeed expanding outward.
2. No, but a shift to blue would indicate that the galaxies were moving toward the Local Group. That would indicate that the universe was contracting, not expanding, as the Big Bang theory states.
3. Four hydrogen atoms have more mass than one helium atom. When hydrogen fuses into helium, the "lost" mass is converted into energy.
4. Because Earth revolves around the sun, the position of Orion appears to change as Earth moves. Orion is in the daytime sky during the summer and thus can't be seen.

Chapter Test C (page 457)

I. Testing Concepts (page 457)
1. false—spectroscope
2. false—on a spiral arm
3. false—The Sun
4. true
5. false—barred
6. circumpolar constellation
7. light-year
8. nebula
9. main sequence
10. Local Group
11. expanding
12. red shift
13. big bang
14. (Order will vary.) spiral; elliptical; irregular
15. steady state

II. Understanding Concepts (page 458)
1. The Sun and Vega are both main sequence stars. Vega is hotter and brighter than the Sun. However, the Sun has a greater absolute magnitude than Vega.

2. Concept maps should show stars originating from a nebula. High-mass stars → main sequence star → red supergiant → supernova → neutron star or black hole; Low-mass stars → main sequence → red giant → white dwarf
3. core
4. radiation zone
5. convection zone
6. photosphere
7. chromosphere
8. transition zone
9. corona
10. X; areas of the Sun's surface that appear darker because they are cooler than surrounding areas
11. blank
12. X; huge, arching columns of gas
13. X; violent solar eruptions
14. X; occur when large amounts of electrically charged gas are ejected suddenly from the corona
15. blank

III. Applying Concepts (page 459)

1. No; constellations form patterns when viewed from Earth, but have no relationship to each other in space.
2. As Earth orbits the Sun, some constellations come into view, while others disappear. The student may be looking at one map from the northern hemisphere and one from the southern hemisphere. He might also be looking at maps from the same location but different seasons.
3. You can refer to its absolute magnitude or its apparent magnitude. The absolute magnitude of a star is a measure of the amount of light it gives. The apparent magnitude is a measure of the amount of light received on Earth.
4. In our solar system, the planets are held in place by the gravitational pull of the Sun. The planets orbit around the Sun. In the Milky Way galaxy, stars are held in place by a black hole at the center. The stars orbit around the black hole at the core.